The Psychiatric Fix

PSYCHIATRY'S ALARMING POWER OVER OUR LIVES

By June and William Noble

THE CUSTODY TRAP
HOW TO LIVE WITH OTHER PEOPLE'S CHILDREN
THE PRIVATE ME

JUNE AND WILLIAM NOBLE

The Psychiatric Fix

PSYCHIATRY'S ALARMING POWER OVER OUR LIVES

DELACORTE PRESS / NEW YORK

Published by
Delacorte Press
1 Dag Hammarskjold Plaza
New York, N.Y., 10017

Manufactured in the United States of America

First printing

Designed by Laura Bernay

Library of Congress Cataloging in Publication Data

Noble, June.
The psychiatric fix.

Bibliography: p.
Includes index.
1. Psychiatry—Social aspects. 2. Mentally ill—Care and treatment.
3. Power (Social sciences) I. Noble, William. II. Title III. Title:
Psychiatry's alarming power over our lives.
RC454.4.N63   362.2   81–9746
ISBN 0–440–07281–6   AACR2

To the memory of our parents:

Lovisa Amanda Gjetnes
and
Ivar Waldemar Brogger

Ethel Kathryn Karsch
and
William Parker Noble

Because of the unique mix that is part of every person's heritage, we have become what we are. In our aim to understand we have come to know them as well as ourselves.

TABLE OF CONTENTS

ACKNOWLEDGMENTS

There is no story in a single thread of thought. The tale emerges from the joining of a multitude of threads. Our deep appreciation, therefore, to the many people who helped us by offering their time and information:

Mitchell Balter, Ph.D., Lyle Bivens, Ph.D., the Honorable Charles Bristow, Walter Brown, M.D., Robert Butler, M.D., Lee Coleman, M.D., Joel Cook, Esq., Stephen Cohen, M.D., Katherine Craven, Carolyn Crowley, Bernard Diamond, M.D., Ann Diamond, Esq., Carolyn Douglas, M.D., Arthur Elliott, Ph.D., Kristin Eriksson-Mitchell, M.A., George Estes, Lynn Shields Feiner, Joel Fort, M.D., James Friedman, Helene Rank Friedman, Ph.D., Alan Gellenberg, M.D., James Gilman, Richard Hansen, M.D., Dona Hoard, William Homans, Esq., Jonathan Horton, M.D., Hans Huessy, M.D., Eric Jacobson, M.D., Frank Jones, M.D., William Kunard, M.D., Gerald Klerman, M.D., Donald Langsley, M.D., Wayne Lavengood, M.A., Philip Lee, M.D., Alan Louis, M.D., Mia Lydecker, Gary Margolis, Ph.D., Charles McConnell,

Michael Murphy, M.D., Edward Macklin, M.D., Carol Nadelson, M.D., David Ogden, Anne Marie O'Keefe, Ph.D., James Paulson, M.D., Herbert Pincus, M.D., William Pollin, M.D., Robert Pressman, Ph.D., Ralph Rybeck, M.D., Melvin Sabshin, M.D., Brig Saran, M.D., George Schumacher, M.D., David Siel, M.D., Larry Silver, M.D., Father Paul Shanley, Ronald Shapiro, M.D., Milton Silverman, Ph.D., Ralph Shafferzick, M.D., Kurt Schlesinger, M.D., U.S. Senator Robert Stafford, Frank Sullivan, Ph.D., Donna Taylor, Patricia Thornton, M.A., the Honorable Win Underwood, William Woodruff, M.D., James Young, M.D., Patricia Perkins at the Middlebury Town Library, Vermont, and Hans Raum at the Middlebury College Library, Vermont.

A special thanks to Robert LaFiandra, M.D., and Fred Wertz, M.D., for their professional critique of this work.

To Cynthia Vartan, our editor, our gratitude for her unstinting efforts to produce this book. And to Josephine Stewart, authors' agent, our love and constant admiration.

NOTE

For purposes of this book we have avoided the use of quotation marks, because the settings of particular dialogue and stories may have been changed. We have also changed some names and locations and some of the people portrayed are composites. However, where a dash (—) is used, the words and circumstances, with minor editing for clarity, are actual. They have been reproduced from documented sources such as tapes, notes, interviews, testimony, briefs, clippings, papers, articles, books, correspondence, releases, and reports, or from personal experience. Where dialogue appears without being set off by a dash, the words and circumstances have been reconstructed from equally reliable and documented sources.

INTRODUCTION

It is the Great Magic Show, a wizardry of power, with methods dazzling and unfathomable. It blends mystery with mystique and claims results never imagined. The Great Magic Show *is* psychiatry onstage.

But magic, alas, has no mystery once we learn the bag of tricks. And when the magicians let us stand backstage while they work, we see the sleight of hand. The magician himself stands exposed as merely . . . human.

Psychiatrists are not magicians, they are simply doctors who happen to have specialized in the mind. There are smart ones and there are dumb ones, sensitive ones and insensitive ones, help ful ones and dangerous ones. They may be the witch doctors, shamans, and voodoo priests of our society, but because we are in the scientific age, we expect that their diagnoses and treatments have a rational base. There should be nothing mysterious about their work.

Since the early 1960s American psychiatry and its practitioners have traveled a gauntlet of criticism, much of it well deserved.

From the hectoring of Thomas Szasz to the gentler urgings of Britisher R. D. Laing to the stark, dehumanizing hospital realities painted by Erving Goffman, psychiatrists have been seen as overly authoritative, overly coercive. Ken Kesey used fiction and showed us that not all the inmates of a state hospital could—or should—be the ones locked away each day. And Joseph Heller and Kurt Vonnegut, Jr., gave us fictionalized psychiatrists every bit as mad as those they treated. Personal stories of psychiatric care gone amuck have also abounded . . . Sylvia Plath's *The Bell Jar*, William Arnold's *Shadowland*, the biography of Frances Farmer, Barbara Gordon's *I'm Dancing as Fast as I Can*. Psychiatrists *are* human, after all.

But a simple book of criticism would be hardly more than a duplication of what has already been written. Something more was needed, a multidimensional look not only at the way psychiatrists practice but at who they are, why they think (and act) the way they do, and whether they remain entitled to the mystique of mindhealer they have carried for so long. In short, what we wanted to do was to pull the shroud of mystery away from psychiatry and expose it . . . for good or ill.

Our research took us across the country, from coast to coast, talking with hundreds of psychiatrists and medical students. We met with some of the most influential people in the field, including the then president of the American Psychiatric Association and the most powerful psychiatrists in the federal government. We also talked with the iconoclasts—rebel psychiatrists who had little good to say about the establishment, echoing much of the criticism that has come down since the early 1960s. Generally the cooperation we received from all psychiatrists was excellent, even though we were careful to point out that this book was to be investigative and might not turn out to pat many people on the back. The usual response was an acknowledgment that the ills of the past needed to be aired, and that it was far healthier to stand in front of the curtain than to hide behind it.

Though this book will show that we are not great admirers of the way many psychiatrists practice, it would be an oversimplification to say that the profession and its practitioners don't achieve some good things. There are fine psychiatrists out there, humanistic, clearheaded, dedicated, intelligent, judiciously operating within a field whose reach continues to exceed its grasp. It is the other psychiatrists, those who see it as perfectly appropriate in the course of practice to comment, advise, or render judgment in inappropriate areas. These are the ones we want to expose. Psychiatric expertise is narrowly confined, and it should remain that way.

Yet the power of psychiatry is both a blessing and a curse to psychiatrists. The power has often been thrust upon them by societies looking for quick solutions. In a culture that believes everything can be cured or fixed, patience and forebearance are virtues long discarded. We fear discomfort or inappropriate behavior or deviations from the norm. When we observe children who can't sit still patiently, or older people who seem confused and slow to catch on, or when we feel disoriented or depressed, we look for fast diagnosis and medication. It would behoove us to do some careful reevaluation.

Medically approved therapy in many quarters still includes lobotomies and electroshock and extensive periods of incarceration. It still includes dosing with drugs that have side effects that sometimes are worse than the original problem. The profession is rife with in-house critics, many of whom told us rueful tales.

In the final analysis it is up to us to learn to question authoritarian dogma. We are endowed with deductive reasoning power for that purpose. We are not simpleminded and should not behave as if we were. We should question, examine, listen to our own doubts, demand answers and explanations, and above all stop perpetuating the myth that psychiatrists have a unique handle on the vagaries of the human mind. That is pure nonsense.

In the last ten or fifteen years the profession has felt power slipping away as the exclusivity of psychotherapy has been broken by psychologists and social workers, as the relevance of psychoanalysis and its long-term, expensive demands have been challenged by shorter-term therapies that can accomplish so much, quicker and cheaper, as medical students have turned their backs on what was once *the* preeminent medical specialty. There has been a late surge to regrasp the power, and this book will point out how the profession is going about it. There is no question that organized psychiatry understands the importance of having and exercising power. In this technological, scientific age the very nature of power is in perceptions and expectations, and this is precisely the training psychiatrists have.

This book, then, is an attempt to demystify psychiatry, to profile it. What you will find are stories and analyses that make it plain that psychiatrists know many games.

And they play them with all of us.

PROLOGUE

Watch what happens. . . . The magician walks onstage. He stands alone, erect, black frock coat, knife-edged trousers, hands that play with the air. The corners of his mouth turn up in a secret smile. We wait, shivering. What will he bring forth for our amazement? What has he up his sleeves? White finches or the brilliantly blooded head of a rabbit? Will we scream or will we cheer?

Ah, that is the suspense that holds us enthralled. Will he scare the wits out of us or bring us laughter?

The sorcerer barely nods in our direction. We know, we *know* the magic is about to begin. . . .

The Psychiatric Fix

PSYCHIATRY'S ALARMING
POWER OVER OUR LIVES

One

BABEL

In the beginning was The Word, and The Word was Insanity. All who observed its affliction knew it and were afraid. Those who were afflicted were sinned against.

And Insanity was The Word. It was a curse of a vengeful God. It was the wily manifestation of the devil. The Word was known in all languages and by all people.

It was the scourge of mankind. And although mankind spoke in many tongues, The Word "Insanity" was well understood.

Insanity begat dementia praecox . . . dementia praecox begat schizophrenia . . . schizophrenia begat psychosis . . .

And in the land voices from every tribe were raised to explain each new phenomenon. And the tribes traveled to the Tower to converse. But in the Tower this was not possible. Each could not understand the other. The language of the Garden had been corrupted and enlarged. And there were as many tongues as there were mental disorders. There were as many tongues as there were therapies.

Babel.

*　　*　　*

The devil has chosen the boy. Lurking behind the load-bearing beam in his basement, he has taken him to his breast and breathed curses into his ears. His cleft tongue has touched the boy's lips and eyes. His tail has flicked his fingers and toes. The boy is four, and now he is cursed.

He will climb the basement steps and be scolded by his mother for venturing *down there*. The steps are too steep for a four-year-old. It is too dark and too damp at the bottom.

The boy will draw his gaze inward as he joins a netherworld not of his choosing. As he stands before his mother his tongue will start to click . . . he cannot stop it. . . . On and on . . . the clicking . . .

Stop! his mother shouts, stop! stop!

But it does no good.

The boy begins to hop . . . then he begins to bark like a dog . . .

The mother cannot understand what is happening to her child. She takes him by the hand and leads him to his bed.

This is but the beginning of the nightmare. The boy is possessed by the devil, the mother is certain. She takes him to church, seeking purification and strength. But the boy squats and wets his pants, over and over. The public disgrace is too much; the mother must hide the boy away at home. She wants to talk with him, but there is no way . . . he repeats his words . . . and repeats . . . until she thinks she will go mad.

It was the basement that brought this misery down upon them! That place of horror. The boy *had* to have been beset by the devil . . . and now he is possessed!

The boy does nothing to disabuse these thoughts. When he is six he begins to scream curse words. His mother keeps the windows closed so the neighbors will not hear. He careens about the house, jumping and whirling, faster and faster, hour after hour, tipping furniture, smashing and breaking . . . destroying. The mother has no doubt, the devil is truly present and thriving in her house. He has lodged in the boy.

The mother prays for guidance and relief, and someone suggests exorcism. The ceremony is painful and elaborate . . . but it does not work. The boy is as unmanageable as before. The mother operates on the edge of hysteria, she never knows when the devil will take the boy and fling him about the house, screaming his violent invectives.

One night the boy cries in her arms. —I can't help myself. I am trying to stop—

Shhh, the mother comforts, shhh. The tears well up, for she knows the boy *wants* to stop. But it is out of their hands, far beyond their power. They are mere instruments.

She caresses the boy's brow, savoring these moments when he can control himself. He will often be quiet for hours, expending superhuman effort not to let the devil cause him to scream or curse or whirl around.

Oh God . . . the mother prays . . . if only the boy were truly *sick* . . .

There is a man from one of the tribes who brings a paper to the Tower. It is translated into many tongues and read. The man's name is Georges Gilles de la Tourette, and he describes a disorder that occasionally afflicts children. The age at onset is between two and fifteen years, the disorder is unrelated to social class. There are usually no histories of mental disease in the family.

It is a *sickness*, the tribal elders proclaim, endowing Tourette with special honors. What heretofore was magic and superstition shall now be science, what heretofore was given over to the devil shall now be lodged in the body of empirical knowledge.

And it shall be known evermore as Tourette's Syndrome, and it shall be chronicled with The Word.

And among the tribes the essential features of Tourette's Syndrome will be recognized . . . recurrent, involuntary, repetitive movements, "tics," including vocal "tics" sounding as yelps, barks, grunts, or clicks . . . irresistible urges to utter obscenities, to scream, to curse . . . to repeat words and phrases over and over . . . often lasting a lifetime . . . three times more common in boys than in girls . . . a *sickness* of the mind.

But how do we *treat* this sickness, question the tribes? And then each tribe puts forth its ideas and there is great expectation.

But it is as a symphony of chaos, for each has its own way with The Word and with treatment . . .

Insanity begat stereotyped movement disorders . . . *or* transient tic disorder . . . *or* chronic motor tic disorder . . . *or* Tourette's Syndrome.

Insanity began choreiform movements . . . *or* dystonic movements . . . or athetoid movements . . . *or* myoclonic movements . . . *or* hemiballismic movements . . . which began hemifacial spasm . . . or synkinesis and dyskinesia . . .

And the tribes cannot decide which words to use and are sorely bewildered. In the beginning The Word was Insanity, and it covered a multitude.

Within the tribes there develop cliques and schools. There are many who dispute Tourette's description of a pathology and its origins. Some believe the syndrome has a biologic cause; others believe it comes from emotional deprivations. There is much disagreeing and arguing and consternation, for all wish to benefit mankind by their work. But it is most difficult.

The furor in the Tower rises, the many tongues compound the confusion. In the maelstrom are the voices of the elders, uttering their theories of treatment, urging compliance and acquiescence. Their dicta are relayed, repeated, translated, distorted, misunderstood . . . followers explain, elaborate, identify, codify, interpret, modify. . . .

A lone tribesman appears at the Tower. I have brought a word, he says, my name is William Cullen, and I have a word for you.

The elders regard him suspiciously.

William Cullen says, The word I bring is . . . *neurosis!*

And neurosis begat hysteria, phobia, obsession-compulsion, anxiety. . . .

And anxiety begat agoraphobia, social phobia, panic anxiety, neurotic depression. . . .

They brought the young woman to a psychiatric clinic in Syracuse in a catatonic state. She was admitted to the psychiatric hospital for evaluation. If she could be "saved," she would be transferred to a sanitarium and from there to her home. If she was irretrievable and there was a lack of funds, she would be committed to the state institution for the insane. The year was 1944.

The hospital staff included a part-time psychiatrist, a resident, and a woman intern. The psychiatrist and the resident were men who wished to be elsewhere. The resident chafed at the two-year program he must endure before he could shuck the institution and begin his practice with people other than crazies. He intended to get into psychoanalysis. Good-bye forever . . . straitjackets, wet sheets, paraldehyde, restraints, bars, steel doors, mesh walkways, three-inch key rings.

The doctors conferred about the girl. They listed the symptoms: chronic, if not constant, catatonia, moaning, disorientation, weeping, head-banging, self-mutilation. They made a tentative diagnosis . . . probably dementia praecox.

The intern hoped to be able to talk with the girl, to reach through the deep despair. The history of the case was heartbreaking. The girl had always been sensitive and very dependent. She was involved in an auto accident and had been the only survivor. Her mother, father, and fiancé had been killed. She came out of it with bruises and head injuries. How much head trauma, it was not clear.

Now she was withdrawn. She sat on the floor in a corner of the dayroom, and at night she was put in a padded block and sedated with paraldehyde.

The intern reasoned . . . The girl cannot face the reality of what is left of her life. The intern was not sure about the diagnosis of dementia praecox. There had been no gross signs *before* the fatal event; the girl had been a reasonably competent, stable human being. The intern believed in talk therapy and decided that this might help break the girl free from her ironclad internal world.

So one morning as the sun streamed through the mesh-wired windows, the intern sat with the young woman. The intern detected a few whispered words—I am nineteen . . . I am waiting for my fiancé . . . We are going to be married . . . My mother and father are getting the house ready for our reception . . . I must get dressed so I will be ready.

Then with a lurch and cry the girl looked at the intern. —Where is my fiancé!

—You must face this, said the intern. —He is dead. But I will help you.

The girl moaned and tossed her long, thick hair over her face. Her eyes stared back into themselves. She became like a stone.

The intern got up and left. —We'll talk more tomorrow. I will help you.

The girl was led back to her room, and for a while she was quiet. Then she threw herself on the floor and bashed her head against the linoleum again and again. When the orderly found her, blood and matted hair covered her face. They called for a gurney and took her across the lawn to the general hospital, where she was X-rayed and cleaned. Skull fracture, the radiologist reported. Quite massive.

Definitely dementia praecox, the psychiatrist said. Irretrievable. She must be committed. She can only become worse.

To the psychiatric hospital came the girl's aunt. The diagnosis was explained. She has a progressive illness, the resident told her, it's best this way.

The aunt said she couldn't believe it, there was never a trace of a problem before the accident. But when the aunt looked through the window of her niece's room, she saw her lying stiff and silent. Restraints bound the girl to the bed and sandbags confined her head. The bloodied hair had been cut back to a ragged cap.

The aunt nodded her head in sorrow. Surely, to look like this, to *do* what she did to herself, the girl must be insane. Demented. Mad.

The resident said,—If you visit her, you may make her agitated.

The aunt nodded at his wisdom. The mystery of the demented mind is more than she could cope with.

The intern was troubled. She wanted to tell the aunt that she had detected a flicker of reality. That it might not be progressive. But she held her counsel. She, too, was baffled by the intricacies of dementia.

Among the tribes are conservatives and liberals. They move amoeba-fashion across national borders and mingle contentedly, even while they dispute.

Among the conservatives are the fundamentalists who believe in the old ways, the simple ways, when in the beginning The Word was Insanity. The fundamentalists cling to the hymnal of dementia and repeat the phrases most comforting and familiar.

The fundamentalists gather in a corner of the Tower and nod sagely to one another. Under the umbrella of The Word they have lumped the stigmata of mankind . . . masturbation, pederasty, homosexuality, hysteria, aging, forgetfulness, disorientation, confusion, noncompliance, intoxication, drug dependency, agitation, depression, eccentricity . . . It is as a litany.

They will cling to the venality of the stigmata, they will resist removal from the lexicon.

The liberals chafe at The Word that decrees or reinforces moral dicta. There is no place in the lexicon for such value judgments, they say, for what may be learned in the Temple is not the root of all sickness.

Then to the Tower come the lawyers. They seek approbation for their own version of The Word—*legal* Insanity.

The conservatives agree that it is as the mountain. Forever and unchanging, a monument to The One who decreed in the beginning that there was The Word and it was Insanity.

But the liberals cry that mankind has come too far to revert to The Word, Insanity. Mental disease or mental defect is more realistic. The time to change has come.

And so the battle is joined.

As Gilles de la Tourette and William Cullen come to the Tower, so do Sigmund Freud and Wilhelm Reich and Otto Rank and Alfred Adler and Carl Jung and Karen Horney . . . searching minds, offering theories to the tribes who struggle with The Word.

Occasionally some in the Tower leave to tend to tribal members who suffer with delusions, paranoia, addiction, sexual abnormalities, dementia, malingering. They also assist the military, the Government, the leaders of Temple and nation. We are as instruments for the use of mankind, they say, The Word is in us, and we can make you understand.

But the tribes do not speak with the same tongue, and changes come slowly, for that which is dementia praecox in other lands is now schizophrenia here.

All is not Vienna.

After the Second Great War there is strong intent to write a Bible to encompass the knowledge of the elders in the Tower. In the beginning there was The Word, but there are now also the Book of Freud, the Book of Jung, the Book of Reich, the Book of Sullivan, the Book of Meyer . . .

And the tribes are sorely confused. Where is The Word, they implore?

There must be An Authority, the elders say. We must publish The Word, The *only* Word.

Verily, the tribes exclaim.

A glossary of diagnostic categories to which *all* the tribes subscribe, say the elders, a listing of personality reactions to psychological, social, biological events.

And so the workrooms of the Tower ring with debate and shudder with travail, for the publication of a Bible that would satisfy *all* the tribes requires great effort and wisdom.

But it comes to pass. And the First Diagnostic and Statistical Manual of Mental Disorders is produced. It shall be called DSM-I, the elders proclaim, for a Bible by any other name would be but a jokebook.

It diagnoses and it labels, and the elders have their Authority. The multitudes are content. The scientific age is upon the land, and this provides The Word.

The Bible becomes unquestioned authority for those who practice the profession of mental health, and it carries The Word even to the poorest and sickest among them and to those they tend. The Word binds all to psychiatric diagnosis and psychiatric definition, as written in the tenets of DSM-I.

But the tribes push out from the Tower, each with its special theory of disorder and therapy. In spite of DSM-I, all is still not Vienna. There are rumblings of discontent and disagreement, for labeling is only so useful as it is current. And the language of the tribes is forever changing. Today's "illness" may be tomorrow's "strength."

Among the tribes some are beginning to question who is "ill" and who is "disturbed." Are the poor "psychotic" and the rich just "neurotic"? We have our Authority, say the elders, the answers are there. Find The Word and it shall make you understand.

But we know so much more now, say the tribes, science has bestowed miracles upon us. . . .

And in truth that is so. The psychotropic drug revolution and behavioral analysis surge has brought new tribes and new elders to the Tower. What was Authority in the 1940s is no longer so.

Revise, revise! chant the tribes.

Hold, caution the elders. Who will provide The Word?

The Word is in *us*, the tribes say. *We* are the Authority!

It is so, the elders acknowledge, and we shall lead.

Verily! cheer the tribes.

And so it came to pass that a new Diagnostic and Statistical Manual was produced, and the elders named it DSM-II. And The Word went forth as it did before.

But *still* there is discontent, for some of the tribes continued to speak in a different tongue. This Bible does not apply to us, they say, we are different, we are psychologists, social workers, psychiatric nurses . . . We don't treat *sickness*, we treat health!

Yet it appears to the elders that these new tribes have great need for a Bible, for they, too, must provide The Word. They are studying and interpreting the Great Books in the Tower, and it will not be long before the Tower could be theirs.

Let us consider a revision, say the elders. Let us give a hearing to new nomenclature, so that all who practice the profession of mental health can speak with a common tongue. It is time to abandon old prejudices and superstitions.

It is right and proper, respond the tribes.

But, warn the elders, let there be no mistake. The new, revised Bible shall be ours, we shall *own* it! As before, it shall provide The Word.

And so chiefs and subchiefs, wise men and apprentices, labor to produce a new Bible. The work commences in the early 1970s, and

year after year The Word proves elusive. For where is it written
that what worked in Vienna would also work in Topeka . . . or
Minneapolis . . . or New York City . . . or Los Angeles?

It must be more scientific, demand the medical insurance companies who reimburse the mind healers. . . .

You cannot limit our work through categorizing, complain the
psychoanalysts. . . .

You can't remove the nomenclature we learned at our elders'
feet, insist the conservatives. . . .

But the elders have much wisdom, and they see who will lead the
tribes in the years ahead, those who believe in the power of psychopharmacology, in brain inhibitors, L-dopa, neurotransmitters, and
the great possibilities of chemotherapy. The Word shall be rooted
in . . . *science*!

Insanity shall be banned . . . *illness* shall be banned. *Psychosis*
and *neurosis* shall be made more exact, they shall be called "psychotic disorder" and "neurotic disorder." *Nervous breakdown* shall
be an "event" . . . and the hysterical personality shall be known as
a histrionic personality disorder.

We must recognize the new standards and values, the elders
proclaim, for otherwise we shall be as relics of retrenchment and
reaction, and we shall be buried in the dust of arid futility. We are
the Authority, we *own* the Authority.

So the Tower blossomed with ideas from the multitudes, and the
tribes took the caveats from the elders to heart. Homosexuality
would be banned as an illness, though the denizens of the Temple
thundered in dispute.

But The Word is with *us*, the elders reminded.

The tribes understood, their faith was fortified, and so they continued. . . . That which was once "dipsomania" and later became
"alcoholism" is now "alcohol abuse and dependence" . . . "Tobacco dependence" is added because of serious medical complications of long-term use . . . Opium, barbiturate, cocaine, cannabis,
amphetamine, hallucinogen use is added. . . .

And we shall call this Bible DSM-III, the elders proclaim. It will
stand as a monument.

*   *   *

In the beginning was The Word, and it is now a multitude, relied upon by millions.

Generations will be affected.

The drug industry will write new advertising copy.

The insurance companies will provide explicit forms.

The talk therapists shall search for proper classifications . . . if they wish reimbursement from the insurance companies.

And the words that fly in the air shall be *explosive disorder . . . phase of life problem . . . atypical psychosis . . . adjustment disorder . . . sympathomimetic abuse . . . psychosexual dysfunction . . . depersonalization disorder . . . psychogenic fugue . . . schizo-affective disorder . . .*

In the beginning was The Word, and it grew into the Bible for mental health professionals. And the conservatives, the liberals, the insurance companies, continue the battle to find a common language . . . a book of common language.

For in their strivings they see that no tribe knows more than another. They are no longer different in the language they speak . . . only in the pretensions they hold.

About DSM-III

The *Diagnostic and Statistical Manual of Mental Disorders* (third edition) is organized psychiatry's latest attempt to codify up-to-date research and learning on mental and emotional states. It was published in 1980 with great anticipation and fanfare, and was much wordier and more specific than either of its predecessors.

The copyright on DSM-III is owned by the American Psychiatric Association, and it was an APA task force that spent more than four years formulating the manual. Its place on the practicing psychiatrist's bookshelf has become de rigueur because health insurance companies will only pay off *if* the psychiatrist notes which emotional or mental disorder he is treating, *as set out in DSM-III*. The copyright, therefore, has some value, and the copyright owner holds extensive power.

What DSM-III attempts to do is to move away from references to the causes or origins of mental illness. The manual is an attempt to be *everymansbook*, a compendium that seeks to be descriptive rather than theoretical. The hope is that it can be used by all mental health practitioners regardless of training and psychiatric bias . . . from psychoanalysts to psychiatric nurses.

One area that caused a great deal of argument was the partial removal of the word "neurosis," which in turn wiped away the neuroses categories that Freud had originally formulated. Removing "neurosis" was in line with avoiding references to causes of illness, but it brought a storm of criticism, especially from the psychoanalysts. Actually, however, it was only a change in style, not substance, because most neuroses were renamed "disorders" and listed according to their symptoms. —The neuroses were still there, of course, said the chairman of the task force. Thus, anxiety neurosis became panic disorder . . . and hysterical neurosis became psychogenic amnesia (sudden loss of memory) . . . more than 350 pages of what is essentially a new language.

The major criticism for DSM-III has come from the psychoanalysts who see this attempt to codify mental and emotional disorders as creating rigid and artificial categories. In effect, they say, DSM-III relegates the psychiatrist to little more than an interested technician with his manual in one hand, his pad in the other, observing symptoms and finding the right category. We are accustomed to using our clinical experience, intuition, and educated inference in making diagnostic decisions, says one psychoanalyst, calling the DSM-III system simpleminded and atomistic. In fact, during the preparation of DSM-III, one psychoanalytic society was so distraught that they threatened not to use DSM-III at all unless "neurosis" was put back in. These psychoanalysts felt that DSM-III ignored the roots of *their* learning, the Freudian categories of neurosis, and so they questioned the value of what was left. But a compromise was reached whereby the old terms relating to neurosis were put inside parentheses immediately following the new terms, indicating that it would be all right to use the old terms . . . at least for a while.

Two

PLAYERS

San Antonio. A jewel of a city commanding the flat land of southeastern Texas; shop-lined boulevards, cozy river banks, and rich history working to spread charm and sophistication.

A nice place to celebrate good news.

Or . . . to ease the pain of bad news. A few psychiatrists, a most important few, have come from all over the United States to talk about a problem in the profession, and if they are meeting in the city where the Alamo claimed every defender, few sense a precedent.

There are people from the American Psychiatric Association, from medical school departments of psychiatry, from hospitals, from government, from private practice . . . psychiatrists all, an assortment of talent and experience that means business.

They are united, they are resolute, they know where they must focus.

On themselves.

They are their own biggest problem. They have brought things to the current sorry state. They have been remiss, self-satisfied, insensitive, unaware . . .

The figures are there for all to see. Fifteen years ago one out of every eight medical school graduates opted for psychiatry. The smartest ones, too. *Only* the smartest ones. Surgeon's hands and a gracious bedside manner never depended on the intellectual traditions of Sigmund Freud and Carl Jung and Alfred Adler and Harry Stack Sullivan and Adolf Meyer. But the mind game does.

Or did. The psychiatrists find themselves like the political official whose approval rating keeps dropping in the polls. . . . People just aren't giving them credit!

The figures show that now only one out of every *twenty* medical school graduates wants to be a psychiatrist. Worst of all, they aren't the smartest ones.

—Something has to be done, the psychiatrists tell each other. —The start has to be made here, today.

In the San Antonio sun they acknowledge that they must lead the way, *they* are the role models for the medical school students.

—We should send senior people, charismatic people, to teach in the medical schools, is one suggestion. Show the students that psychiatrists are classy and charming with magical talents, persuasive, insightful healers. *This* is what *you* can be if you choose to walk through our doors. Charisma, young doctor. Psychiatrists have it!

The students aren't impressed so far, that's for sure. —These days students who want to become psychiatrists stay in the closet, says someone from a major medical school. —They are ashamed of it, they don't want people to know.

The psychiatrists look at one another. Ashamed? Sure, we've been sitting on our complacency for fifteen years, but . . . ashamed?

The psychiatrists acknowledge they can't expect too much from the medical students, even though they *are* the future of psychiatry. But the medical students are still young men and women, easily baffled by esoteric lore and learning. When they come for a clerkship in psychiatry in their third or fourth year, some are tense and fearful. —They actually fear that the psychiatrists will psychoanalyze them, a medical school dean reports. On a couch, the fifty-minute hour, Oedipal fantasies, anal retention . . . all the while wondering if the shrink is reading their minds. It's nonsense, of course, but the fear is real.

Respect, that's what has to be achieved. People have to learn to respect psychiatrists once more.

San Antonio . . . the Alamo . . . respect was earned here, too . . .

He's out of medical school now, just finished four years of grueling work at one of the country's most prestigious institutions. In the beginning he would have crawled from class to class, if that's what it took to be a psychiatrist. In the beginning he would not have been a worry to the concerned bunch in San Antonio.

—I was someone who was very pro psychiatry and only went to medical school to become a psychiatrist. I had this profound fascination with behavior, I think it's one of the most intellectual pursuits there is.

The first two years of medical school went according to plan. In fact he decided he'd also get a Ph.D. in psychology to go along with the M.D. —Let's face it, some of the biggest problems man has had to deal with have been behavioral ones . . . crime, for instance. . . . He would learn *how* the brain functioned, its biochemistry and physiology, and *why* we do the things we do. A perfect mix of disciplines.

Then came the third year of medical school and clinical clerkship rotations.

—I had never been in an operating room before and I was really surprised that I was so interested.

Still, he was consumed with his plans for behavior study, even to analyzing just how he could get the various groups and ideas in the field into unified working order. —I wanted to bring the whole area, the psychiatrists, the academic psychologists, the clinical psychologists, together, cooperating with each other, sharing ideas and information. I thought I could make the whole field over.

But then he went into a surgery rotation and . . . —I just loved it. Right afterwards I spent two months in adult psychiatry where I could compare the two services.

In San Antonio the group huddles to thrash out the plays that have gone wrong. How do they lose these students, even the ones that seem committed at the start of school?

The young doctor recalls what happened to him. —Medical students pretty much decide the field they go into on the basis of role models, and I had two of them; one a resident in surgery, the other a child psychiatrist. I talked over my feelings with both of them.

He had a glimpse of his evaluations in clerkship. In the psychiatry rotation he had been written up as "uninterested in psychodynamic formulations." —That was a polite way of saying that basically I wasn't of the faith, that I didn't buy much of the psychoanalysis they spread around.

It was too oriented to pat theories of mother fixation, penis envy, and castration complex. He began to think of psychiatry as a problem instead of a solution . . . the behavior field was so fragmented and so unconcerned about coming together. Was there any point in pursuing this? Not likely.

There was no way to get this fellow back in the game. He was fresh out of chips, and there was no obvious reason for the house to stake him to more.

NEW YORK PSYCHIATRISTS USE PR FIRM FOR "IMAGE PROBLEM"
—Headline in *Psychiatric News*.

What do we know about these people? Freddie, the writer, asks.

Here's some background, his boss, the vice-president, says, indicating a briefcase full of documents. He thumbs through them quickly . . . throwaways, studies, articles, letters . . . you can start from here.

They sit at the foot of the long conference table, contemplating the idea that about three thousand psychiatrists actually need public relations help. Just like the politicians. Just like unions and big business.

We've been asked to submit a bid, the boss says. We're dealing with Area II of the American Psychiatric Association, that's mainly New York.

Freddie glances at the bid requirements. The successful bidder will work for one year "on trial," though it's implied that if the campaign has enough impact, there could be more work down the road.

They could probably use something, Freddie says. My sister's a nurse at a hospital on the Island, and you should hear the way *she* talks about the shrinks.

You better not listen to your sister for a while. We've got to believe in these people. They've spent a year worrying about what to do. Negative image, that's what bothers them. . . .

In what way?

They feel they've been marshmallows. They get a bad press, and what do they do? They respond like *gentlemen*. . . .

So they don't want to be pushed around anymore. Who can blame them?

The boss consults a sheaf of notes . . . Remember these words . . . *suspicion, cynicism, distrust* . . . that's what really bothers them. People look at them this way, and they're tired of it. They're called "sadistic meddlers with people's brains" . . . "greedy exploiters of patients' dependency" . . . "charlatans who hide their quackery behind a medical degree and a quasi-scientific jargon" . . .

Freddie grins in his lopsided way. Well, I'd say that is an image problem.

I'd like you to get the bid together by the end of the week.

Freddie nods, jotting down more notes. . . . Let's see, what do we know about these people?

Some psychiatrists have been captivated by the profession since junior high school, a quest that has influenced their choices of courses right through college and into medical school. Others don't wake up to a special interest in psychiatry until the middle of medical school. One thing they all have in common, though . . . they want to know, they *really* want to know why we do the things we do, *what* makes us behave.

The academic preparation begins in college. "Premed" is more than just a sobriquet, it is a yardstick for budding doctors. It means college courses in biology, physics, organic and inorganic chemistry, it means a special devotion to the sciences.

These undergraduate courses are a "must," says Johns Hopkins University . . . "required," says Stanford Medical School. . . . "required," says University of Southern California School of Medicine. . . . That still leaves a lot of area for other things, and the medical schools like to see a liberal-arts education in undergraduate school.

—I was one of four people in my class of 160 at Harvard who wanted to be a psychiatrist, says a student at the medical school. —None of us came from what you'd call scientific backgrounds. There were no doctors in the families, and in college we had majored in humanities rather than science. I thought first I'd go into family practice and pediatrics, but in my first year I took an introductory course in psychiatry, and I thought the mind set was not too different from the study of literature. When you read a novel, for instance, you read on different levels. You keep in mind the story, and the theme and the technique. And to me a person's mind reads like a novel.

Four years of undergraduate school, a college degree, and the budding psychiatrist is really only beginning. Next come four years of medical school, the first two of which are generally in the classroom studying diseases and human biology. Then come the clinical rotations, the clerkships, and they round out the other two years, along with certain advanced special courses such as psychopharmacology and radiation biology. In these last two years the medical student gets involved with patients, under close supervision, putting into practice what comes out of the classroom. Some even wait until this point before deciding on the type of doctor they want to be.

The Harvard Medical student tilts her chair back, remembering how it had gone. —I still hadn't committed myself to psychiatry until I began clinical work. My first patient turned out to be someone with Munchausen's Syndrome. She *wanted* to be sick to get the attention that goes with illness. She was a fascinating case because she was determined to be hospitalized. She had been in and out of hospitals for years.

—On this trip she contaminated her own urine, but I didn't

realize this until the staff picked up on it. We were supposed to heal but there wasn't anything physical to heal.

—What do you do in a case like that?

—Send the patient home. She sighs. —She'll find another hospital to play games with.

—So that was the turning point.

—No. She shakes her head. —It was a young girl who had slashed her wrists in a suicide attempt. My age. This brought home with a force that we could stitch her up but she'd try again. There was the same problem. Something in the psyche to be worked through. I felt very frustrated. It seemed to me then that psychiatry had a very practical use. It was not just a theoretical discipline.

The result of four successful years in medical school is the M.D. degree. For psychiatrists, however, come additional years of service and training, usually four years of internship and residency specializing in psychiatry.

Then comes the opportunity to be board certified, a position perhaps on the faculty of a medical school, a directorship of a hospital project, private practice, or a research position at the Alcohol, Drug Abuse and Mental Health Administration. For some, administrative positions in clinics, institutions, community mental health facilities.

Now, amazingly enough, it is not necessary to have all this background to call oneself a psychiatrist. It is not necessary to be board certified, nor is it necessary even to have a residency in the field. An M.D. can hitch the title to the name, and thousands have done so.

Nevertheless, board-certified psychiatrists seem to occupy the influential positions within the profession, and they make up the department heads, psychiatric association officers, and directorships of the best hospitals. (State hospitals have frequently taken the doctors who for one reason or another were ineligible for board certification. Their foreign medical education might disqualify them, or their lack of up-to-date continuing medical education. They are often regarded, unfortunately, as the blue-collar guys of the trade.)

A psychiatrist by virtue of education is scientifically trained and oriented. The emphasis on the medical aspect of behavior supports the title, and behavior is seen in a medical framework. Behavior in this aspect is referred to as part of the "medical model." This model has been criticized for being narrow, arbitrary, and for overlooking things such as cultural and social influences. Psychiatrists, the critics say, tend to treat anyone looking for help as if he is "sick."

Psychologists, on the other hand, who have not been schooled in the discipline of treating the "ill," may be more concerned with the cultural aspects of why people behave as they do. Nevertheless, they have still been exposed to as much, and, some say, more, psychoanalytic training and sensitivity to human frailty.

Psychologists like to repeat this quickie:

Q. What's the difference between a psychiatrist and a psychologist?

A. About twenty-five dollars an hour.

An editorial in an issue of *American Psychologist* stated in part, —For most psychiatrists the knowledge they have garnered about human behavior, and the vast array of theory and data associated with the study of human behavior, is transmitted in the context of the residency program. There is typically no training in advanced statistics, mathematics, methodology, research design or related basic issues of scientific work in human behavior. . . . In short, psychiatrists have little formal training in the broad study of human behavior, little contact with problems and methods in science, particularly those aspects of science dealing with complex social events, such as social programs and the like. . . .

—Doctor, why did you decide to become a psychiatrist?

Pause. Smiles. —I suppose sex had a lot to do with it. In my senior year in medical school in Chicago I had a love affair with the head nurse at the hospital where I was working. She had been in analysis, and at one point she screamed at me . . . "You have to go into therapy . . . I'm *not* your mother." I began to think about how people practiced therapy and the idea seemed very interesting.

—As simple as that? Really?

—No. No. That just opened my eyes. I really hadn't made up my mind until I came to California for my internship. I was on the acute treatment ward at the state hospital and I came to realize that I really wanted to do this type of work.

—You mean you *liked* working with acute psychotic cases?

—Let's just say I was comfortable with them.

—Most psychiatrists don't feel that way, do they?

Shrugs. —I grew up in an asylum. I was used to them.

—An asylum?

Nods. —For the first seventeen years of my life. It was run by the county. If people didn't get well in the hospitals within a short period of time they were sent to the asylum, which was actually a working farm. Part of the idea was that people got better working on a farm.

—You lived there?

—My mother and father ran the asylum. It was a three-story castle-like building sitting on a beautiful knoll in the middle of the valley. The building was in the shape of a cross, and men patients lived on one side, women on the other. Those who took care of them lived in the middle. Actually I was born there.

—It couldn't have been easy for you.

—I never felt any fear until I was thirteen years old. Somehow I sensed I was there to entertain people, and from the early days I got the message . . . "You're the powerful little boy who's going to save us when you grow up . . . you've got to be a lawyer or a psychiatrist and get us out of here. . . ."

—Then sex didn't start you on the path to psychiatry.

Laughs. —I guess not, although I've not admitted this before. People were there for many years, and when I went back for my mother's funeral a few years ago I was just amazed to see and recognize people I had known as a child. They were still there. The asylum . . . they don't call it that anymore . . . had become their home, they were so used to living there. Their dreams of leaving dried up.

—What is the place called now?

—A mental hospital. When the name was changed it made it legitimate for doctors to come on the staff. A few did.

—Weren't either of your parents doctors?

—No, no. Laughs. —My father was a farmer, as a matter of fact, and a good businessman. He convinced the trustees he could run the asylum in the black, and he did. When my parents took the job they planned to stay only five years but they soon found it was a good job, the best-paying job in the area during the Depression.

—The county was rural with a population of perhaps twenty thousand. I went to a one-room school two miles away for eight years and I was one of the best dressed. But I'd dirty up my overalls so I wouldn't stand out from the rest who were really quite poor.

—There must have been "incidents" with some of the asylum inmates.

—Well, one time, when I was about three, a lady who was quite manic and hyper had broken through a window of our living quarters and had come up the stairs bleeding. It was the middle of the night. She came into the bedroom where I was sleeping with my older brother in one bed and my father in the other. She was bleeding from the window glass, but she lay down next to my father and bled all over the bedclothes. I remember my brother who was just five screaming and scurrying under the covers. But I just sat up and looked at her. I was curious, not at all afraid. They came and got her, of course.

—You've never had nightmares about that?

Shakes his head. —Never. She did that a second time some months later. It cost her a lobotomy, the first person at the asylum to have one.

—You said your first fear was when you were thirteen.

—Yes. I was pushed off the top of the building onto the wing of the floor below by a man who was very disturbed. This was the first time I became aware of being so scared I didn't want to stay there anymore. Many of the people just weren't in control. Before drugs that could alleviate, you see.

—What did your parents think of your decision to become a psychiatrist?

—They approved. I remember my father saying, "Well, don't be

one of those psychoanalyst types who only treat ten or twelve patients in a week. There are thousands of people who need treatment, so the place to do that would be in a state mental system,
even a state hospital. It would be good if you could do something
bigger."

—And so I did.

Freddie the writer snaps a page of copy from his typewriter. His
boss will be on the phone any minute, looking for the proposal,
reminding him of the bid submission time.

Freddie gives himself a mental kick. Schmuck! You didn't have
to spend time on your own research, they gave you the information.

Some of it, Freddie corrects himself, some of it. Laundered, so
to speak. I had to find the warts too, it's the only way to do the job
right.

He inserts another page and continues writing . . . *A key goal of
any image campaign is reaching those who can mold opinions,
those who can reach hundreds of thousands of people. In short, the
media: television, radio, newspapers, magazines, lecture series* . . .

The phone rings.

Is everything ready? It's his boss.

Not quite. Twenty, maybe thirty minutes . . .

You're three hours overdue.

Last-minute checking on some stuff. It took time.

Freddie could type this boiler plate with his eyes closed. *Access
to the media is crucial in an image campaign, and we have the
capability to provide such access, the type of material they like to
see, who should talk to whom* . . .

Being so goddamn thorough could cost the job, the boss complains.

Listen, they *need* an image campaign. Believe me. I looked up
some recent studies of psychiatrists *by* psychiatrists. First thing,
they better clean up their act among their own people. One out of
five psychiatric residents *right now* would not go through medical
school if they knew then what they know now. . . .

He snips clean copy from the jumble of typed pages. . . . *Our media experience is extensive. We have prepared speeches on a variety of topics, we have organized lecture appearances and tours, we have coached and readied numerous people for television and radio appearances, we have scripted their dialogue, we have put together letter-writing campaigns, we have ghostwritten numerous articles and fillers, we have prepared testimony to be presented before governmental and quasi-governmental agencies and commissions. We offer these communications skills to you . . .*

Another study says three out of four young psychiatrists are *anxious,* Freddie goes on . . . from moderate to incapacitating. Now what are you looking for in a shrink? Solidity, right? But . . . *anxiety?*

Clean up the image, the boss says.

He continues as if he hadn't heard. . . . More than half the young psychiatrists entering practice today are *depressed.* You'd think they were in PR or publishing. If I'm going to go to a shrink, do I want depression?

So find someone older. . . . The boss is visibly strained. . . . Get someone who's been around awhile. We have to paint a picture of *stability.*

I knew you were going to say that, so this is what I propose. We can't let depressed or anxious people run off at the mouth and get the profession in further trouble. So I suggest *we* become the official mouthpiece. . . .

Hmmm . . . not bad.

Then I'll go with this copy, and you'll have it in an hour.

You said twenty, thirty minutes.

I can't make up for lost time. You've been on the phone . . .

Think shrink, says his boss, who likes epigrams. . . . And move it!

Freddie types with super speed and gives his secretary the first three pages for final.

. . . *Certainly an important function we would perform would be to act as a clearinghouse for all those who might be writing about, broadcasting about, or studying the topic of psychiatry. We would offer help and information, arrange interviews, obtain research materials, suggest approaches. In short, we would become the public*

*information brokers for the profession, bringing together the media
people with the psychiatrists who could help them the most. In time
we would expect all (New York–based) media representatives to
turn to us for whatever they need on the profession of psychiatry. . . .*

That wraps it up. Mazeltov.

—I know the American Psychiatric Association and how it
works, and I believe I have a realistic view of where psychiatry fits
within the rest of medicine and within society. I hope you will elect
me vice-president.

So reads in part the election campaign statement of a candidate
for office in the American Psychiatric Association, the organization
for psychiatry in America. People take various routes to the top,
but someone who becomes an officer in the APA can claim to be in
the heady atmosphere of psychiatric leadership.

It usually entails a steady climb with one eye on commitment to
the *profession*. Service to fellow psychiatrists is the key. Service.

In his list of career service the aspiring vice-president points first
to APA duties . . . president of his district branch, member of the
nominating, membership, program, and public affairs committees
in his district; area representative, chairman of the public affairs,
legislation, divisional meeting, and nominating committees of the
area; nationally, speaker of the APA Assembly, member of the
statistics and nomenclature, post graduate education, budget committees, chairman of the Joint Commission on Government Relations, member of the Joint Commission of Public Affairs, and first
chairman of the APA Political Action Committee . . .

A joiner.

Of course he is elected.

Freddie the writer hopes there are no calls to return as he stops
by the receptionist's desk on his return from lunch. He has a congressman's speech to write and the dinner is four days away. He
plans to spend the afternoon on the first draft.

There's only one message. The boss. See me, it says.

Is he in? he asks the receptionist.

She nods and reaches for the intercom.

I'll surprise him . . . and he wheels past her desk and knocks on the door.

Come . . . is the muffled invitation.

I got your message, he says, slouching into a comfortable chair.

We got the word an hour ago. The New York psychs have picked another firm.

Freddie grimaces, mostly for effect. He feels detached, even though he has worked hard on the bid. . . . What was it, price? . . .

Mostly. We offered pretty much the same services. But there were some other things. We weren't as aggressively *positive* as the other firm . . . The boss reaches for a yellow lined legal pad . . . I made some notes. They suggest they can "dispel myths and misconceptions about psychiatrists" that now appear in the media. That means they've got to define the psychiatric role . . . the *professional* psychiatric role . . .

Freddie does not like postmortems. *If* you can figure out their professional role.

The boss shrugs. Maybe it means showing how they are different from psychologists, social workers, and so forth. They want to keep away from "newer, trendier nonmedical schools of therapy and self realization." They want to pull the wagons in a circle. . . .

Freddie gets to his feet. He sighs. Some of the enthusiasm for starting the congressman's speech has left him. . . . At least I don't have to think shrink, he says. My sister, you know, is not madly in love with them.

The boss says, I'm still sorry to lose the account. . . .

I'll make up for it, Freddie says, hitching his pants and walking out. He raps wood as he passes the receptionist's desk.

—It's the clannish quality of psychiatrists that disturbs me the most . . . a kind of religiomystical system, a cabala, that they are somehow the possessors of this secret knowledge, and yet it is still called medical art, still more art than science. They pull out their union cards and form a phalanx. In terms of general humanitarian care for the mentally ill, the troubled, the disenfranchised, the leaders of reform rarely include psychiatrists.

So says a psychiatric social worker with twenty-five years' experience in mental health.

About the Players

A recent study by a major polling organization indicated that most people think of psychiatrists as highly trained, well educated, and deeply concerned for the individual. The problem, the polling people say, is not in the way other people view psychiatry but in the way psychiatry regards itself. Psychiatrists have a negative self-image, leave themselves open to criticism, and even invite such criticism.

There is now a well-directed effort to dispel the so-called negative image among psychiatrists. The profession is organizing itself to deal with the problem from the medical school level up to the highest levels of the APA. Studies such as a 1980 survey of 220 residents in all medical specialties, which showed only anesthesiology as a less fulfilling career than psychiatry, will be challenged or otherwise neutralized. The medical student was singled out as the most significant individual in psychiatry's future, and efforts to attract more into the practice are now under way. Emphasis will be placed on generating excitement among the students, the students will have more exposure to patients in clinical settings and there will be "better teaching." To ensure more suitable teachers there will be a limitation on the number of non-M.D.'s on the staff. For each non-M.D. who teaches medical students, the theory goes, there is a corresponding drop in psychiatric prestige.

The key issue, as many psychiatrists see it, is . . . *we have to correct the impression that psychiatry is still practiced as it was twenty-five years ago.* . . . There have been many changes, and the task is to make others aware and to make psychiatrists proud to be part of the profession.

Three

THE GENDER MENDERS

The hospital is prepossessing in the manner of understated good taste. It has the character of old Eastern Seaboard money. The style is that of a dowager who would prefer tea from mended Limoges to newly minted Syracuse glaze.

The brick for the building was fired before the Revolution. Architecturally the hospital belongs in the country, compatible with other eighteenth-century houses in the area of Richmond.

The staff at the hospital say with pride, —We're one of the oldest. Period.

Like that of a CIA or FBI "safe house," its use is incongruous with the setting. *Gender identity clinic?* The fact is not posted.

As far as the trustees of the parent hospital are concerned, certain psychiatric evaluations and counseling go on here, while at the general hospital certain surgical procedures are performed that one does not discuss at board meetings. . . .

Dr. Charles Scolatti, psychiatrist for more than fifteen years on this particular staff, walks with an athlete's stride up the brick walk. The street is part of an area restored to architectural authenticity, including gaslights that now gobble up diminishing energy reserves.

A bronze plate near the doorbell says "psychiatric unit." It is freshly buffed.

Once inside, Scolatti takes the stairs two at a time.

What are you bringing me, love? His secretary is halfway into his office with an armload of morning mail and professional journals.

Penis envy, she shoots back. —Mother fixations.

He groans. Once inside his office he sheds his jacket and turns to his morning calendar. The first appointment, he sees, is with someone named Mary Gensler. . . .

This Gensler is tall, heavily built, a woman with close-cropped hair and loose-fitting shirt. Her face is round.

How did you hear of us? Scolatti asks.

Friends, people I've met. You know.

Yeah. Scolatti knows that the grapevine works with added efficiency in these cases because of the urgency the patients feel. Have you thought about what might be involved? How long it's going to take?

She shrugs. I'll do whatever is necessary.

Scolatti leans forward, stretching himself tauter. We don't take just anybody. We . . . I . . . have to decide if your reasons are good ones, if your head is in the right place. I turn down more people than I accept.

Look, Mary Gensler says, I'm twenty-seven years old, and ever since I can remember, I've felt something was wrong with me. I was born a girl, but I think of myself as a man. Isn't that the kind of thing you correct here?

Scolatti nods. In the right kind of cases, yes. He riffles through the pile of correspondence on his desk. These are just a few of the requests I've been getting since we set up the Gender Identity Clinic. From the time Christine Jorgensen went public, every male or female born with self-diagnosed gender displacement thinks they can get it corrected with some well-placed medical treatment. Well . . . He sits up to his full height. It just doesn't work that way.

She persists. When I was a little kid, I was always happier playing with the boys. I've always worn boys' clothes . . . She frowns. . . . except when my mother forced me into a dress.

A lot of people like you come through here. Not long ago I had a construction worker sitting where you are. You know what he likes to do?

She shakes her head.

He likes to put on his wife's panty hose. For years he's been doing it when no one was at home. Then one day his wife caught him. A week later he was in here telling me he guessed he better have a sex-change operation. Anyone who wants to wear panty hose has got to be a woman, right? His wife, though, promises to stick by him. "Wait a minute," I tell him, "have you got kids?" "Three," he says, "three little girls." "Do you still make love to your wife?" "Sure," he says, "five to ten times a month. It's as good as it's ever been." Scolatti pauses, watching Mary's reaction. The soft face remains attentive, without embarrassment. "Well then," I tell him, "you don't need surgery, you need to come out of the closet. You like your penis too much, you get up on it, and I'm not about to cut it off." So he goes back to his wife and tells her what I've said. He comes back for counseling. Well, within a year he and his wife have worked it out. Every morning he gets up early and puts on his wife's panty hose and a dress and cleans the house or cooks or does whatever he wants. Then when his daughters and wife get up, he stays that way, they all meet for breakfast, and he changes for work.

Kinky.

Just a transvestite.

But I'm not a transvestite, Mary says, pleading. I'm a man. I'm a man everywhere but here and there . . . pointing to her crotch, touching her breasts.

Have you ever had sexual relations with a woman?

Sure, Mary says, but I always felt as if I was a man. I'm no lesbian.

We'll have to see about that, won't we?

I didn't know you'd be so hard to convince . . . it's my body, after all.

Not quite, Scolatti says. If we go for this, you'll belong to us . . . the plastic surgeon, the urologist, the breast surgeon, the pathologist, the neurologist, the endocrinologist, the internist . . . *and me.*

Wow!
So we make sure . . . is this trip necessary?

Psychiatrists have always made it difficult for transsexuals, transvestites, and homosexuals, mirroring, of course, the social, cultural, and religious biases of the times. From the middle of the nineteenth century, when psychiatry in America began to bloom, the homosexual, especially, was the object of some of the most brutal, mindless treatment.

The psychiatrists had right on their side . . . the practice of homosexuality was clearly against the law. Therefore, encouraging it was out of the question. The Bible had some choice things to say, too, and public morality followed the Bible.

What could a psychiatrist offer, then?

Hope and change. Homosexuals needn't suffer in silence. They could become neuter, maybe even heterosexual. The medical profession could provide some "help." For instance, a clitoridectomy for lesbians, especially for those poor souls suffering from *eroto-mania*, the nineteenth-century definition of being turned on. (When the sex urge was directed at another woman, it was diagnosed as erotomania.) Or . . . they suggested cold sitz baths. That would numb the old urge.

The surgeons were the hired guns, with the psychiatrists diagnosing the pathology. Lesbians were also offered hysterectomies or ovarectomies, and male homosexuals were sentenced to vasectomies, pubic nerve obliterations (to prevent erections), and even lobotomies. The ultimate "treatment" for males was castration, and while the surgeons were doing the cutting many psychiatrists began to wonder if perhaps things hadn't gone a bit too far.

So they turned elsewhere. They tried hormones, deducing that one's homosexual bent was the product of an imbalance in male or female production. Alter the mix and change the drive!

It wasn't so easy. Homosexuals had a peculiar habit of retaining specific sex drives in spite of hormones. And then of course there were the unpleasant side effects . . . higher blood pressure, baldness, increased cancer risk. Had to face it . . . hormones might make a man more or less male and a female more or less female, but homosexuality is much broader than just gender. It covers a multitude of feelings, emotions, appearances, and drives, none of which are exclusively male or female.

Another special treatment, developed in the 1940s, involved the use of electric current. The psychiatrists were shy about talking about it. They referred to it as aversion therapy. Negative conditioning.

The theory went like this: If a person got a jolt of electricity whenever a stimulating sex photo, a homosexual sex photo, was presented, eventually the pleasures evoked by the photo would diminish or disappear with the jolt of pain. The treatment had several stages. First an emetic, a vomit-producing pill, was administered. Then out came a dirty picture. Over and over. The pill, nausea, the picture. Next there would be hormones. And while they were supposed to be pumping away in the system out would come a heterosexual picture.

Still a problem? Then time to move to the big leagues. Shock time. Wired up, dry-mouthed, nervous, and wondering, the patient waits in front of a screen, a control at the fingertips. First a homosexual picture is flashed. There are eight seconds to wipe it off the screen. Eight seconds to decide *no go*. If not . . . blaaaast. Blue bolts. The pain subsides. Another sexy picture appears. The message rings clear . . . you want a homosexual turn-on, be ready for blue bolts. You want a heterosexual turn-on, no pain, no strain.

But that's not all. Some psychiatrists introduced a bit of random shocking, a Russian roulette of blue bolts. At irregular intervals the patient would get zapped *even if he had wiped the image off the screen in eight seconds*. Sometimes he tried to wipe it off and couldn't. And again blue bolts. This was done to build up aversion to "homosexual stimuli." Effective? For a time.

Yet it didn't take long for both psychiatrist and "patient" to realize there was backsliding. What to do then? Back to the old medical technique of the booster. Minor blue bolts. Booster shocks once a month or every six weeks. The expectation was that the final debris of the homosexual urge would be exorcised from the psyche.

Throughout this cruelty the "patient" thanked his psychiatrist while the psychiatrist congratulated his "patient."

Now, if you're looking for some way to get in step with the multitudes, to duck the universal scorn you've contended with since you can remember, the anxieties you felt from *feeling this way*, you'll go any route to reach the promised land. Small wonder that the *scientifically approved* way held allure.

But while the shrinks were offering hope they were also writing the game plan. In order to offer a *cure* there had to be a *disease*, and for generations that's what homosexuality was labeled. A disease. A neurosis, a disorder, unnatural. A disease.

Scolatti is breezing right along now, undaunted by Mary Gensler's frequent questions and comments. He's spoken the same words or a slight variation many times in the months the gender identity clinic has been open. You might as well know what you could be in for, he says. It takes a hell of a long time, it's damn painful, and when you get through, you may not like it anyway. But, baby, then it's too late.

You think this is a snap decision? I don't care what it takes.

First you're ours. For a year you'll come here for psychotherapy, at least once a month. We talk about the whys and the whens. You tell me all about yourself, and when we're through I'll tell you if you pass the test. During that year you'll cross-dress as a man, live the way you think a man should live, do the things you think a man should do. Get used to . . .

I've been doing those things for the last five years, Mary interrupts quietly.

. . . becoming comfortable as a man. You think you'll have a problem with that?

No, I won't have a problem with that. She shakes her head.

Good. Scolatti pushes himself to his feet and stretches mightily, gently patting his flat stomach. He examines Mary closely. You could do with some firming up. Are you athletic?

They always called me a tomboy when I was growing up.

Scolatti slides back into his chair and picks up where he left off. During the year you're cross-dressing and coming to see me, you'll also be taking some male hormones—possibly testosterone. It will make you feel different and look different. You'll be taking the hormones all the way through the treatment and maybe for the rest of your life.

What things will happen to me?

I'll have our endocrinologist speak . . . He stops and shakes his head. Damn, you haven't even filled out the personal history sheet or taken the psychological tests.

She waits. What can she say?

I'm talking to you like you're already in the program, like you're one of my people. He gives Mary a penetrating look. What I've been saying today doesn't mean anything, you get no brownie points just for sitting there and listening to me. *If* we decide to let you in the program, even for the first year, it's going to be based on a lot more than one conversation.

Yessir.

Scolatti nods. Then, after at least a year of psychotherapy, if we want to continue with you, we get to the cutting. He pauses. The way you're doing it is tougher, of course.

How do you mean?

With you we add equipment. Most others we cut it off. *That's* much easier, less time, less complicated, costs a hell of a lot less. He watches for her reaction. There is none. Anyway, he continues, the first thing is to remove the fatty tissues in your breasts, but we save the nipple and stretch your new chest nice and flat. You'll get a total hysterectomy, and that should clean out the inside plumbing. All of this, you understand, is taking place over a period of a couple of years. None of these operations happen . . . bing . . . bing . . . Then comes what you've been waiting for . . . your very own penis. We'll build you a penis.

He stops, noting the questioning look on her face. You want to see how?

She nods, and Scolatti pushes himself to his feet. With his two index fingers he outlines the surgical procedure on his own abdominal area. There are several stages to all this, he says, but first we make two parallel incisions, vertically, about where you'd have a cesarean section, maybe an inch and a half wide and about six inches long. We carry the incisions down to the groin and then make a roll of the skin flap and sew it closed lengthwise. This is called a pedicle. Then we walk the pedicle down your abdomen, flip by flip, to keep the blood supply intact. We make a scrotum from your vaginal lips and insert a couple of fake testicles—something like Ping-Pong balls—and there you have it. Of course, the urologist has to operate to hook up your urinary system, and that's probably the most difficult surgery of all.

You say all of this will take several years?

Three or four at least.

Mary is undaunted. That sure doesn't bother me. I've spent about thirty years living a lie, what's three or four more to make things right?

Psychiatrists are good at helping to do away with lies in people's lives. For transsexuals such as Mary Gensler they try to see whether the mind and body are out of step, and if they are, then it's cut . . . and stitch . . . and back together. Where the mind dominates, it becomes easier to change the body . . . and it's the psychiatrist who decides when and how the mind dominates.

But it isn't always easy.

—Help me, I'm a woman in a man's body, the patient says.

Not so fast, the psychiatrist thinks, does this character know what a woman is like? —Very interesting, but what's a woman?

—A woman's soft and gentle and has feelings and can cry and be tender . . .

—What's a man?

Oh . . . rough, drinks too much, never shows feelings . . .

Damn, the psychiatrist thinks, stereotypical behavior again. Back to square one . . .

With homosexuals the lie was the other way around. Mind and body at odds with convention, don't change the body, change the mind.

Could psychiatrists help?

Of course.

But *only* with the proper perspective. Homosexuality: it's usually against the law, has been for hundreds and hundreds of years, it violates our religious tenets, it has often been considered corrupt and destructive behavior. . . . But was it wrong? Wrong medically?

Yes, said the psychiatrists. . . . Was someone sick who practiced homosexuality? Yes . . . Was it a disease, a pathology? Well . . .

It was the psychoanalysts' ball game because psychiatry was theirs for so many years. They set the rules, they were the umpires. From the time of Freud they knew how the sociocultural winds were blowing . . . that a society so hung up on heterosexual expression could never, *never* buy homosexual deviation. We can explain it all, they said, we know what happens to make a person homosexual. It's really a mind problem.

It's evil, sinful birth, Religion answers.

It's a sociopathic personality, Law intones.

A mind problem, the psychoanalysts insist. You have a person who acts differently from others, who wants to have sex differently from others, *sex we know is wrong and unnatural*, that person's mind needs clearing. There's a sickness, a pathological neurosis. Since we're the mind people, we'll take it from here. . . .

The homosexual's problem lay in the early years, the psychoanalysts said. An inadequate development of the Oedipal complex that made the person both fearful of and turned off by physical attraction and sex with someone of the opposite sex. In the early years each of us is attracted to the parent of the opposite sex, but at the same time we sense a rivalry with the *other* parent, and this will give us guilt and anxiety. No problem as long as the parents understand all this, don't feel threatened or encourage the attraction too strongly . . . if they just let it play itself out.

But where this doesn't happen, the homosexual monster can appear, given a boost by the cloying, smothering parent, that all too familiar stereotype.

The psychoanalysts were especially interested in the child's guilt and anxiety resulting from rivalry with and attraction for the parents. Punishment was one way to wipe away the guilt and anxiety, but it had to be an appropriate kind of punishment, something that definitely fitted the transgression.

Aha! Let the child design its own punishment. Since all of this has to do with sexual feelings, why not . . . castration! That's a punishment all right, a severe, frightening experience, definitely anxiety producing.

Hence, castration anxiety.

But anxiety's almost as bad as the actual punishment. Can the anxiety itself be avoided?

Create a defense. We do *that* all the time. So we *deny* our original interest in the parent of the opposite sex, and by extension any interest in members of the opposite sex.

The psychoanalysts could rest, the enigma of homosexuality was unraveled. It was obviously a mind problem all along. . . .

That's pretty much where things stood until 1957 when Evelyn Hooker did a new study of homosexuality, and her conclusions were startling. No, she said, all the studies, all the research that's been done since Krafft-Ebing and Freud in the nineteenth century *doesn't* support the idea that abnormal development during the Oedipal stage is the *only* way a person can become homosexual. It may be one way, but cultural factors, social conditioning, play an important part too. Socio-sexual learning can take place right up into early adulthood, it may have nothing to do with guilt and anxiety and attraction for Mother and castration. . . .

No way, the psychoanalysts came back. Why, we can work through that poorly developed Oedipal stage and change a person from homosexual to heterosexual. Just give us enough time, and we'll show you.

Along comes Irving Bieber, a New York psychoanalyst. A defender of the faith, he proposed the scientific approach: let's expose homosexuals to full, in-depth psychoanalysis, let's monitor them from day one and see if they come out of it as heterosexuals; let's compare them with a group of heterosexuals also going through analysis and see the similarities and differences.

The profession cheered.

In 1962 Bieber's study was published, and the results showed . . . whatever you wanted them to show.

Bieber took 106 homosexual or bisexual people and followed them through the daily, weekly, monthly grind. When it was all over he came up with: *fewer than one in five homosexuals transformed to complete heterosexuality, one in two bisexuals transformed to complete heterosexuality.*

See, the psychoanalysts and their True Believers said, we *can* change people, we have the key. Homosexuality is not a permanent disability. All psychiatry should benefit.

You had time on your side, the critics carped, pointing to a greater success rate when the patients had 350 or more hours of psychoanalysis.

In-depth psychoanalysis is not a quick fix, the True Believers retorted. These are deep-seated, primal problems.

The success record is hardly remarkable, the critics persisted. With homosexuals the record is dismal. You've failed four out of five times. Those are lousy odds.

But we've shown psychoanalysis *can* make a difference. The problem is a poorly developed Oedipal stage.

The sample is hardly representative of all homosexuals. These are only people who really *wanted* to change. A lot don't.

Many would come around if they knew what we could do now.

That's if you assume homosexuality to be a sickness, a neurosis.

Well, of course it is.

So it went through the decade of the 1960s, not much changed from decades past, except that now each side had more studies to support its "scientific" theories.

For the psychiatric profession as a whole it was further confirmation of long-held beliefs. Though Freud had always been careful about his characterization of homosexuality, he never thought it the biologic norm . . . and psychiatry was content to build on that.

Charles Scolatti leans back in his chair, confident now that Mary Gensler is impressed with the severity and complexity of the transsexual operations. He knows, however, he must reinforce the lesson. Many times all the patient thinks about is that beautiful new body, never mind the problems along the way.

You remind me of someone who came here three years ago, he says, a big woman, good body and all. Like you she wanted the female-to-male change, and she was so damn impatient! Couldn't wait for the hormones to work, didn't want the psychotherapy. Well, I told her straight out, I make the rules around here. If she didn't like it she could get out of the program.

Did she?

Scolatti twirls some kinky curls in his sideburn. She's in limbo right now. She started with us, but something happened where she worked and she still is not sure whether to get on with it.

She couldn't have been as determined as I am.

Oh? Scolatti says. I wouldn't be too sure of that. He pats the hair of the sideburn into place. It was after she had been cross-dressing for almost a year and taking the hormones. There was a teacher's strike in the city schools, and the school board was advertising for substitute teachers. She decides to apply *as a man*. Her college transcript has only her first initials, so no one suspects she's anything but what she says she is. They assign her to sixth grade, and for the first time in years she's really enjoying herself. No one knows anything . . . so she thinks. Her voice is lower because of the hormones, she's big and dresses in jackets and slacks. There's only one problem. Every day she has to cross the picket line outside the school but she doesn't think anything of it, only that the kids are getting an education and she's helping to provide it. Then one day a man comes up to her and says, "As a scab how do you like teaching sixth grade?"

She starts to walk by without answering when he grabs her arm and says, "I happen to know you're no mister. Now do I have to go any farther? We'll blow the whistle on you unless you quit. Get out of the school system and stay out."

Jesus! Mary Gensler says. How shitty.

It's life, dear girl. Now do you see why we don't just shoot from the hip around here?

Scolatti has voiced what a tough responsibility it is to pick and choose among the characters who come through the gender identity clinic. Who needs to play god like this? Values change and maybe in twenty, thirty years transsexual operations will be out. No sooner is the *homo*sexual thing taken care of than we have the *trans*sexuals.

Above all else you have to have a secure ego to get through this, he says suddenly to Mary. Strong ego.

*   *   *

The step to calling homosexuality a sickness, a neurosis, was inevitable. Prominent in the *Diagnostic and Statistical Manual* was homosexuality, then considered a psychiatric disorder of substantial magnitude. Yet by the mid-1960s it became apparent that cohesive political action could work wonders for those who had been shoved around too long.

For the psychiatrists the first rumblings came during a convention of their association near the end of the decade. Leo Alexander, formerly head psychiatrist at the Nuremberg trials and a man most respected by his brethren, was chairing a panel dealing with treatment of homosexuals. Aversion therapy was the topic, electric shock and reactions the focus.

Alexander clears his throat and makes the requisite introductions of the panel; a speaker rises and smooths the pages of his paper.

A whistle blows, there is shouting from the floor. Voices begin a tirade from all sides of the room as people push through the doors holding banners condemning psychiatrists for using electric shock. There are shouts that shock kills, that psychiatrists are modern-day witch doctors, unknowing and uncaring.

Gay power. Murderers! How many of us have committed suicide because you've made life unbearable with your antiquated moral judgments!

A few psychiatrists recover their aplomb.

On the dais the speaker pulls the mike closer and starts to read. But the psychiatrists in the audience are agitated. The din grows louder, and it's apparent the speaker is outmatched.

For another few minutes the tug-of-war continues, but the demonstrators prove too numerous and too loud. Look at us, they shout. We're gay and proud. Take a good look, because never again will you consign us to the garbage heap. Stop trying to make us into your image of *normal*.

Reluctantly the panelists, led by Alexander, stand up and slowly make their way off the dais. They tried, but who could read a paper in this chaos?

The spark of gay power takes fire. Wednesday evening, the traditionally social evening of the American Psychiatric Association

Convention, will never be the same again. It is the occasion of the president's dinner dance, the psychiatrists dressed in formal wear.

A few blocks away three young psychiatrists sit around a small table in a neighborhood pub. Each has come alone and has been surprised to find the others. Now, with certainty born of place and situation, they acknowledge their mutual homosexuality. It would have been awkward for them to attend the dinner dance stag, and they certainly had no desire to escort a *woman*.

They talk. How many of us do you think there are? Who knows, no one wants to risk coming out. Is it crazy to suggest we have our own party during the president's ball? Why not?

So, at next year's convention, when Wednesday comes a modest announcement is passed around. For those who feel uncomfortable at the president's dinner dance a special evening with refreshments and conversation will be offered.

It is a judicious, tentative step reflecting the concern of a few gay psychiatrists who have shed the protective mantle of anonymity. The uncertainties abound for these men and women. What will this do for their careers? Will they be frozen out of referrals, the life-blood of a psychiatrist's practice? Will there be coercion from the Association?

They feel they are the cutting edge of an irresistible movement. They know they have to do this. If their profession regards them as neurotic, outside the biologic norm, then how tainted is the mental health they practice!

The fears dissipate as the first social evening turns into a surprising success, and people realize there are more "open" gay psychiatrists than anyone suspects. Other social programs are planned, and there is talk that gay psychiatrists may soon be presenting and reading papers on homosexuality. There might even be a booth at the convention.

In spite of this, through the early 1970s the gay psychiatrists remain the hushed orphans of the profession, sullied by psychiatric labeling of psychiatric disability. There is the *Diagnostic and Statistical Manual* to prove it.

Beyond psychiatric jargon, gay power had already made its mark. From Kinsey's work in 1948, which first showed evidence of homosexuality as a statistical norm, through the 1960s when long-held prejudices were held up for scrutiny, it became apparent that psychiatry, like conservative religions, was anachronistic in its labeling.

Gay psychiatrists decided to approach their Association. We think you should take another look at homosexuality, they said. Many psychiatrists do not hold with the view of psychiatric disorder.

Right, right. We'll look into this. The big stall.

A year, two, passed before straight shrinks joined the request. We want action. Gay people are being denigrated by and within the profession. They are being asked to conform to a straight's view of normality. Civil rights, in fact, are being violated.

And so they asked for a resolution by the trustees of the APA supporting the rights of homosexuals not to be discriminated against in employment, housing, public accommodations, licensing, and performing homosexual acts by consenting adults in private . . . and . . . a statement that homosexuality does not constitute a psychiatric disorder.

Suppose a homosexual wants to *change*? A bleating call to hold the fort.

Then call that anxiety a "sexual orientation disturbance." But distinguish this from someone who is content with his sexual orientation.

The trustees voted the resolution in December 1973 and put it to a vote of the membership in 1974.

There were angry mutterings. Why don't we vote on schizophrenia as well? Or manic depression. Or paranoia. What is politics doing in medicine?

Indeed, what is medicine doing in politics? Check out history.

When the vote was counted, 59 percent, a heady majority in light of the mutterings, voted that homosexuality should no longer be labeled a psychiatric disorder and should be removed from the *Diagnostic and Statistical Manual*.

Thoughtful gay psychiatrists pondered the vote: 59 percent is a nice number. Yes. *That still leaves 41 percent of those voting who still think gay is sick.* Is this attitude good for the mental health of someone gay who wishes or needs psychiatric help? Would you send a Jew to a Nazi?

It is yet another convention of the American Psychiatric Association. During the next few years gay psychiatrists have organized themselves into the Gay Lesbian and Bisexual Caucus of Members of the APA. There are over four hundred members holding regular meetings, reading and presenting papers. They have been provided recognition and support by the Association and now have a convention booth.

This year's theme is that gay psychiatry covers the country, and at the booth there's a large map of the United States with pins locating caucus members in every state. In Iowa, Alaska, Alabama, New Hampshire. A network of gay shrinks.

As a member of the caucus mans the booth a florid, middle-aged man walks up. He points to the map. —I still think you people are very sick, and I know that it has been proven you are. His badge identifies him as a psychiatrist from Boston. —Take a look at Bieber's study. It's right there, the proof.

The gay shrink answers politely. —The study, if you want to call it that, was hardly representative.

Boston-badge is enmeshed in his rhetoric. —You people are probably going to take over the world. The map apparently worries him. —Look where you've gotten in *our* country.

—I doubt that we'll take over the world. That is not of the slightest concern.

Certain now. —You can't fool me. That's what going to happen. You can seduce anybody. A lot of us know it and we're ready for you. Keep *that* in mind.

A woman bulging in a polyester pant suit beckons Boston-badge to hurry up. The gay shrink catches something in her eyes. Fear? Unease? My god, could it be *jealousy*?

About Sexual Preference

It seems clear that the number of transsexual operations being performed across the country is on the increase. This is partly the result of publicity given to the successful treatment of celebrities such as tennis player Renée Richards, and partly because the medical uncertainties of matching body and mind have been eased. There are now close to twenty major gender-identity clinics across the United States, and there are, in addition, physicians who will perform the surgery outside the constraints of such a clinic. The emotional aspects of transsexual surgery are important, and someone trained to evaluate a patient's emotional stability, maturity, and comprehension of the consequences would seem to be essential. But does it have to be a psychiatrist? There is no mental disorder here, no mental illness. Should the standards inherent in the medical model apply? Is a person seeking transsexual surgery *sick?*

Much of the current transsexual tide started in the mid-1960s at Johns Hopkins University, where one of the first gender identity clinics was opened. Thousands of patients were treated over the years, and people like Dr. John Money acquired international reputations. Now, however, Johns Hopkins has decided to stop doing the operations, and a major reason is a study by a Johns Hopkins psychiatrist, Dr. Jon K. Meyer, that those who have had the surgery are no better adjusted than those who were denied the surgery. This will undoubtedly slow the response to requests for transsexual surgery. But there are many psychiatrists who don't agree with Dr. Meyer. In fact, a current study done at the University of Minnesota shows that of those transsexuals contacted after treatment, the great majority indicated a significant improvement in psychologic functioning. It's clear that a major reason why psychiatrists rather than nonmedical mental health professionals do psychotherapy with transsexuals is because all other aspects of the treatment are medically based. It is a doctor's monopoly, yet few people have asked whether a psychiatrist's training prepares him adequately for such work.

The gay psychiatrists section of the American Psychiatric Association feels that *no* nongay psychiatrist should treat a homosexual, no matter what the complaint. The section claims a membership within APA exceeding five hundred psychiatrists; they are well financed and well organized. It is their aim to remove all psychiatric discrimination against homosexuals both within the profession and outside. They are adamant . . . sexual preference, they insist, is *not* a psychiatric disorder.

Four

COMING
THROUGH THE RYE

You're drinking too much. . . . Janet hears the words sharp and clear. He said the same words last night, didn't he? She can't recall. Maybe it was a couple of days ago. But he's always on her back. She dances over to her husband to give him a hug. Let him know she has no hard feelings. He disengages her arms from his neck.

You're stuffy, she says, and puts a record on the stereo. She begins a whirling dance. The volume is high. Janet, he says, you'll wake the kids. . . .

She barely hears him now as her fingers click to the music . . . watch . . . tele . . . vision . . . she murmurs in syncopation.

He gets up from the couch, disgusted, and goes back to their bedroom, where they keep the television set. Janet dances faster and faster to the music, bumps against the doorjamb to the kitchen but scarcely feels it. The record finishes, and she goes into the kitchen without turning off the stereo. She opens the refrigerator and takes out a half-full whiskey sour that she had poured while she washed the supper dishes. She wants to do something, an overpowering need comes over her to move, to go out or call someone on the phone. Has to keep in motion. Certainly not tired enough to go to bed. Can't sit still for television. She starts dialing a friend. A sleepy voice answers on the other end and Janet is off and running. . . . I have to talk. Listen, how are you? . . . There is no stopping her until fifteen minutes later when her friend finally pries herself away. Janet looks at the half inch left in her glass and can't stand the sight. She pours it down the sink. She looks at her reflection in the night-blackened window, and for a minute she thinks she is her own mother. The eyes and cheeks have fallen, age lines are *there*. . . . But she poured the drink out, didn't she? I'm not an alcoholic, she mouths to the window. . . .

In the seven hours since she started drinking this day, Janet has consumed a half quart of whiskey sours and a quarter gallon of wine. There is vodka within reach too, but she keeps *it* back for late-night drinking. She drinks for one reason . . . the sedative effect.

Alcohol is among the quickest-acting soporifics in a family of drugs that includes paraldehyde, barbiturates, ether, and chloroform. It reaches the bloodstream quickly as significant amounts are absorbed through the stomach lining. When it hits the stomach, it increases the secretion of hydrochloric acid and becomes a direct stomach and intestinal irritant.

Janet drinks because it depresses her central nervous system. As some of the neurons stop working she experiences pleasure. She floats. Her anxieties diminish. There is a golden haze between her and the demanding, rushing world.

After Janet had her first drink in the late afternoon, she found she was no longer jumpy. She became calm, cool, relaxed. And she felt so good she didn't want to lose the high. She sipped another, a little faster, and now a clarity came to her. She basked in her own self-control. Another couple of ounces, then she noticed energy. She moved faster, organized the meal, helped with homework, set up a car pool, ran down to the basement to do a load of clothes . . . and stumbled. Another bruise. But she didn't feel it. Her thighs and shins had been bruised for ages. Accident prone, she declared.

She decided to cool the drinking and tried to sit down with a book. She couldn't keep still. She was agitated. . . .

As the short-term sedation of alcohol wears off, the psychomotor activity becomes more noticeable. There is always some psycho-motor activity or agitation from a sedating drug. If Janet felt tense again, it was only natural. She needed more alcohol to calm her down. Agitation, sedation, on and on. Eventually it would be al-most impossible to decrease the agitation to the point where she could relax.

She lay in bed with her eyes open. The room was not clear, and she felt dislocated. She was outside her body and not sure where she was. She had to go to the bathroom and lost the way. But she felt wide awake. She could drive all night if she had to. She wished, in fact, she could go outside and run until exhausted. She forced herself to return to bed and lie as quietly as possible next to her sleeping husband.

What is wrong with me, she wondered? She drank to relax. She can't figure out what's going on inside her. . . .

There is diminished oxygen being carried to her brain because of the alcohol, and already there is a deterioration of more than the normal amount of cells. She's in her thirties and thinks she's aging normally. She is wrong.

Psychiatrists, no less than other physicians, are often baffled and frustrated in the attempt to deal with alcohol addiction. There are *so* many views. . . . In 1979 some psychiatrists decided that men (and, by analogy, women) in their thirties could not have *de-tectable* organic brain syndrome. The aging process simply could not progress that far, that fast. *Wrong!* say the alcoholic psychiatric specialists. We *know* it can happen, we've seen it happen. . . .

The whys of addiction are easier to trace. From the earliest days people have been looking for something they could take that would alter reality . . . and alcohol is one of the oldest substances, and certainly the most socially acceptable. Diarrhea? Try a little black-berry brandy . . . Chilly? Have a shot of bourbon . . . Bad appetite? A sip of port . . .

Hard on the heels of alcohol came other drugs; chloral hydrate, morphine, barbiturates, jungle powders and esoteric alchemy . . . And there was belladonna, a derivative of deadly nightshade that enlarged the pupils of the eyes and affected the central nervous system.

The whys of alcohol addiction *do* intrigue. —Why is it so many people use alcohol and it doesn't cause problems? Yet why does a significant and varying minority use alcohol and find that it dominates their lives? asks a psychiatrist who does alcohol research and also has a clinical practice. We need to know if there is a common chord of personality behavior that predisposes toward addiction. Is it like eating too much? Some people face stress by eating, some get a high from sweets, some gorge themselves as a reward or to gain a form of nurturing.

But eating doesn't set off the cycle of sedation . . . agitation . . . sedation . . . agitation . . . that goes with alcohol. And so the addiction propensities are not so strong.

By having a drink with meals or drinking very slowly, the alcohol sedation-agitation cycle can be avoided. Then the alcohol is gradually dispersed through the system, and the agitation is just as diffused. But a person who drinks for sedative effect doesn't want that. He or she might just as well not drink at all. The drinking is not for taste or for sociability. It is for *effect*.

Janet holds her hands up to the morning light streaming into the kitchen. She had awakened at five and stumbled to the bathroom with a raging thirst and a dull, soporific ache behind the eyes. When she lay back down, sweat beaded on her neck. She wiped at her face with the hem of her nightgown and closed her eyes. She cursed herself for not taking aspirin while she was up, but she couldn't bear the thought of getting up again. Her good friend at work had told her an infallible trick to lessen a hangover. Drink a pint of cold water and take two aspirin before going to bed. Janet could never remember.

Now, alone and blurry, standing in front of the light, she studies her hands. They feel as if they were shaking off her wrists, but they *look* steady. The agitation she feels must be in her *head*. She has a glass of juice and a Librium. Her body feels hot and cold at the same time. Could she be going through change of life in her thirties? Absurd.

*   *   *

At dinnertime she takes her whiskey sour to the table and spoons a few peas and a small piece of chicken onto her plate. Her sons and husband start to eat, and she toys with her food. Aren't you hungry? Her husband pauses with a forkful in his hand.

He raises his eyebrows as she sips from the glass. Why didn't you finish your cocktail before you came to the table? How can you mix that with *wine*?

Her sons pick up on her husband's disapproval. Mom got rammed in the rear, the older one says. It dented the trunk.

What's this?

The boy rushes on. She picked me up from scouts and on the way home she came to a stop all of a sudden in the middle of the block and a truck rammed the car. Almost threw me into the windshield.

Her husband looks squarely at her. Did you get his license? His insurance company?

Janet shakes her head. It wasn't his fault. I shouldn't have stopped so suddenly. I dropped my purse and it got tangled in my foot.

Was she drinking? Her husband directs the question to the older boy.

I could smell something.

The younger boy kicks him. Tattletale.

Janet looks from one to the other. Why are you picking on me again? Haven't you anything better to do? She's furious now and downs her drink in a gulp. I'll have the damn car repaired, don't worry. And you can pick him up from scouts in the future. Or he can get another ride. Her son's disloyalty is more than she can bear.

She gets up and leaves through the back door. Enjoy your dinner! She has plenty of friends she can go see. Plenty of friends where the vodka isn't measured and parceled out.

But she doesn't get in the car. Instead she walks around the yard, then up and down the street. Her temper and agitation abate and she's ready to go back to apologize.

When she sneaks in the back door she hears click, click, click, click and shouts from downstairs. They have gone to the basement to play Ping-Pong. She'll tell her husband she's sorry. Everything will be okay. But she has to get up nerve to talk, to settle down the excitement inside. She opens the cabinet where laundry supplies are kept and pulls out a plastic bottle marked bleach. She pours half a glass.

Hey, Janet! In a stride her husband is across the room, wresting the glass from her hand. My god, honey, what are you doing? He grabs the bleach bottle with the other hand. Then he sniffs the glass. What? It's vodka? I thought it was *poison*. I thought . . . He tries to take it all in. You hide *vodka* in bleach bottles? Are you crazy? No, don't bother to answer. You are crazy. You are sick. Sick. And you're going to see somebody. If you don't see somebody, I'm leaving and taking the kids. Better yet, I'm kicking you out. . . . His anger knows no bounds. He wants to pound her.

Janet is in shock. Up to this point she has been able to balance everything out. She has kept a pretty good secret, she thought. Now here is this man, almost demented, dialing the number of the local hospital and asking for the name of a shrink. A psychiatrist.

You're the one who's crazy, she yells. But without conviction. She is not together enough to counteract his threat. For all she knows he could put her out, with suitcase and clothes. Her mind is in such a haze. A shrink? The final degradation.

Psychiatrists generally detest alcohol addiction problems. There is little chance of working cures, let alone miracles. Alcohol addicts are masters at denial. They are devious. Their psyches are usually so addled that they make the worst possible candidates for psychoanalysis. And if they achieve some sort of breakthrough on the psychiatric couch, surely they will have lost the thread the next day. If there is impaired memory, how can there be psychological progress? And until there is a rational, drug-free mind to work with, how can one get to the psychological reasons why an alcoholic wants to be in a sedated state?

The field is scattered with burned-out psychiatrists who in all earnestness and with every skill at hand have attempted to work with the actively drinking alcoholic. Psychiatric leaders thump tables and say that one-to-one therapy does not work with an active alcoholic. The drunk will lead one down the garden path, will have impaired faculties, will find every excuse to continue drinking. Some go so far as to say that a psychiatrist working with an active alcoholic impedes any progress to recovery. The doctor becomes part of the problem. The doctor is the rescuer, the traditional role. He has been trained to *do for* the patient, rather than to expect the patient to do for himself. Yet countless practitioners insist there must be a cause and then exert full effort to discover what it can be.

Psychiatric specialists in alcohol addiction claim they will find definite organic brain syndrome, even in young addicts. The alcoholic *looks* different. Active alcoholics can be spotted. They are like a different species! But, they counter, this does not mean that there is such a thing as an "alcoholic personality." In a recovered state the former alcoholic is no different from anyone else as far as personality goes. Craving sedation? Yes. But no more nor less creative, no more nor less angry, no more nor less successful, no more nor less sensitive.

Alcohol treatment as a psychiatric or medical specialty is relatively recent. It was only in the 1960s when the first treatment center was set up at McLean Hospital in Boston. Doctors with any knowledge in the field were scarce when young Ralph Ryback, an assistant professor of psychiatry at Harvard Medical School, was tapped for the position of director of Alcohol and Drug Abuse Services. Dr. Ryback had become a celebrity in the field when he hit the pages of national magazines with his alcohol tests on fish. The punsters of the day joked about his getting the creatures stewed to the gills. And in fact he often did. Curious about memory deficits created by alcohol, and curious too about the absorption of alcohol in cells, he set out to cocktail the fish.

What is not generally known is that fish can be trained to solve mazes and perform memory tasks. Ryback got them a little inebriated and trained them. Sobered up, they forgot. But when he would serve another mild pick-me-up to return them to the happy state again, they *remembered*. This revelation had implications far beyond the tests in the alcohol-infused water in which his little carp cavorted. Further intrigued, he got their alcohol blood level up to high intoxication and sent them through their paces. Sobered up they could remember nothing. Blackout. Intoxicate them again? They could not recall. Same as humans.

The fish told Ryback something else. Wherever water goes in the body, alcohol can go too. To the intestines (to create irritation), the stomach (to annoy the lining), the face, the fingers, legs, toes (to make them puffy), and to the kidneys (to inhibit the waste-ridding process). And what's happening inside shows up outside. *An alcoholic looks different.*

At McLean Hospital, Ryback examined and treated thousands of alcoholics, as inpatients and as outpatients. He observed psychiatric and psychological counseling, studied community support groups such as Alcoholics Anonymous, and came up with the simple yet workable theory that guides his research at the National Institute of Mental Health . . . *An alcoholic must stop drinking before he can be helped!*

When the hospital gave the names of three psychiatrists to Janet's husband, he shoved the list in his pocket. He would call them from the office and choose one for her.

At the office he closed his door, then thought of the switchboard and the possibility he would be overheard. He could not take that chance. As if he were making an assignation, he decided to operate in secrecy. He took the numbers and a palm full of dimes and went to the lobby, to the pay phones.

With the first two psychiatrists he blurted out his wife's problem. Alcoholic, he told their secretaries. They told him there was no free time in the schedules for the foreseeable future. They suggested a treatment center, like a hospital or an alcoholic's retreat. With the third psychiatrist's secretary, he became cagier. . . . She has . . . um . . . troubles . . . probably from overwork. Maybe an identity crisis . . . He liked those words. *Identity crisis.* Buzz words for disgruntled females and perhaps he could get her to a shrink under that guise.

It wasn't difficult. He got her an appointment for the next week.

*   *   *

The secretary asked Janet if she had a rider in her health insurance for mental disorders. She had major medical, Janet told her. It covers, the secretary answered.

The psychiatrist was slow and easy with Janet. She looked at the couch, wondering if she'd be asked to stretch out. There was no such suggestion. Instead the psychiatrist asked her if she wanted to sit on some cushions, but she declined, holding herself upright and tense. He asked her why she thought her husband was worried about her. She shrugged. . . . It's *his* problem, she said, not mine, and it's my son's problem. They pick on me.

There were no raised eyebrows or sidelong glances from the psychiatrist. As soon as the words were out she thought she must sound paranoid. Instead he nodded and said that there are usually scapegoats in every family under stress. Maybe she was the scapegoat. They'd have to find out.

She could have kissed him. That's exactly the way she felt. He asked her why she felt that way, if she could think of incidents. Was she ready to remember?

Janet felt close to tears. She had not had a drink for fifteen hours, and her emotions were raw. She said she wasn't ready.

They talked about other things, her sons, where she had grown up, how she came to marry her husband.

The next day her husband asked to talk to the psychiatrist and got him on the phone between patients. He said he didn't know how much Janet had told him, but he thought the doctor ought to realize Janet was a heavy drinker. Surely he would not drop Janet as a patient now, since he had made room for her. There was no response from the psychiatrist, except to ask if that's all Janet's husband wanted to tell him. Yes, the husband said, furious now that the man didn't want to hear about his *own* angers and frustrations.

The psychiatrist could have cursed this turn of events. He could do without a female alcoholic patient. He had seen his share, and they were what in the old days people called "hysterics." His own mother had been strong, unbending, in control of herself. It was his father who had been the lush. If it had to be one in the family, let it

be the man . . . not the woman! An image-breaker, that's what a
female alcoholic meant.

But the psychiatrist was also humane. He believed alcohol abuse
was nothing more than a symptom of deeper hurt. The woman
was trying to survive. He could never countenance going back to
the time when drunks were treated like criminals and thrown into
barred rooms to sober up. The woman had problems, he was sure
of it. Why else would she want to escape into a sedated state? He
wouldn't turn her away, but how the hell was he going to treat her
unless she sobered up? He'd have to confront her.

In recurring issues of *Psychiatric News*, the tabloid-size newspaper of the American Psychiatric Association, he had seen double-
page ads featuring actor Patrick O'Neal advertising Antabuse, a
drug that will cause anyone taking even one drink to become vio-
lently sick. He hardly ever prescribed Antabuse, though he knew
general practitioners used it frequently.

But this testimony of Patrick O'Neal's was seductively com-
pelling. There, big as life, next to O'Neal, was the truth that hurt.
You've been lied to, Doctor . . . by the alcoholic . . .

There isn't a psychiatrist who likes to think he can't get at the
truth. It may lie under the surface, but surely it can be reached.
Yet here is this admitted ex-alcoholic telling all . . . that *he*, just like
his fellow boozers, schemed, obfuscated, *lied*, avoiding the one big
issue. . . . He had denied. Even to himself.

And O'Neal in the ad tells the psychiatrists they have to confront
the patient. Never mind the searching and tentative probing of the
psyche. Confrontation. And after confrontation, perhaps Antabuse.

The picture of O'Neal shows him sitting at a grained wood table
in his dark pin-striped suit, with muted polka-dot tie, his cuffs shot
just so, and in front of him an on-the-rocks glass upside down,
placed over a prescription-sized piece of paper.

The psychiatrist can't escape the stepped-up promotion of Antabuse. The manufacturer is hitting the profession with a harder sell
than when Antabuse, the trade name for disulfiram, first came on
the market years ago.

The pill to create negative feedback. Negative reinforcement.

You have a drink while taking disulfiram and . . . whammo! . . . down on your knees. Sick! Throbbing headache, copious vomiting, chest pains, vertigo, blurred vision . . .

The psychiatrist recalls his residency, when the drunks would be brought into the psycho ward to be sobered up and dried out. Tell you what we're going to do, the staff doctors would announce to the hard-core drinkers . . . we're going to give you a pill. Now you don't have to take it, but we guarantee it will make you want to give up drinking. . . .

He recalls one man, a slight, shaky inmate who was very willing. My wife doesn't want me back this way, and I've lost my job, and you say I have to stay here until I'm better. . . . Bring on the pill!

Sounded easy. He'd been without booze for a week, and the water had flowed from his engorged cells, his appetite was slowly returning, and maybe there was a future.

They took him to a stripped-down room with a cot. Ominously there was a bucket in the corner. The orderly gave him a glass of water and a pill. Nothing to it.

By the way . . . the orderly spread a rubber sheet on the cot . . . we figure you might want some vodka on the rocks a little later.

What are you talking about? The patient was confused.

Some people get a little queasy with alcohol after taking this pill, but you can see for yourself.

The pill made his heart race a bit. It sure would have been nice to calm down a little. The orderly came back with a water glass of ice and vodka. . . . Sure, I'll try it. . . . He took a drink. It soothed him, and he felt wonderful. The orderly asked if he wanted another. . . . Sure . . . He had never turned down a drink in his life.

Two days later the psychiatrist talked to the man. He was still clammy and weak.

I was never so sick in my life. I wanted to die. It seemed like I was trying to vomit for hours. I couldn't get my breath and ended up on the floor. They let me go on like that, on and on . . .

You drank a lot of alcohol, the psychiatrist tells him. A third of a bottle was finished. What do you think about drinking *now*, when you've taken Antabuse?

The man had shaken his head. Never. Never again.

The psychiatrist knows that, unlike a hangover that follows excessive drinking, the reaction to disulfiram is immediate and violent. Even small amounts of alcohol can cause throbbing headache, sweating, vomiting, chest-pain, weakness. The reaction continues as long as there is alcohol in the blood. A swig of cough medicine could make someone sick for half an hour or more. A good amount of alcohol could kill.

The psychiatrist had been reluctant to prescribe it ever since he saw the results. Now the drug ad with Patrick O'Neal made him even more cautious. It mentions the possibility of congestive heart failure and death. Not to be trifled with . . . *unless the risks of continued drinking outweigh the risks of taking the drug*. He'd have to think about that, but with luck he'd never have to make that decision.

He doesn't consider Janet one of these cases. In fact, he certainly doesn't think of Janet in terms of alcoholism. He put down on her chart for insurance reimbursement purposes that she has an affective disorder from midlife stress. About as harmless a diagnosis as he could make.

But the next time she comes for therapy she is loose and almost disjointed. There is the residual smell of alcohol on her breath in spite of the Binaca spray she totes around.

She talks volubly, but he interrupts her from time to time to get her back on track. She has trouble following his questioning, and when she tells him at the end of the session that she thought things "went well," he suspects his original diagnosis. He decides she may have an acute drinking problem that is compounding evident anxieties and depression. He is tempted to prescribe a benzodiazepine. There are plenty of good ones on the market for anxiety and depression, but he is uncertain if he can persuade her to substitute the medication for alcohol. If she starts to take the two together, there will be added central nervous system depression, and this could be not only tricky but lethal. He is one psychiatrist who never forgot the effects of multidrugging that he saw in the Veterans Administration hospital wards and the disastrous side effects that often resulted.

Seeing her in this state probably means she has liver involvement that would hinder the body's ability to dispose of the drug. The psychoactive metabolites in the drug he'd *like* to use, say, Ativan, stay in the body so much longer than the old barbiturates that the half-life could stretch from fifty to a hundred hours . . . and if she took a pill every night there'd be a considerable buildup. Can't take that chance with an alcohol addict, he decides.

He asks her to go to work late the next morning and to come in to see him instead. He figures he'll get her in a reasonably sober state. He will confront. After she leaves the office he opens Psyche News to O'Neal's dramatic statement. . . . You've been lied to, Doctor.

He phones a colleague who works with alcoholics, a colleague who in fact once ran one of the better-known rehab programs. His friend tells him that when they analyzed the outcome of the patients who went through the program, they found the results were terrible. Our program didn't really work, he admits. We were reinforcing the drinking. The benefits were too good, the vocational training, special programs for the family, the *attention* paid to the alcoholic. It made the alcoholic feel, well, *special*. He had to keep on drinking to maintain this center-of-attention phase.

The psychiatrist wonders what to suggest for Janet, and it boils down to agreeing that confrontation is the only route. The woman wants to please. She is threatened by the loss of her family, but more, if she can be urged into a treatment center, she'll be able to stand back and see herself in context of the damage already done to herself and others.

The psychiatrist always believed that if one could understand the problems causing the drinking, *that itself* would be enough to make one want to stop. But alcohol experts like his colleague were telling him that this has no support in reality. Alcohol-addicted people were *addicts*. And as with other substance-abuse, one had to be free of the drug before analytic therapy could work.

So it may come down to the basics to get Janet off the sauce. The threat of loss. And getting rid of her delusion that because she isn't skid-row material yet, she can handle alcohol. Getting her into a treatment center. Getting her into a support group. Help her with psychoanalysis when she really gets sobered up. He'll do it. Or at least give it his best shot.

As the psychiatrist writes up his notes, an article in the pile of papers on his desk catches his eye. It's about fingering the alcoholic through blood tests. He reads that hospital tests can now determine who is a chronic abuser. Fantastic! What that can mean in terms of modifying hospital medication, or the amount of anesthesia. Forget the lie. Ignore the denial. The test will tell. This bit of news makes him feel better. He doesn't like the idea that doctors, scientific men, can be fooled.

Janet is calm and floaty as she sits in the psychiatrist's office. The extra Librium that she took in anticipation of seeing her doctor is working well. Yet, what her psychiatrist sees is a woman whose mouth is drawn down, whose eyes are showing tinges of yellow, the early signs of jaundice. He sees a person who holds herself as if the day were more than she could bear.

He talks to her gently but firmly about the treatment center and the threats that hang over her if she won't let him help her. At first she answers him in a monotone, explaining that there is a conspiracy within her family, that she harms no one, that her drinking is greatly exaggerated, that she is cold sober right now. He notices that her words seem to stick on her tongue. She has dry mouth, a side effect of antianxiety drugs. He asks her straight out what pills she took this morning. She shrugs and evades. He tells her she is kidding no one but herself. He *knows* she is on a tranquilizer, but he wants to find out how much of a liar she is. He has never before been this rough on a patient. Always the "savior" of his patients, he has tried to capture their trust so they can work through from there. If they trust, they will tell. The dictum of psychiatry. He knows that isn't always the case. Clinically he knows it, as well as deep in his bones. Maybe that's why he has always avoided treating addicts.

He asks who gave her the Miltown. Librium, she corrects. The same, he tells her. My doctor, she says. Why, he asks. I told him I couldn't sleep, that I wake up during the night, that I was tense.

Outwardly he is calm, but he rails inside. The damn GPs give out Elavil, Valium, Librium, to every sneaky fool who walks in. Of course, she never told the GP she was a hefty drinker. The GP himself probably tosses down his lion's share. So why would he search for alcohol impairment in her? Yet any clinician who wasn't simpleminded could look at the woman and see early signs of alcohol abuse. She's running around with water retention, and after you rule out heart failure and kidney impairment, you have a fair idea where the water comes from. And if the damn GP was in doubt, he could have done a lab work-up.

He tells her to cough. She does. He tells her he knows she must get lung infections pretty easily. She nods. *That* will get worse, he tells her. Janet seems surprised but gradually respectful at the psychiatrist's straightforward approach.

It will all get worse, he repeats. He's riding close to the edge now of what is medically sound, but he doesn't care. He knows that pulmonary infections are enhanced by alcohol abuse. He knows cancer and heart disease dramatically increase. He knows what a cirrhotic liver looks like from the autopsies of his internship.

The last Surgeon General's report he read listed almost a quarter million deaths a year directly related to alcohol. That didn't take in the mixtures of smoking and mood-altering pills. With those it could go as high as a *fourth* of all deaths.

Janet is thinking clearly enough to wonder about a number of things. Why should she go to a treatment center, when she could stop on her own? What will the neighbors think? Will she lose her job? Aren't the only people in treatment centers down and out? She doesn't consider herself an alcoholic.

He is tempted to tell her that she would just be going for a rest, or midlife crisis. But he has come this far and he won't back down. You need expert alcohol counseling. It is hard to admit he can't do the job for her. This is an area that eludes him. But he's not alone. He can think of only a handful of psychiatrists who know how to work with alcohol.

The center is tied in with AA and other support groups, he says.

Janet laughs out loud, a mirthless, stinging laugh. I'll have nothing to do with AA. They're a sanctimonious, never-take-a-drink-again bunch of people. I know *all* about them.

He asks if she has ever been to an AA meeting. Of course not, she says. Have you?

He confesses that he has not. But he has a colleague who has worked with them. And there are other groups, he insists.

You don't want to work with me, she challenges.

I do. Very much. But not yet. In a couple of months. I can't help you now. It's an admission, not a brush-off.

What will my employer say? Again the bottom-line question.

He doesn't trust her employer to understand. He doesn't recommend the truth. Like many psychiatrists he has a fear of divulging anything about his patients. Her company may have a covey of top executives who are heavy closet boozers, and like many of the self-righteous in positions of power, they'd have difficulty forgiving another person's weakness.

He suggests she get a leave of absence with no excuse, in fact let them think she has to save a family member. She should plan to be gone for thirty days.

He never intended to take on an alcoholic. But maybe among his patients, or clients, or whatever he was supposed to call them now, there already were people deep into the booze and fooling him. Would he have looked for it in Janet if her husband hadn't phoned? In hindsight he wasn't sure. Would he then have been as idiotic as her GP and prescribed diazepam for her anxieties? Or phenobarbital to help her sleep? Or amitriptyline for depression? He was not known as a candy man, but even *he* used psychopharm for at least a third of his clients.

He had been warned against alcoholics since medical school. They are horrible people, was the distinct message. And in complimentary tape cassettes supplied by the drug companies on ways to build up an office practice, it was stated unequivocally . . . *don't scare off lucrative patients by treating alcoholics.* Booze doctors were stigmatized, just as sloppy boozing was stigmatized. We haven't come far from drunk tanks and death by delirium tremens. VA hospitals, city clinics, coroners, still saw death by dt's. And jails were still used as back wards.

With all the mystery about alcoholism, all the searching for cause, all the theories about controlling the drinking, about finding the roots in deep analysis, all the garbage of pro and con of this or that kind of therapy, the psychiatrist knew this much. His fellow psychiatrists were as baffled as he. At the last APA convention he heard alcohol problems again referred to as dealing with the *unknown*. And the biological people and pill pushers were dusting off their anger at AA. They called it pseudospiritual drivel. They were determined to tackle alcohol addiction from a medical point of view.

Though how, he had no idea.

At the treatment center Janet quickly learned a few things. There was no magic to make her stop drinking or end her dependence on pills. She decided she didn't want to go the Antabuse route at this point. She discovered staff people who knew every lie or excuse she could dream up. She found out that being away from the house removed her from the habit-forming setting. Every moment there was an undercurrent of the problems (within relationships) caused by drinking to excess. She began to see that she herself had been a scapegoat, a role she accepted . . . when? Her husband, her boys, were all playing the game.

She jogged every morning and swam in the pool. She went to group therapy and two AA meetings a day. Strangely, she felt unpressured. They weren't tight-assed. You have a choice, they kept telling her. You never had that choice before. You knew you *had* to drink. You had to plan your day around drinking. Now you have a choice. You'll be able to decide at any time how important that first drink is to you. And you only have to decide this today. Don't worry about tomorrow. Put that decision off until then.

By the third week she looked in the mirror and saw a face she hadn't seen in years. She laughed aloud at the young woman who laughed back.

The public relations director of a telephone company in the southern part of the state called the psychiatrist one day. She said they were setting up an alcohol program for the company and she had heard he had been involved in working with alcoholics, or at least with heavy drinkers.

So much for confidentiality, he thought. How the hell could they have figured this out? No, he told her, you're mistaken. But I think your program is laudable, and I can put you in touch with colleagues. You could start with the Alcohol, Drug Abuse and Mental Health Administration.

She said they were thinking of getting a consulting psychiatrist on the staff.

He wanted to tell her not to do that, to go instead to the people who have recovered, to the treatment centers that know how to confront, to the national headquarters of Alcoholics Anonymous. But his medical training and his natural reticence stopped him.

You really have me confused, she persisted. I understood you do treat alcoholics.

Never, he replied. He was out of patience. I have never treated an active alcoholic, nor would I. Nor can any psychiatrist. We are not equipped. There is no way a person under the residual or direct effects of alcohol can profit from our medication or our analysis. In fact, intensive psychoanalysis can be unsettling for someone who is drinking. Not to be recommended. But recovered? Or recovering? Yes. In that case I would take referrals.

He congratulated her again on the good sense her company had in starting such a program.

It's not entirely altruistic, she said. The message will be quite clear. If the person agrees with us that there is a problem, then we'll help in any way possible. If not, then he or she will face layoff. Shape up or ship out . . .

You're on the right track, he told her. That seems to work.

On his appointment calendar he saw that Janet was penciled in for a session the following week. He was not assuming a guarantee that she'd stay relatively dry. But the fact of the appointment gave a certain lift to the day.

About Alcohol Addiction

Alcohol addiction continues to elude medical people. Among psychiatrists one of the most thoughtful analyses has been presented by Frederick B. Glaser, M.D., Head of Psychiatry, Clinical Institute Addiction Research Foundation in Toronto, Canada.

His ideas are drawn from three studies that point to the fact that problem drinking and depression or psychosis are clearly related. Depending on dosage, alcohol can relieve or cause depression. A small amount can make one elated, too much causes depression. Problem drinking can also cause a psychotic state. Glaser also feels that drinking and heredity may be related, but that the relationship has been simplistically overemphasized. Perhaps the only genetically related circumstance where problem drinking and heredity go hand in hand is with identical twins. If one is a problem drinker, the chances are slightly more than fifty-fifty that the other will be.

Historically, alcohol abuse/addiction has been looked upon as a type of madness. The term "dipsomania," which was first used in 1819 to describe all drinking problems, implies psychosis. Even to the present the issue of alcoholism and psychosis are linked. In a 1979 case in California, *People* v. *Duffy*, the defendant's counsel attempted to exonerate his client on the grounds that his alcoholism per se met criteria for insanity and that he should be judged not guilty because of it. The defense lost, but not without a stirring battle.

As to heredity, Dr. Donald Goodwin, Chairman of Psychiatry at the University of Kansas Medical Center, cautions that although alcoholism can run in families, it is pure conjecture to believe that genetics influence whether a person will become an alcoholic. Yet, epidemiologists appear to thrive on the theory of genetic influence and long for an opportunity to provide a solid scientific base, seeing it as an opportunity to engineer the genes and create an effective control to problem drinking. Nevertheless, Goodwin doesn't see "effective control" on the horizon.

We can conclude there is no pat psychiatric answer in the approach to alcohol dependency. Diagnosis and treatment require individual attention. What works for one will inevitably not work for another. We can surely count on *no* major breakthrough in the field of alcohol treatment and cure. Dr. Frederick Glaser submits that alcohol studies should be an independent scientific discipline, related to but not subsumed by a discipline such as psychiatry. And if, as the literature indicates, alcohol problems are sui generis and not necessarily related to other problems, then the need to develop a separate discipline becomes not only sensible but immediate.

Five

VIENNA WALTZ

The famous patient has been dead since 1936, and an exercise to review her symptoms is under way. Psychiatrists gather to offer clinical recommendations for treatment of this woman, who was twenty-one when she first became ill in the late nineteenth century.

Patient symptoms: eyes glazed, troublesome cough, right arm and both legs paralyzed, recurrent headaches, poor vision, frequent sleepless nights, in a trancelike state . . .

In the false warmth of late fall 1979 they flocked to New York City for two days. Many of those attending are psychoanalysts, and *this* patient is clearly a challenge.

They review her symptoms carefully, noting that there was sickness all about her in the house. She was weak and anemic, refusing to eat anything but a few oranges from time to time.

Insulin therapy, one psychoanalyst suggests. It might have worked. Insulin shock therapy, developed by Manfred Sakel in Vienna in the 1920s, a deliberate dose of insulin to bring on convulsions. Sometimes a coma. Sometimes death. The right dosage wasn't as exact as measuring a cup of sugar. But it might snap the patient to . . . it might . . .

Electroshock, another psychiatrist suggests. ECT, zapping the brain with bolts of electricity, simulating the grand mal seizures of epilepsy, *that* might snap her out of it.

I think we should try medicating her, still another psychiatrist offers. Put her on some strong tranquilizers, she's obviously retreating from the world.

No, no, says a member of the New York State Psychiatric Institute, no ECT, no major tranquilizers, no antidepressants. He'd give a minor tranquilizer like Valium. Maybe some hypnosis as well.

But a professor of psychiatry at New York University's School of Medicine has other ideas. The woman is suffering from the consequences of repressed rage. *She is furious* . . . and she's never let it out! She's afraid to assert herself, she's dependent, and she's learned how to make and keep herself vulnerable. Our culture encourages this . . . and . . . it . . . is . . . wrong! In my treatment there would be no predetermined ideas as to what type of person she was supposed to be. Find the anger, help her to express it. . . .

Other ideas and suggestions spurt forth: individual or family therapy, group therapy, Gestalt therapy, transactional analysis . . . a kaleidoscope of treatment for one unfortunate twenty-one-year-old patient.

The psychiatrists indulge themselves. Their imaginations are set free . . . for their suggestions are academic. That they speak with many tongues is of no interest to *this* patient. Nor is the fact that they would treat the same symptoms so differently.

The truth is, the patient was the famous Bertha Pappenheim, known as Anna O., who lived and suffered more than one hundred years ago.

Take any six psychiatrists, the saying goes, and you're guaranteed six opinions. Even for Anna O.

It was November 1880, and Dr. Josef Breuer hurried along the streets of Vienna on an emergency call. He was one of Austria's best-known physicians, often called the "doctor with the golden touch." He healed those that others couldn't heal, and at the age of thirty-eight he had already made major discoveries in nerve breathing control and inner ear balance control.

He strode down Lichtensteinstrasse and spied the Pappenheim home. The father, Siegmund Pappenheim, was a successful businessman, and the family was obviously well off. When Breuer was let into the third-floor parlor, Mrs. Pappenheim came immediately. What worried her, she said, was that her daughter Bertha might have contracted tuberculosis. That troublesome recurrent cough of hers just wouldn't go away. . . .

Breuer could understand her anxiety. His own younger brother had died of tuberculosis.

What made matters worse, Mrs. Pappenheim explained, was that Bertha's father lay in a rear bedroom coughing *himself* to death . . . he, too, had tuberculosis, and he was dying. The family had watched over him for five months, tending him, caring, wishing the dreaded cough away. Mrs. Pappenheim spent the days with him and Bertha the nights.

Until Bertha, too, began to cough, that lung-bursting cough echoing her father's.

Let me see her, Dr. Breuer said, and Mrs. Pappenheim led the way.

In her darkened bedroom Bertha was frail, obviously weakened, her cough-wracked body hidden under a lace coverlet.

As Breuer bent to examine her he noticed that when she looked at him she squinted as if she could make out no more than the barest outlines.

Such a symptom certainly wasn't connected to tuberculosis. He mentioned this to Mrs. Pappenheim, who said they had been aware of the condition. We've consulted nerve and eye specialists, she went on, some of the very best. They all say the same thing . . . there are no physical causes to explain it. *Nothing physical.*

Breuer continued his examination. He soon discovered that Bertha's legs were paralyzed, that she could not move her right arm. Strange. Weird . . . but a glimmer of understanding was coming to him.

He tried to have her move her head, but she was unable. There was a paralyzed muscle in her neck.

The nerve specialists, Mrs. Pappenheim repeated, can find nothing *physically* wrong.

How is her hearing?

Very bad, she appears to hear little. And when she talks, many times the words stop in midsentence. For no reason the words just stop.

He glared down at Bertha; noting the weakened condition, he suspected she was probably suffering from anemia as well. Her appetite, I suppose, isn't good?

Mrs. Pappenheim shook her head. She's refused almost everything for days.

Things were becoming clearer to Breuer. Clearer, but not any easier.

Sometimes, Mrs. Pappenheim said, she *does* show something. She cries out, she screams . . . things . . .

What kind of things?

She sounds terrified . . . so scared . . . she screams that "black snakes" and "death's-heads" are invading her room . . . horrible things . . .

He'd have to think about this some more, but he was quite sure now what was going on. She had the woman's disease . . . hysteria . . . he'd seen it in a number of others. No apparent physical cause for the symptoms, it was an *imagined* disease. Something of the mind. He knew how to treat it.

Hypnotism.

Talk her out of it . . . the cough, the paralysis, the hearing, seeing difficulties. Under hypnosis.

It was just a bit more than one hundred years earlier that medicine stumbled across the idea of using hypnosis to treat physical ailments. It happened in Vienna in the middle of the eighteenth century, and the doctor's name was Franz Anton Mesmer. His treatment became known as *mesmerism.*

Mesmer, however, really didn't know that the effect of his technique was hypnotism. He stroked his patients with magnets, believing that the magnets had some magical otherworldly effect that "cured," among other things, gout and paralysis. Mesmer stroked . . . and stroked . . . and the patient grew better through hypnotic suggestion and relaxation. He was sure there was some un-fathomable power *out there* operating through his magnets.

Mesmer had a pet magnet that he carried in a sack around his neck. "Animal magnetism" he called his treatment, and set about "magnetizing" everything around him, the desk, chairs, and tables in his Vienna office, the trees and shrubs in his garden.

But his success was short-lived in Vienna. Other practitioners were able to achieve the same cures without wearing a magnet clunking against the sternum.

Mesmer moved his practice to Paris, and the gullible French adored him. Animal magnetism became *the* cure in the early 1780s. And those who weren't seen in the carriage trade that thronged to his Place Vendôme establishment were calling him to their silk and velvet boudoirs. . . . Lafayette, Marie Antoinette, Montesquieu . . .

But at the Place Vendôme, what fun. Maestro would appear in billowing fiery robes, waving a wand, chanting, background of string instruments, flickering candlelight. And the *sack*, the sack with the magnet, a pendulous scrotum of magic. There. Look at it. Then the joining of hands, the sliding from one to another in the circle, touching, crooning, stroke, stroke.

The magic of seduction, wealth, superstition, susceptibility, leisure, indulgence.

In spite of Marie Antoinette and the believers, Louis XVI felt a certain unease and appointed a scientific commission, which found Mesmer a quack. Animal magnetism drifted into disuse. Hypnotism, meanwhile, has continued on the fringes of therapies up to this moment.

The institutions for the truly mentally deranged at the time of magnet magic had none of the Place Vendôme chic. The treatment was as vile and brutal as anything recorded. The sick were chained, beaten, usually confined for life. Not to offend the eyes of the gentry was the purpose then. And banishment for that reason continues to be the purpose of the intolerant and cruel.

But modern psychiatry was born in the institutions for the insane. Doctors such as Philippe Pinel and Isaac Ray thought that abnormal behavior was truly the result of a disease, just as swollen glands were the result of mumps. Cure the disease and behavior returns to normal.

When Philippe Pinel, during the French Revolution, became superintendent of Salpêtrière, the huge institution in Paris, it marked the first time a medical man, a *doctor*, had held the job. Medicine and medical science would now be applied to the problems of the insane.

By the middle of the nineteenth century Pinel's work at Salpêtrière was adopted at other institutions across Europe and in the United States. A psychiatrist came to be seen as a certain type of doctor . . . he worked with the insane. In fact, for over three quarters of a century, starting in 1844, the official magazine of the American Psychiatric Association was known as the "American Journal of Insanity." And the Association itself was first known as the Association of Medical Superintendents of American Institutes for the Insane.

Yet, side by side with the growth of psychiatry in the asylums, the legacy of Franz Anton Mesmer—hypnotism—was used by other doctors. No magic wands or Oz-like fantasy rituals, of course, but the idea spread of inducing a trance, of a "power" that could bring on a cure, of even suggesting that cure while the patient was in a suspended state. The search for hidden meanings in the subconscious personality had truly begun. . . .

But was psychiatry very different from other therapies in other cultures? Were psychiatrist-hypnotizers merely the medicine men of a budding industrial society, practicing witchcraft and voodoo in coat and tie and watch fob? Take the Shona, an African people who for generations have relied on *their* shrink, alias *nganga*. If Mesmer and those who followed him suggested their cures, so too does the *nganga*.

The demons of mental illness are otherworldly to the Shona, angered spirit-forces that must be exorcized from the afflicted person. The *nganga* collects leaves and grass, burns the mixture to ashes, and gives it to the patient, who is under a blanket where he can inhale the smoke. This is supposed to induce the angered spirit-force to speak through the patient, telling why it is angry. The *nganga* then takes the patient, along with a black hen, to a pool and orders the patient to sit under a certain tree. The *nganga* cuts off the hen's smallest toe, makes a tiny cut on the patient's neck and lower back, dips the bloody hen's-toe in powder so the powder itself becomes bloody, and rubs the powder into the cuts he has made on the patient. The *nganga* then dips the hen into the water, rotates the patient's head . . . and chants to the spirit-force . . . *remove yourself from the patient . . . come to the hen. . . .* The hen is then freed to run in the woods, where it will soon disappear, carrying the spirit-force with it.

Exorcism . . . stroke . . . stroke . . .

Dr. Josef Breuer had had quite a lot of experience treating "hysteria." He knew the symptoms could come on quite suddenly and that there would be no apparent physical cause.

I'm going to try hypnotism with her, he said to Mrs. Pappenheim. At this point he wasn't a true believer in hypnotism. But even if the results were merely *temporary*, it could provide some relief, and so he could not ignore the therapy. Also, many of his Viennese colleagues considered it the standard treatment for these types of cases.

They both gazed down at the unmoving young woman, trying to fathom the scope of this strange malady. Once the patient had been put under hypnotic trance, most doctors would use suggestion . . . *give up your symptoms . . . you are not sick . . . there is nothing really wrong with you . . . you will feel better . . .*

I'm going to try something a little different, Breuer decided, a few questions, perhaps . . .

Mrs. Pappenheim nodded her approval, and Breuer made ready to hypnotize Bertha. Once he had her in hypnotic trance, carefully choosing his words, he asked . . . *How do you feel, Bertha?*

No answer.

Is anything bothering you?

She shook her head. No words, but she *did* move her head.

Is anything bothering you? he repeated.

Then she spoke. But it meant nothing. The words were incomprehensible. Gibberish.

He debated whether to use hypnotic suggestion but decided against it. He finally left her bedside, determined to follow this strange case of hysteria to a resolution.

I'll be back tomorrow evening, he announced to an anxious Mrs. Pappenheim.

And he did return. Once more he placed Bertha under hypnotic trance.

Is anything bothering you, Bertha?

She spewed forth more gibberish, only this time the stream of words continued unabated. At first Breuer just thought everything was unintelligible, but gradually he saw some pattern. She was speaking in different languages . . . French, German, English, and Italian . . . the sentences meant nothing, whatever meaning she was conveying *had* to be in the very fact she was speaking in different tongues.

Now, Bertha, why don't we just speak German to each other?

The flow of gibberish continued . . .

Bertha?

. . . and continued . . .

Bertha?

. . . and continued . . .

The torrent was unstoppable, so Breuer reluctantly brought her out of her trance and left.

But the next evening he was back, and the evening after that, and most succeeding evenings as well. Such attention was unusual for someone who was suffering from mere . . . hysteria.

An imagined disease . . . no physical cause.

Breuer's professional curiosity was aroused as it had rarely been. What was she *trying* to tell him?

A most unusual case. Intriguing, genuinely mystifying.

He returned again and again to the frail girl's bedroom, wondering what it would take to break through. Then one evening after he had put her into the usual hypnotic trance, Bertha began to speak in German, a rational, comprehensible German . . . and she told him a story.

He dared not interrupt while she spun out a tale of a nervous, upset girl sitting at the bedside of a man, a very sick man.

Her father!

Breuer knew that for months she had been caring for her father at night while her mother watched over him during the day. In the afternoons Bertha would lie down for a short rest, just as regular home-care nurses did. He learned that during her afternoon nap she would sleep peacefully for an hour or so and then grow restless, tossing and uttering "tormenting . . . tormenting . . ." while her eyes remained shut.

Then Breuer noted that one day someone responded to her cries and she immediately launched into a story, hesitating at first, but with increasing confidence . . . and in German! A few moments after she finished the story she woke up refreshed and relaxed.

Breuer wondered . . . could the evening trance be replacing the afternoon nap? Could she be acting out the part of her father's nurse and mixing it with a daughter's grief at his dying?

He returned the next evening and once again put her into a trance. Without much coaxing she started a new story, again in German, with the central character a girl anxiously sitting by a sickbed. Sad stories, Breuer thought, charming but sad, modeled after the fairy tales of Hans Christian Andersen.

The pattern repeated itself evening after evening . . . the hypnotic trance, the imaginative little stories always with the girl by the sickbed and a refreshed and relaxed Bertha afterward.

Do you write children's stories? Breuer asked her.

No, though I do like to daydream, I spend hours daydreaming, it's my private theater.

Breuer began to develop a theory: Bertha's consciousness was oscillating between two levels, her normal one and a "secondary" one where she did her daydreaming and developed her sad little fairy tales. She was actually living in two worlds. In one there were fearful images that were caused by and reinforced her emotional nonrational state. In the other world she was in control and clearheaded, *as long as the monsters did not intrude*. When they did intrude, her unconscious was stimulated.

Unconscious?

Breuer had used a word few had considered. But there it was, the gem that would be the centerpiece for the psychoanalytic theories of another man from Vienna . . . Sigmund Freud.

By the end of the nineteenth century, psychiatry was essentially split along two lines. There were the *psychiatrists* (often called psychologists in spite of the fact they were medically trained), who worked with the insane in the institutions and hospitals . . . and there were the psychoanalysts, who worked privately, often with those who clearly were not demonstrably ill but who could afford intensive and long-term analysis. The psychoanalysts were destined to dominate the field for many years.

Though Freud used psychoanalytic techniques in the 1890s, it wasn't until 1900 that his ideas had much impact on general psychiatry or on anyone outside his tight circle. But after he published his book *The Interpretation of Dreams*, things were never quite the same. He differentiated between the conscious and the unconscious. Sufficiently distressing matters are avoided by the conscious and sink to the unconscious, where they continue to fester and amplify themselves *in dreams*. Interpret the dreams and fantasies and the *unconscious*, and free the conscious!

While Freud's following was gradually growing in Europe he received an invitation to visit the United States. Granville Stanley Hall of Clark University in Worcester, Massachusetts, suggested he make the trip in August and September of 1909. At this point there were few American disciples, and the invitation seemed like a good opportunity to make new contacts. Traveling with Carl Jung and Sandor Ferenczi, two of his closest supporters, Freud spent his time as both tourist and peripatetic expert. But the real *paying* purpose of his visit was a Clark University series of five lectures to a convention of psychologists. For the first time he envisioned the possibility of his work on psychoanalysis translated into something more than coffeehouse theorizing. As he stepped up to the lectern that first time he looked around and *knew* . . . he had arrived.

In Europe he was still something of an oddity, but *here*, he could tell, the most powerful and influential came to hear him and treat him as an equal.

Europe-worship was strong then. Why should Freud be any exception to the value the enlightened Yankees placed on Europe's culture, Europe's science, Europe's *theories*. And he wasn't.

At about this same time general psychiatry was beginning to emerge from the institutions and state hospitals. In Boston neurologists dealing with the physiological problems of the brain picked up on a characterization that had been bandied about in Europe for half a century. What about adding the designation *psychiatrist?* What about the term neuropsychiatrist? Done.

That word had such . . . panache. And medical overtones, yes. Analyst? Not scientific enough. Medical superintendent for the insane? Lacked drawing-room chic. Psychologist? Would be joked about in surgery. Psychiatrist. On our own. Damn the prefix, full steam ahead.

And in 1921 the group that began as the Association of Medical Superintendents of American Institutes for the Insane officially changed its name. From this time forward it would be known as the American *Psychiatric* Association. Done.

Does a name change the care that patients receive? Is a *psychiatrist* any more intelligent or effective or humane than a *superintendent?* Any more enlightened? Not likely.

The psychiatrists who escaped from the institutions found cozy rooms and easy practices waiting for them. Most of their patients were elite and only rarely ill. The brothers back in the institutions had the bad eggs, the catatonic, the manic, the demented elderly, the screamers, hallucinators, the paranoid, the violent. Would anyone in his right mind want to spend a career treating people like this?

A few, yes. The rest were the profession's dregs: the alcoholics, drug abusers, foreigners who could only wangle an institutional license, the has-beens and never weres. But psychiatrists, yes, most of them were so labeled.

The palliative measures they practiced were primitive and crude. "Shock," the old standby from the days when the demented were lowered into pits of snakes, was a word these healers found hard to relinquish. From chains and beating to straitjackets and being wound in wet sheets, to high-pressure hosing to . . . insulin shock and electric shock.

Woodshed philosophy. Spare the rod, spoil the child. For your own good. Hurts me more than it does you. You'll thank me later.

But the crudities of mental institutions were being more than matched by the crudities in Germany of the 1930s. Many European psychoanalysts saw the anti-semitic writing on the wall and took heed. It would only be a matter of time before Vienna, the renowned center of analytic learning and practice, would be a Nazi target. And then what? Prague? Paris? The haven, of course, was the United States, where psychoanalysis was sought after and properly appreciated.

And so the psychoanalytic greats came from the major European centers to settle in major United States cities. And although they brought with them the internecine battles within the profession, psychoanalysis as a kindly and healing art would absolutely change the face of medical psychiatry.

Mental disorders are not generally culturally based, yet healing techniques may be. Occasionally there are certain traits or phobias seemingly endemic to a particular group.

In portions of China, for instance, there is something called *Koro*, an anxiety peculiar to men and arising from a conviction that the penis is shrinking into the body. If it happens, the man believes he will die. So, once afflicted by *Koro*, these Chinese go to extraordinary lengths to prevent the penis from shrinking, using every device and theory their imaginations can produce. To Western eyes it can become quite ludicrous, but to this group of Chinese it is deadly serious.

Although our culture has nothing like *Koro*, there have been attempts to categorize it: anxiety neurosis . . . conversion reaction . . . phobia secondary to masturbation . . . hypochondriasis . . . psychosis . . . extreme castration complex.

Healing practices and procedures nevertheless have a commonality. The witch doctor can be a good role model for the Western psychiatrist. Psychiatrist E. Fuller Torrey says that if one is magic, then so is the other. If one is prescientific, then so is the other.

They all start from the confessional mode, and, in telling, one finds relief. In talking, one establishes a healer-patient relationship.

Just as witch doctors or shamans or voodoo priests start from the premise that something *afflicts* the troubled one, so do psychiatrists. Psychiatrists schooled in the *medical model* call it an illness, an affective disorder. The Yoruk Indian shamans of northern California would blame the distress on black magic, on an evil sorcerer. Yet both seek the same healing, a purging of the symptoms of distress.

In western Kenya, in Luo country, the devil is also at work. Mental illness is the result of an angered ancestor or the fates and never because the patient has done something or had something done to him. The bush psychiatrist might diagnose "worms on the brain" and the treatment might include animal bloodletting, poultices, and ritual degradation, but the coherent purpose is to purge the mental illness. Africans may never complain of depression, but to their healer they will moan about disinterest, a bad appetite, a general malaise—the usual symptoms of depression.

Our psychiatrists create hope by having us look to *them* for relief. It's also the way shamans create hope among the Apache Indians. An Apache looking for help knows better than to be skeptical of his shaman. He must humble himself totally, put himself completely in the hands of his shaman. *Only you can help me*, he pleads.

You have the gift, we say to our psychiatrists. . . .

We dream . . . and it can be like opening a door to ourselves. We talk about our dreams, psychiatrists interpret them, and the ritual tells us who we are, what we want. Dreams are important in psychiatric therapy . . . as they are to Navajo medicine men and Ute Indian shamans. To the Utes dreams depict drives and motivations; healing depends on discussing and interpreting them. To the Navajos dreams and their dynamic interpretations are so important that first waking moments are spent thinking about and analyzing dreams just experienced the night before.

Guilt, too, is part and parcel of any healing exercise. We know how pervasive it is in our western psyches . . . from the Crucifixion to motherhood. The wiser among us say guilt *isn't* like the common cold, you just don't catch it out of the air! Someone has to lay it on you. Psychiatry has built a foundation on the who, when, where, why, and how of guilt . . . and so have the medicine men of the Shona tribe of East Africa. A Shona who is depressed will most likely blame it on witchcraft and consider himself an evil person. He suffers from guilt that only the medicine man can purge. . . .

As we take to the couch.

There are about thirty psychoanalytic institutes around the United States, mostly in the major cities. These are the monasteries of psychiatry, temples of Sigmund Freud and the others who followed him, the learning cloisters of psychoanalysis. Most have no university affiliation, they exist separate and apart from academia, *and they like it that way.*

We'll take care of our own, they say. We don't want anyone messing around with our specialty. It's a bit of a secret world, suspicious, intellectually charged, unresponsive to the casual visitor. Drop-ins are not welcome.

The building of this particular institute was built in the late 1940s with private funds, the product of a burgeoning interest in psychoanalysis following the war. It is an unimposing cinder-block structure in a modest-rent district, wood-shingled and resting on concrete pylons tall enough for cars to drive under. A wide stairway leads immediately to the two operational floors.

On the first floor there is a reception desk, a library that can double as an auditorium, and two classrooms. On the upper floor are offices for faculty. There are no laboratories, no medical paraphernalia.

How many students do you have in your institute? a visitor asks.

There are seventy *candidates* here.

Candidates?

Candidates.

And how many will you graduate this year?

Five candidates will graduate.

To be a psychoanalyst one must usually have graduated from medical school and taken a psychiatric residency. It is, by far, *the* most specialized of the psychiatric disciplines, because some eight

to ten *additional* years are required. This institute has a four-year
academic program, but in addition every proper psychoanalyst
must also have gone through personal psychoanalysis. And that
can take years. Then there is clinical training, too.

And how does the budding psychoanalyst pay for all this training after those years in medical school and residency?

He has his own psychiatric practice. Part of his fees pay for his
psychoanalytic training, and for some there can be medical insurance reimbursement for the personal analysis, though that's being
stopped now.

In the institute library there is a pen-and-ink drawing of . . .
Freud.

On the landing, just outside, there is a bust of . . . Freud.

On the adjoining wall . . . Anna Freud.

In the hall, offered for sale, lithograph prints of Sigmund Freud,
suitable for framing.

The priest has his Christ, the rabbi his Star of David, the analyst
his Freud.

The candidates study just about everything ever written about
psychoanalysis and learn the relevant theories. They take courses
such as Introduction to Psychoanalytic Technique, Neuroses,
Analyzability (not everyone is intelligent or sane enough for
analysis), Depression, Theory of the Therapeutic Process.

Can such an institute operate from the fees the candidates pay?

Not quite, but grants are common.

Is there a printed history of the institute?

Yes. But only for members.

Could there be secret rites? Skull and Bones stuff?

Why is there such suspicion?

Merely careful.

You bet.

—Doctor, why did you become a psychoanalyst?

He is friendly, open, a psychiatrist with years of analytic experience.

—When I finished psychiatric training I just didn't feel I knew
enough . . . and I also felt the personal need for analysis. It's a kind

of thirst for more understanding, that there's more to this, that I didn't have a grip on what human psychology is really about. We like to think the brighter people, certainly the more intellectual people, go into psychoanalysis, those who like to conceptualize along those lines.

—How do you think other psychiatrists, nonpsychoanalysts, regard you?

—The general profession probably has some envy of us. There's the feeling that somehow what we do is better, easier, although we certainly aren't better off economically. Now, the envy my colleagues feel is somehow tied with all this intellectualism and intellectual capacity. I hate to say it this way because it sounds so arrogant. But implicit in the statement is that we *are* intellectual. For instance, I go into a teaching situation with general psychiatrists and they present material to me. Now, because I'm analytically trained I am able to find nuances. On the other hand they can admire that. But because we're all human, along with that admiration comes envy.

—Doctor, how does analysis work?

—A successful analysis is one where there's been basic change, not just symptomatic change. For example, all of us in growing up require some feedback from those closest to us, to establish a coherent sense of ourselves, to gain what we call self-esteem. Now that just doesn't happen out of the air. We have inner structures to set that up . . . but we need someone or several someones to get it going. When it's incomplete in childhood, adults have to continue getting it from others . . . in their love relationships, work relationships, social lives. Such a person in analysis might demonstrate to me, *without being fully aware of it*, that they had a tremendously high dependence on me, the analyst, for self-esteem.

—To the degree the person felt I was meeting his need he might actually feel better, although the problem would still be there. But in emotional interaction with me over time, through verbal interventions that can be internalized, we hope to produce an inner sense of self-esteem, no longer looking to rely on anyone else. Now *that's* a successful analytical experience . . . when one is no longer dependent on external things but on internal things.

—Most psychoanalysts just sit there and let the patient do the talking, don't they?

—Not so. I *do* have to be careful that my interventions aren't just for the sake of hearing myself talk, but it's not the idea of being a blank screen. It's more the idea of not throwing in other variables that would complicate things.

—Doctor, just who can *afford* analysis? It takes years and thousands of dollars . . .

—No doubt psychoanalysis is a luxury, though I think every analyst worth his salt tries to see some patients at no charge.

—Do you have a clinic at your institute?

—It's all but invisible. Eight out of ten applicants for the clinic are found unsuitable for analysis. Some of my colleagues don't even want this type of clinic. They really have a siege mentality.

—Aren't they elitist as well?

—The attitude stems from a fear of diluting our entire discipline . . . and from a misunderstanding. We aren't keepers of a holy grail, we're the practitioners of a specialty that has to be accepted in the marketplace. They haven't understood that yet. *You can't get by any more with mystification.*

But mystery and magic and unfathomable doings were very much tied in with psychiatry in the middle of the twentieth century. World War II went a long way to legitimize *medically* the art of psychotherapy. The Army said, we want our battle casualties back in action . . . and fast! Many were suffering the emotional wounds of war and needed only short-term therapy. Doctors, the bulk of whom had no intention whatsoever of becoming psychiatrists, were drafted and became ninety-day psychiatric wonders. And many liked it!

They weren't psychoanalysts, but psychoanalysts with prestige, routed from the great intellectual centers of Europe, were in the wings. And they were in the *United States.*

With the end of the war many of the psychiatrists with their new skills decided to just continue in the profession as *analysts* instead of reverting to general medicine. They mingled with the gurus of the psychoanalytic institutes that were being formed.

And finally, there was some real money for psychiatry. The National Mental Health Act was passed in 1946. Medical schools could now get funding for departments of psychiatry. Before the war there had been only a handful of academic departments, the most notable at Johns Hopkins, presided over by the venerable Adolf Meyer. At most medical schools psychiatry was lumped with neurology or internal medicine, and the teaching was done by part-time staff.

As psychiatry achieved its own identity in the medical schools the psychoanalysts took over. Their influence was powerful. Until the middle 1950s, when a different kind of short-term therapy came along. Drugs . . . antidepressants . . . first the tricyclicates and then the monoamine oxidase (MAO) inhibitors . . . imipramine . . . desipramine . . . nortriptyline . . . phenelzine. . . .

State institutions became more manageable, and patients could eventually be released, maintained on medication and supportive therapy. Many psychoanalysts, who did not prescribe medication, saw patients making great strides *with* medication and *without* analysis. Even if drug therapy did not solve most of the root causes of anxieties and depression, it sure lifted the fog enough so most could get through the day.

Other drug discoveries followed, providing relief for anxiety and depression, as well as overt psychosis. The areas that psychoanalysis had monopolized slowly broke away, leaving psychoanalysts to minister to a narrow, well-heeled patient population.

Then in the 1960s and 1970s still newer forms of psychotherapy became available. *Nonmedical* therapy. Psychologists and social workers were banging on the gates, making it known that not only could they provide counseling and lay therapeutic analysis, but they could do it, *in their judgment*, as well or better. And there was no mucking around with the medical model. They didn't have to unlearn the *aplomb*, the *gentleman's distance* taught in medical school.

Josef Breuer's treatment of Bertha Pappenheim continued for some months, and there was noticeable improvement. He came almost every evening, hypnotized her, and continued to ask his questions.

Is anything bothering you, Bertha?

Tell me what's wrong.

He came to realize that whatever it was, she had been deeply traumatized. She had simply decided it was too awful to talk about. And so she refused to talk at all, except in a mindless form of four-language gibberish.

But gradually she began to respond to hypnosis, conversing with him and enlarging her sad little fairy tales. Then, after hypnosis, she continued conversing with him. Within three months after he began seeing her she started to talk, and he was sure hypnosis had dislodged the block.

Very shortly the power of movement came to her left side, and by April 1881, four months after Breuer first came to her, she was able to get out of bed, moving unsteadily across the room.

But still, whatever it was that bothered Bertha, Breuer could not fathom.

Then, on April 5, 1881, her father died, and the reaction on Bertha was grave. At first there was rage, followed by a two-day stupor that left her changed. She was passive, withdrawn, recognizing only Breuer, and only when she had first felt his hands. She *knew* his hands, they had ministered to her for months, they had hypnotized her.

Once again she fell into the old sleep pattern . . . a deep sleep in the afternoon, waking just before sunset. She would be highly excitable and confused, sometimes hallucinating or screaming insults and abuse at her mother and nurse. Breuer could only speculate that the sleep pattern was a re-creation of her work as her father's night nurse, when she would catch a nap in the afternoons before going on duty.

One day, during a hot spell in the summer of 1881, Breuer was sitting with her while she was under hypnosis.

Is there anything bothering you? he asked.

Well . . . she said, *I have a new friend, an English lady . . .* and Bertha described seeing a lady's "horrid little dog" licking water from a glass. It was repulsive to her.

Then, to Breuer's amazement, Bertha's face grew pinched with disgust . . . but she asked him calmly . . . *May I have a glass of water, please?*

When she woke from hypnosis, she drank a full glass of water, and Breuer was stupified.

Before the hypnosis she had not been able to drink any water, in spite of the heat and her thirst! She would raise a glass to her lips, but then push it away, again and again . . .

Breuer's wonder took shape. . . . Was there a connection between talking about her phobias, what had caused them, and then being able to overcome her physical disabilities?

Another evening, under hypnosis, she gave more clues.

Is there anything bothering you, Bertha?

Well . . . one night I was there by my father's bedside, and it was so sad, he was suffering so . . . I couldn't help crying . . . my father asked me for the time . . . I couldn't see through my tears . . . I brought my watch up so close, *I had to squint . . .*

By his next visit Breuer noticed that Bertha's squint, the one she had had all these months, was gone!

So Breuer finally had the key. They would talk out her symptoms, talk them away. Bertha began to refer to Breuer's treatment as "the talking cure," and gradually, one by one, the symptoms *did* begin to disappear. . . .

But what of her cough, Doctor, I'm still so worried about *that*, Mrs. Pappenheim said.

We'll work on it next . . .

Tell me what's bothering you, Bertha?

Well . . . there was an evening when I was sitting by my father's bedside . . . dance music was coming from a neighbor's parlor . . . oh, I wanted to be there dancing . . . everyone was having such a good time . . . and I felt so bad because I didn't want to be with my father . . . and I started to cough, just like him. . . .

Acute guilt, Breuer decided. Identifying with her father's cough and illness.

And the next time Breuer saw her, the terrible, racking cough that had plagued her for so long was gone.

Finally, after more than a year and a half, the treatment was finished. Bertha Pappenheim's myriad symptoms had been washed away by the "talking cure." A few months later Breuer related the entire case to a young friend who was training to be a medical research scientist.

Why, you have made a major breakthrough in the treatment of hysteria, the friend said. You should write an article about it. Other doctors should know, you owe it to medicine.

I have had enough of hysterical women, Breuer said. What we are dealing with here is the power of the unconscious. . . .

Yes, the unconscious, the friend said, I had never thought of it that way before. . . .

The date was November 18, 1882, and the friend was Sigmund Freud.

About the Talking Cure

The original psychoanalysis of Sigmund Freud and the contributions made by Josef Breuer have spawned a pastiche of therapics, some as different from the original as modern surgery is from bloodletting. The old psychoanalytic model is being challenged. For decades it was psychoanalytic gospel that the Oedipal relationship was at the core of inner conflicts and repressed sexual and aggressive wishes. One had to return to the subconscious of childhood to seek out and resolve the difficulties. Freud's hope, the ability *to love and to work*, was considered then, as now, the best achievement for each person and the sign of a successful analysis.

Recently, Heinz Kohut, a Chicago psychoanalyst, has advanced the theory that it is the empathy and responsiveness of one's parents that determines whether a child will develop into a healthy adult. Kohut suggests that the Oedipal conflict is not a major factor in the formation of a narcissistic character disorder, which in simple terms means that the child, deprived of parental pride in his assertiveness, continues to search for someone to provide him a sense of reaffirmation. Kohut and his growing followers see the narcissistic character disorder as the disease of our time, reflecting the alienation and rootlessness of a technologically oriented society

and ever smaller and less involved families. In Freud's time alienation was not a major problem—but sexual repression was, and it
was women and their "hysteria" that gave psychoanalysis a spring-
board in the first place. But today sexual repression is not a major
problem, and the psychoanalysts are finding fewer and fewer cases
of it and, in the process, also finding that some of the most resolute
of Freud's theories are no longer relevant.

Newer therapies are also invading the territory once monopolized by psychoanalysis. In fact in the last decade applications for
low-fee analysis at the Psychoanalytic Institute in Boston have
dropped by 40 percent and by the same amount at the New York
Psychoanalytic Institute. What's happened is that people are turning to newer therapies, including a form of psychoanalysis that is
much shorter in duration than the classical five days a week, month
after month, year after year. . . . The therapist today gets more
involved with the client, not just acting as a backboard but urging
responses and making judgments. Even classical psychoanalysts
admit this new technique is having results comparable to extensive
and expensive Freudian analysis.

Behaviorists are also getting involved, rejecting emphasis on
emotions, mental states, and internal conflicts in favor of behavior
modification. Most are not psychoanalysts, they're usually psychologists or social workers. They deal with symptoms, not root causes,
teaching the patient to relax in tense situations, for instance. For
some, changes have been effected in as few as five or six sessions.

Some of the newer therapies have moved quite far from psychoanalysis, such as *Gestalt*, an experiential technique developed by
Dr. Frederick S. Perls. The Gestalt method (note use of the Teutonic term, a subliminal link to Vienna and Freud) tries to get the
patients to focus on their emotions with talk or bodily sensation or
even screaming. . . . Then there is *est* (Erhard Seminars Training),
the child of Werner Erhard, a former management consultant by
the name of John Paul Rosenberg who adopted the Teutonic
Werner Erhard to go with his new therapy. He keeps large groups
cooped up in a hotel ballroom for successive weekends and three
weekday evenings while giving them intensive training in the self-
realization that *they* are the cause of their own experiences. . . .

And there is *Rolfing*, the contribution of Ida P. Rolf and also known as "structural integration," where the psyche is approached by observing the way the body looks and then manipulating the body so the psyche can be freed.

The talking cure started it all, but in a recent count there now seem to be more than 250 different therapies in use.

NUTS AND BOLTS

It was a far cry from the mountains of Africa. But the baboon may or may not have remembered. Ever since he was six months old, his days had been composed of solitary confinement in a laboratory cage smelling vaguely of Lysol.

There was no way anyone could call life in the laboratory "good" for the baboon. Of course he got his fruit and eggs, but he could not grub for roots, and *that's* what he liked to do best. If he were to live long enough in the laboratory, his canine teeth would become tartared and weakened. But he was not destined for old age. He was an experiment in the effects of prolonged convulsive stimulation of the brain, with and without modification of anesthesia or muscle relaxant, with or without oxygenation. The process was called electroconvulsive therapy . . . ECT . . .

He was the kind of candidate for experiments that didn't generate much empathy or concern. Baboons are not lovable creatures. As a species they tend to glower, they look mean. Hardly anyone cares about baboons as they do about seals and koala bears.

Baboon (he was not dignified by name) had been mildly tran-

quilized so he would be more manageable. He had been spread-
eagled on the worktable and secured at the ankles and wrists. (A
baboon's hind and front limbs are proportionate, so he can travel
easily on all fours. When stretched out he looks like a little man.
He's from the subfamily *Cynopithecus*, a monkey with a low facial
angle and with cheek pouches. He has a doglike muzzle.)

Behind the baboon's head a syringe is being prepared. There is
no getting away from it. His head is locked in place so the convulsion will not cause him to thrash into fractures. Whatever fears or
adolescent fury are hidden behind those deep-set, morose eyes the
researchers will never know. They don't speak his language.

The syringe is filled with allyglycine, a chemical to induce brain
seizures. Similarly effective seizures are also produced by using
electric current. The researchers have a special interest . . . they
want to know how many minutes of sustained seizures an adolescent baboon can tolerate before exhibiting signs of epileptic brain
damage.

The baboon has been put through these seizures before. Wired
up to graphs he does not know and cares nothing for, he could care
less about the scientific outcome of these jolts. Where are the female baboons he is supposed to be courting? What does he do with
his growing sex drive? He is a gregarious creature, so where is the
tribe he would travel with? He is timid, but because his forehead
shadows his eyes he has been called sullen. He's hairy and has
calluses on his buttocks, so he's labeled a filthy brute. They say he
is intractable and ferocious, but at one time the Egyptians built
monuments to him and called him Anubis and invested him with
divine characteristics. How did it come to this?

Soon the baboon will be injected with a muscle relaxant. This
time he will get anesthesia. It is a mixed blessing. This time the
seizures will go on for more than one hour and twenty minutes.
This time, deadened to the pain but awakened to a vegetable state,
he will suffer irremedial epileptic brain damage. So much for the
baboon.

At the 1975 American Psychiatric Association Convention in
Anaheim, California, a group of psychiatrists met to consider

countermeasures against the activities of individuals and organizations that proposed limitations on the use of electroconvulsive therapy. Disenchanted psychiatrists dub the shock treatments associated with ECT as "Edison Medicine."

The psychiatrists who believe in, use, and continue to profit by electroconvulsive shock therapy were jarred into self-protection by what they described as diatribes against ECT. Specific legislation curbing indiscriminate use of the therapy and court challenges in states such as California, Michigan, and Oregon became as tools of the devil to the true believers of ECT. *They*, said the Edison-Medicine men, would delay or deny a safe and effective treatment to people . . . *they* add unnecessary second-opinion costs to patient care . . . *they* violate the confidentiality of the doctor-patient relationship . . . *they* discriminate against poor or marginal-income groups (who have access to ECT in the state institutions).

The Edison-Medicine men decided to band together. The International Association for the Advancement of ECT was the result.

The organization is now worldwide, though most of the more than 350 active members come from the United States. The international association is a resource for educational activities and political research affecting electroconvulsive shock therapy. Funds from the group are ready to help those threatened by political or judicial "interference" in their practices. The first symposium on ECT with the cooperation of the American Psychiatric Association was held in 1979. By the next year a closed-circuit television show demonstrating an anesthetized, muscularly relaxed white middle-aged depressed woman undergoing electrically induced brain seizure was shown to casual and professional visitors in the exhibition hall at the annual convention of the American Psychiatric Association.

The Edison-Medicine men felt the show was positive and enlightening. . . . See? The muscles hardly jump!

In the 1930s psychiatrists were at their wits' end about what to do with schizophrenic patients. Wards were a mess, patients could grow suddenly violent, suicidal, or catatonic, and managing things could get difficult. Catatonia was almost a preferred state, at least the patients weren't tossing chairs. One aging psychiatrist recalls what it was like . . . —For a long time the psychotics were ignored, and I think because we had nothing much to offer. We locked them up or straitjacketed them and put them in the care of wardens. The beginnings of change came with shock therapy.

By the late 1930s large numbers of schizophrenics were given chemically induced seizures. The psychiatrist closes his eyes. —It was a gruesome treatment. The patients hated it, were frightened by it. They had reason to be. It could be very harmful in terms of causing physical damage. The injection induced a grand mal convulsion, and a heavy, muscular person with that degree of convulsion could come out of it with fractured bones. It was very common to get compression fractures.

How come schizophrenics were singled out for injection-induced convulsions? Because there was a half-baked idea that *epilepsy and schizophrenia were antagonistic*. In other words, schizophrenic epileptics were *calmed* after "natural" epileptic seizures. Psychiatrists chose to go for broke and began using this chemical injection that put the fear of hell into the psycho wards.

But the idea had its early doubters and detractors. Never mind the patients, who at this point had no rights to refuse anything, there were also some nurses and staff doctors who saw other effects besides docility, unbroken furniture, and less bedlam. They witnessed the fractures. And after the seizures were supposed to have ended, some brains just refused to shut off the heightened activity. Then . . . whap, right there in the dayroom when the nice lady patient was supposed to be crocheting her afghan squares . . . she flips out on the floor and has another epileptic attack. Was it any wonder the ward patients were uptight? Did the shrinks think these inmates were 100 percent foolish as well as *crazy*? Who in his right mind would subject himself to *this*?

Meanwhile, two Italians, Ugo Cerletti and Lucio Bini, were cooking up something dramatic. They were into Edison Medicine. Electrically induced epileptic attacks. Bring on the baboons.

It is early spring of the year, a time when a lot of people get . . . well . . . depressed. It's a down time in Oregon, with mud underfoot and the children sniffling or hacking. The prescription bins at the local drugstore are bulging with small white envelopes containing bottles of antibiotic pills, codeine-laced cough medicine, and tranquilizers. Today Pat is picking up a bottle of lithium.

It is hard for her to make it to the drugstore. She wants to sit quietly in her house while she imagines her children dying accidentally . . . at the bend in the road where the school bus lets them off, in the playground where the little one falls from the ten-foot slide onto the blacktop and squashes her skull. She can't get rid of these anxieties. Last year . . . ah, last year . . . she could sip beer and the fears would subside. In fact she would often get a high, a really beautiful high, where she wanted to dance and sing, grab her children, and say, oh, what the hell, let's have a picnic. Who cares if it's drizzling or muddy. We'll picnic under a tree on some bales of hay.

But the children shied away. They feared her manic state. She will not go back to beer. She has forsworn alcohol. She will not go to a restaurant that serves drinks.

Her children come home and they are safe. She has kept the blinds drawn because she can't bear to see whether or not they will come up the walk on a stretcher or on their own feet. She cannot tell anyone about this particular fear that depresses her to her toes. Especially not her husband. Anyway, he says she's no fun anymore.

Pat tears open the little white prescription bag and looks at the bottle of pills. She does not understand the label. It's as if it were written in a foreign language. She bangs the bell on the druggist's counter and brings the pharmacist's head into her line of vision. How do I take these?

Behind the bifocals he raises his eyebrows. I don't understand. Any way you want, I suppose. With water, juice, whatever.

Patiently, as if talking to a child, she says, I can't read your label. I don't know what you wrote. How *many* and *when* do I take them?

She pushes the bottle at him. The instructions are clear. He points this out to her. She wonders if he thinks she's crazy. Of course he does. Why else would she be on this medication!

At her therapy group she sits twisting her fingers. She can no longer knit, and she surely can't talk to the people around the table. A woman next to her puts her arm on her shoulder, and she feels tears backing up behind her eyeballs. They clutch at her throat. I'm on lithium. It feels as if she has shouted it to the whole town. But her voice is a whisper.

Why? asks her friend. You're so depressed. I thought lithium was for when you're manic, or very hyper.

Pat flashes with anger. Who is this person to question her psychiatrist? It will help me. You don't know anything.

Maybe not. Her friend retreats. In this therapy group they're supposed to speak out and not take offense.

I don't want to go back to drinking, says Pat, calming down again. Her hands shake as if it were a rough morning after.

In three weeks Pat's depression is worse. Her denim skirt begins to sag around the hips. Ordinarily she would be glad to lose the weight, but now she doesn't care. She cannot shampoo her hair. Her husband gently suggests it would be sensible if she had a bath. She takes more lithium.

The children come home safe every day, but by now she sees blood dripping from their knit caps. She will have to take care of that slide where her little girl smashes her skull every day. She'll have to show them something awful so they'll take it away. So she pulls on a down vest. Over her greasy hair she fits a brilliant red stocking hat with a green pom-pom. It was a Christmas hat for . . . which child? She doesn't recall. On her head it is stretched out of shape.

There are fifteen steps to the top of the slide. She drops the hat before climbing. She leaves on the down jacket because it is her skull she wishes to crush, not her ribs.

The janitor, emptying a trash barrel, watches wordlessly. Until he sees that she doesn't intend to slide. She intends to *dive*. Stop. Damn you. Stop.

He catches the full force of her as she comes down.

In the psychiatric ward she tells the psychiatrist who gave her lithium, I will do it. I will find a way.

He has stopped the lithium. Now he leans back in the visitor's chair as she sits on the edge of the bed twisting her fingers. We are going to try another modality, he tells her. It's called ECT and I'll explain it to you. It's a simple procedure and doesn't hurt a bit.

Hurt? She wanted to smash her skull on the blacktop. How could it hurt more than that? Thank you, she says. He is like the priest who heard her confession when she first talked about sinning with her own body. Six Hail Marys and one Our Father. This too must be penance.

In 1938 Cerletti and Bini presented a paper for the May supplement of the *American Journal of Psychiatry*. They set forth the effects of electrically induced seizures in animals. The electric technique was relatively simple. *Controllable* seizures could now be induced. Word about electric shock soon spread, and within a few years it was firmly established, especially in the United States, as the dominant somatic therapy for schizophrenia. But enough was not enough. Attempts were made to establish its efficacy for every known problem, from bad behavior to homosexuality.

In its most sophisticated use it was coupled with an injection of a derivative of curare, which slowed everything down and blocked muscle responses to the convulsion. And the use of mild anesthesia made it almost a painless process.

—You would have to be in the state and private hospitals at that time to appreciate what a blessing we considered electroshock, recalls the aging psychiatrist. —It was extremely effective against severe melancholy and depressions. While we found it couldn't cure schizophrenia, it did calm the patients down when they went into rages. But what a help it was to those severely depressed, mostly middle-aged women who might otherwise be condemned to sit in a back ward for the rest of their lives!

Virtual salvation.

Naturally in the state hospitals things were a little quicker and dirtier than in the private sanitoriums. Anesthesia? Nerve blockers to keep the muscles from going into frenzied convulsions? Patient permission? No. At a state hospital in California in 1956 the psychiatrist in charge of the acute treatment ward had recently arrived from the East. The first order of business was learning to twist the dials on the electroshock machine. For him, in the fullest sense, it was a power trip. Electric power trip.

He says, —Looking back, I'm horrified at the number of shock treatments I gave . . . probably two to three hundred a week. I was not in a position to decide who would get them, or if there should be shock. I was only told *when.* There was a shock ward where the patients were brought and cuffed to the beds. We had panels around the beds so there was at least visual privacy during the convulsion, and patients couldn't see another in the throes. But there was noise associated with it. We moved the machine around from bed to bed and I turned the dial. It was easy to learn. Sometimes I would do twenty-five patients at a time. The sedatives cut down on the noise but in retrospect I wonder how I could have done that. At the time I was inured to the whole process.

Aplomb.

Pat's psychiatrist does not have to get a signed permission from her to use ECT. She has already signed herself into the psychiatric unit and agreed with the fine print that she will go along with appropriate treatment. But the psychiatrist is more comfortable knowing that if she doesn't exactly *request* ECT, she is ready and willing to try it.

He wears Bass penny loafers, twill trousers from Cable Car Clothiers, and a houndstooth jacket from J. Press. He picked the jacket up at his last reunion.

He is not an indiscriminate user of ECT. In fact he would prefer to stick with psychopharm but what can you do? Pat appears to him to be docile enough to be suffering from endogenous depression. The attempted suicide raises the risk of just turning her loose with pills. And she did not respond to the lithium carbonate.

—I am thinking about a two-week course for you, he tells her. —Three sessions a week. The words are quite encouraging. Like a two-week course in Chinese cooking. Or a two-week course in how to manage household affairs. Pat has hopes that a two-week course will make her proficient in . . . whatever.

The psychiatrist discusses Pat's case with the hospital resident. The resident has shown a certain reluctance to use ECT, and the psychiatrist would like to get this squared away. He makes some concessions about the limitation of ECT. This tactic is a psychologically sound way to eliminate arguments early in the discussion. The words fly around Pat like swallows to a boathouse.

—Neurotic depressions generally don't respond well to ECT. Nor do personality disorders. But vegetative features such as we see here . . . decreased libido, daily variations in mood, sleep disturbances, anorexia, have been considered hypothalamic symptoms corresponding to an area of the brain which can increase the norepinephrine levels. ECT is known to increase norepinephrine turnover. It appears that subcortical structures in the reticular core of the brain stem may be involved in ECT's therapeutic effect.

The resident starts to interrupt, but the psychiatrist will have none of that. He holds up his hand. I have already instructed Pat that this will be some of the most pleasant therapy she may ever undergo. She won't feel a thing. It will be like taking a nap and waking refreshed. He is not about to let this resident make his patient nervous. So Pat will get a little jiggle three mornings a week for two weeks, and that should do the trick.

Just like that. A little jiggle. A two-week course. A holiday in the Bahamas. A trip to Hawaii.

All ECT devices produce an electric stimulus characterized by wave form, frequency, and duration, with a wide enough range of adjustable factors to cause generalized seizure activity in almost all individuals. Two machines commonly used in the United States utilize the sine-wave stimulus. (This is the sixty cycles per second found in the standard wall current.) One machine is called Medcraft B 24, and the other, Reuben Reiter Molac. The Reiter is the least expensive but does not have a built-in timing capability for stimulus duration and has limited variation in voltage setting. The Medcraft on the other hand has a glissando control that allows for gradual buildup of stimulus voltage intensity. There are claims that the use of muscle relaxants has made this glissando control an unnecessary feature. In fact the glissando effect, they say, functionally increases the seizure threshold, and in this there is danger.

Another machine, the Mecta, dishes out a brief pulse-charge:

short bursts of current interrupted by longer periods of electrical inactivity. Because current is interrupted, the entire session lasts longer than with the other two machines. This type of ECT was used back in the 1940s but was replaced by the fast-turnover models. The Mecta uses less electricity. There are indications that because generalized seizures can be evoked with one third the amount of energy there is a lessening of brain abnormalities and cognitive defects. The uneasy question arises: If a psychiatrist can get $40 to $100 for a single ECT jolt that takes two, three minutes, does it make sense to use another machine that takes twice, three times as long? Insurance policies *pay* for ECT. What's the percentage in waltzing around with them on the payment issue asking them to up the amount for another couple minutes' work?

Pat's hospital does not have the Mecta machine that delivers fewer zaps. But her psychiatrist is not concerned. He uses anesthesia, a mild relaxant, and, if Pat should start to develop anoxia, some standby oxygen.

Lack of arterial oxygen in the brain is the most feared side effect of convulsive seizures. It causes loss of memory, dislocation, even permanent gross brain damage.

While the baboon goes the limit for the testers of ECT, his body responses flip into orbit. A minute of intense convulsions have wracked his shackled body. His spine arches, pushing his head against the restraints. His dog-mouth is braced open, the tongue held retracted. At first the dials register a period of cerebral vasoconstriction, then there is a sustained increase in his cerebral blood flow. The test is going A-okay. It's a good rocket-launch. Now the brain shows an increased metabolic need and the systemic blood pressure begins to zoom. The seizures continue past the hour, and it looks as if his pressure could zoom as high as seven times baseline value. This is compensating for the brain's metabolic need. It is also causing a breakdown of the blood-brain barrier. The anesthesia and muscle relaxant control this as the seconds tick away and the shock goes into seventy minutes. Can the brain hold out any longer? The electroencephalogram (EEG) is registering . . . what? Brain damage? That's it. That's the wrap-up. Four thousand

and eight hundred seconds of intense convulsive seizure. Irrevocable brain damage. Okay, baboon. You've had it. They unstrap him and dump the vegetable into his cage. He'll be kept for some additional EEG's, then destroyed and shipped out with the rest of the lab garbage.

So much for the mountains of Africa, adolescent sex drive, and running with his tribe.

The ECT vendors read the report from this test and are relieved. Those eighty minutes sustained by the baboon represent more than ten times the duration of seizure activity for an ECT course. Not to worry. Home free.

Pat has been tranquilized and a muscle relaxant induced. Her psychiatrist waxes eloquent with the resident. We've come a long way since I first worked with shock therapy. Now, I'm not so old that I remember insulin use, he laughs, but I understand that insulin would leave the patient in a coma for ten to twelve hours, with convulsive periods during that time.

Both doctors wear white coats in the ECT room. This is the medical model. In fact when any psychologists come in for staff consults, he likes to shuck the streetwear. Reminds them he's an M.D. First, last, and always. He continues to reminisce. Now, when we went to ECT that coma stuff wouldn't happen. And we'd use a memory blocking drug on the patient. Didn't eliminate the pain, but afterwards they wouldn't recall anything. So it was zip . . . like it never happend. Like twilight sleep in childbirth.

No. Don't use memory block now. With Pat we'll be using a fast-acting anesthetic. I like methohexitol, which produces less cardiac toxicity than thiopental. Especially good for the oldsters, too.

The resident has a question. You don't use ECT on cardiac patients, do you? Even with methohexitol.

The psychiatrist grimaces. Controversial point, that. Got a lot of psychiatrists who think that's the way to go, even when you get a compromised cardiac status. Especially with depression after heart surgery. I don't favor it, myself. Nor with hypertension. Rather go the drug route.

The stimulus electrodes are placed over separate hemispheres on

Pat's head. If you drew an imaginary line between the top of Pat's ear and the corner of her eye and then found a point one inch above that, you would have the spot where the electrode is placed. Since the current will be diffused through the scalp, exact placement is not necessary. The spots are wide enough apart not to result in skin burns. A large black mouthpiece, like a gargoyle's tongue, is pushed into Pat's mouth.

The psychiatrist had spread a little conductive jelly on Pat's temples. Usually with old people, he says, we have to rough up the skin a little, and maybe throw a little extra current. But this one will not be a problem.

Pat is asleep. Hawaii.

The resident turns the dial. Current pulses into Pat's head. Nothing to it.

The psychiatrist says, You won't get the practice at this that I had. Did thousands. But now the bleeding hearts have interfered so much in the state hospitals that you have to go through a Mickey Mouse routine to use it. Watch that meter. We'll give her a minute and a half.

In spite of the relaxant there are muscle contractions. Pat's feet stretch into a toe dancer's mode, straining toward nothing. Then with a tremor her body enters the clonic phase with rapid and erratic contractions. Monitor that EEG, says the psychiatrist. Are you satisfied we got a good seizure?

Adequate, the resident says. Why do you want to go for a minute and a half? Sixty seconds should be plenty.

He shrugs. He does not like second-guessing. What's so holy about brain tissue anyway? Does he think something magical is going to be disrupted?

The women in Pat's therapy group hug her. Pat feels fragile and ready to weep. She did not want to leave the hospital for home. Even though she feels better.

You look super, someone says. How are you feeling?

Lots better. I really do. She smiles to show how normal she is. She can't remember her friend's name but was told this kind of memory loss was not unusual.

Heard you had ECT. Most of the people in the group had been in recovery units of one kind or another and had strong opinions about the various modes of therapy.

She nods.

Did they force you to have shock?

Oh, no. She giggles. I had a two-week course.

And it didn't hurt?

No. She lights a cigarette. Why are you asking me these questions? I don't want to talk about it.

What's my name? Can you remember?

You know what your name is, so why should I tell you. Don't be an ass.

Okay. She leans over and squeezes Pat's hand. I hope it helps.

This is the last therapy session Pat comes to. Within two months she has begun to get shaky again, and her psychiatrist talks about another series. Maybe some unilateral ECT, he suggests.

It sounds like another trip . . . the northern peninsula of Michigan . . . the ferry to Prince Edward Island . . . Pat is ready. A jiggle three times a week? Why not?

So that's what's happening, Pat's friend tells her own psychiatrist.

I think it's an abomination. Barbarism!

Pat says she felt better for a while, but now she's sitting around with the blinds drawn again. And she's going back *in*. Maybe it *will* work. What've you got against it?

The young psychiatrist sighs. Anyone who knows what ECT is like and still wants it is pretty pathetic. People like Pat are willing to bludgeon themselves into temporary oblivion . . . it's like being on a steady drunk or in a constant drug haze . . . when you come out of it, the problems are still there.

She says it didn't hurt and she doesn't ache now.

The psychiatrist forces a smile. I remember when one of the well-known ECT people said, *You know you can hardly see a finger twitch.* I say, so what? You didn't see a finger twitch when they did lobotomies, either. Hurt? That's the least of the problem. He gets up and strides around the room, punching the air for emphasis.

And what kind of half-assed way is it to measure a treatment by how much the body moves? If you're the brain, you don't give a *damn.* . . . you're *still* being insulted by electricity.

But what's so holy about the brain?

Are you serious? He stops, his face working to gauge her reaction. When he resumes, his tone is more conversational. When you asked me for ECT that time, you were in one hell of a depression. I told you most depressions are self-limiting, that they will disappear with or without treatment. And it may not be in the best interests of some patients to prescribe mood-altering drugs. I said I would never, *never* use shock on anyone except my worst enemy. Even if it doesn't hurt. In fact, the very drugs that block your convulsion and put you to sleep actually make it necessary to increase the amount of electricity used . . . *and that sure as hell doesn't diminish brain damage.* . . . That's the way shock works. *It damages the brain.* It's not a side effect you can get away with by using fancy footwork.

You mean I could be a—a vegetable?

He shakes his head. Probably not that. But you could have memory gaps, and you might find it hard to retain new information. He starts pacing again. Are you chilly? Do you want me to light a fire?

She rubs her arms. Not on my account.

He notes her shiver and strikes a kitchen match on the mantel. You want to hear something?

She nods.

He bends to the fireplace and crumples some nearby newspaper and lights it. He sticks the torch under an already laid fire, and quickly flame ends lick at the logs. He straightens and holds up a magazine turned to a particular page. One of the most respected doctors around makes *this* miraculous finding . . . people who don't put much stock in their memories will not complain about ECT, but those who think their memories are pretty important will have a complaint! My God!

She shifts uncomfortably. He is so *angry.*

Maybe Pat worries more about getting well than about her memory. And don't forget. She consented, it was her choice, nobody forced her.

On his desk is a new report from the department of psychiatry at Dartmouth Medical School. He hands it to her. He says, they ask some interesting questions about making these kinds of choices. Who's competent? Who's rational? Who knows enough to decide about this kind of trauma to our brains? Do *you* know enough? Do *you* want to take the chance you won't get brain damage because they shoot some electric current through? He kicks a log and sparks shoot. There are those who swear by laetrile. There are those who swear by Billy Graham. He shakes his head. There's no accounting.

About ECT

The use of electroshock to produce convulsions is still an accepted "therapy" among many psychiatrists. The controversy within the profession about its use continues. Some claim it should only be administered to a person suffering from endogenous depression (depression caused by internal factors), others say it should be administered only to those who suffer agitation and depression after heart surgery. Still others say it must *never* be administered to anyone with a defective heart system. Then, there are those who claim ECT causes impaired memory and permanent brain damage, but others say that's not so, that whatever occurs is only temporary with no lasting effects.

And there are some psychiatrists who believe that ECT should never be used *on any account*. They prescribe either drugs or psychotherapy or both.

Recently, Joseph Morrissey, Ph.D., and his coresearchers from the Bureau of Special Projects of the New York State Department of Mental Hygiene collected data on ECT from around the state. Their study covered five years—from 1972 to 1977—and shows a decline in ECT use in state facilities, yet an *increase of 130 percent* in the six private hospitals that were contacted. State hospital inmates are "a younger group," with a median age of thirty-six, while in the private facilities and in the general public hospitals with psychiatric wards, the median age during the study period ran between forty-six and fifty-four years of age. White females seem to be the primary ECT recipients, and over 80 percent of those given electric shock were patients in the private facilities.

ECT remains a quick, cheap, insurance-reimbursable item of therapy. An American Psychiatric Association task force on ECT, in randomly surveying four thousand of the Association's members, reports that *only 7 percent* of those who responded think ECT is obsolete.

Pro-ECTers now have the bit in their mouths. They have data and surveys to juggle and selected statements from satisfied "customers" to use in their promotion push. You can believe it will still be a hot item of controversy through the 1980s.

Seven

TURF

You can trace it back to June 1976. It was the day the psychiatrists decided to counterattack. No more Mr. Nice Guy, no more purrings about the unseemliness of competition. It was time to face the realities. Psychologists were *not* psychiatrists, they could never *be* psychiatrists, it was time to draw the boundaries.

The psychologists had hit the psychiatrists right where they live . . . in the hospitals. They were asking for full staff privileges, including admitting and discharge rights and voting participation on hospital planning, policy, and programs throughout the country. It was unheard of!

Ridiculous!

They aren't medical people!

Dangerous!

They're not trained!

The psychiatrists' counterattack began in proper corporate fashion . . . at the June 1976 Board of Trustees meeting of the American Psychiatric Association. The heavy guns of the profession were pointed at the entire range of the psychiatry-psychology battlefield

. . . how *dare* they? . . . they don't even *understand* what they're asking . . . it was time to teach them a lesson!

The matter is thrown open to discussion at the board meeting. The first to speak is John Spiegel, a past president of the APA. Strategy, he says, that's what we have to work on. We need a strategy to deal with these people. And we need time. I suggest some peaceful negotiations. . . .

A few heads wag. Peaceful negotiations? *Talking* it out? That won't do any good, they're beyond that and so are we.

But Spiegel has only given the board the slow curve. He delivers the fast break . . . *until we've prepared ourselves for something more decisive!*

Playing for time, getting the chance to arm themselves, to hone a strategy. Negotiate and fight!

But the negotiating part sticks in the board's craw. Negotiate? Hell, no, we've talked too long. Past President Judd Marmor puts it in simple terms—*If we lose this one, we have lost our identity completely.*

It's time for a clear stand, echoes Vice-President Daniel Freedman, who several years later will become president. Continue negotiating, by all means, keep talking, he urges. —But we must now have our own clear and unequivocal stand.

The air in the boardroom that day was combative, there was indignation, resentment, frustration. But psychiatric pragmatism was there too, unruffled, sensing that changes were needed, that the psychiatrist could learn from the psychologist. Vice-President Alan Stone, who also will become president a few years hence, notes the psychologists are organizing. They file lawsuits against psychiatrists all over the country, they have hired a blue-ribbon law firm, and who does the public look to as patient advocates? Not the psychiatrists. The psychologists have gotten the ear of patients, the psychologists even have a couple of lobbying groups.

We *need* a lobbying arm, suggests Stone. Political action . . . health care *is* political . . . it's time, others agree.

It is Judd Marmor who makes things official. Of course, no psychiatrist can operate without doffing a cap to those twin pillars of medical respectability . . . *in the interest of better patient-care . .*

the needs of psychiatric patients within a hospital setting . . . and Marmor makes sure they provide the foundation for his proposal. Then he lines up the weapons . . . legal and judicial action . . . joining and filing amicus curiae briefs . . . lobbying . . . *the spectrum of political action . . .*

All in favor say, aye!

There is one negative vote.

The battle is on.

There *are* differences between psychiatrists and psychologists. Psychologists are trained in behavioral and social science, psychiatrists are trained in *medical* science. Historically psychologists have been involved with academia and in research; psychiatrists have been much more involved in clinical work. It is only recently that clinical psychologists have been licensed to provide individual health care without supervision by psychiatrists. . . .

While psychiatrists themselves have been providing one-on-one psychotherapy since they first moved into the asylums and state hospitals, it was Freud, of course, who brought it close to an art form.

The psychologist is *not* a medical person. But he or she is a healer with a Ph.D. or an M.A.

The psychiatrist is a medical person . . . and a healer . . . with an M.D.

The president-elect of the American Psychiatric Association, Robert Gibson, sits before the House Interstate and Foreign Commerce Committee. He is testifying on proposals for national health insurance and where and how mental health will fit. Up for grabs is the answer to who should have first crack at the patient, a psychiatrist or any other mental health professional of the patient's choice.

Gibson states that national health insurance is assumed to be a *health* program for *medical* treatment, and therefore a *physician*— a psychiatrist—should make the initial diagnosis and determination that a service is medically necessary. —It wouldn't seem realistic to me, he continues, —that any individual who happens to feel a need for help should, on the basis of what would amount to a kind of self-diagnosis, be able to seek out any practitioner of their [*sic*] choice without some sort of evaluation and diagnosis by a physician at the outset.

The magazine writer is an old hand at politics. Living in Washington, he knows that politics is the lifeblood of the city. He has written articles about the people of Washington and their preoccupation with politics, comparing this to the obsession of landowners with real estate values in fast-growing new towns. An endless source of discussion, gossip, rumor, prediction, and rehash, on the *inside* of a quicksilver world.

In Washington if you aren't in politics, you're in limbo. Look in the Washington phone book, the writer urges, the unions, the businessmen, the religions, page after page of trade associations. Lobbyists, every one of them. *Politics moves!*

The magazine writer blinks as he realizes he is about to step off the curb against the flow of traffic. His mind has been wandering in the early afternoon springtime, he better pull himself together. Up ahead he spies his destination, the headquarters of the American Psychiatric Association. Politics and psychiatrists, it's done quite subtly. . . .

—You have an appointment? asks the secretary.

—Oh yes.

While he waits he glances about. This is *old* Washington, it exudes tradition, stability, and professionalism. High ceilings, deep carpets, spacious rooms, mahogany woodwork, oil portraits, thick walls, it *really* is a mansion . . . outside, the brickwork is vine-covered, someone might mistake it for a museum.

—He will see you now.

He follows her up a wide, winding staircase. She motions him through an open doorway and smiles as he thanks her.

The doctor, one of the American Psychiatric Association's policymakers, greets him with the briefest smile. A slender man in his forties, he is a longtime resident of Washington. He understands that modern psychiatry needs to talk to magazine writers. . . .

The office is more like someone's opulent sitting room, paneled walls, fifteen-foot-high ceilings, dark walnut side table with silver coffee service, a thick, wide couch and circular coffee table, a large walnut desk . . .

The magazine writer has a recent press release tucked in his pocket. The Association is to build a new headquarters, they expect to move in three to five years. They will build from scratch, and it will certainly never look like the current building. You can't duplicate a mansion like this anymore.

The doctor motions him to sit and walks to the side table. —Coffee?

The magazine writer nods, and the doctor pours into a bone china cup, resting on a bone china saucer. He places cup and saucer on the coffee table and returns for his own coffee. Then he sits, smiling.

The magazine writer decides to start with the building itself. —You're moving?

. He nods.

—Why?

He takes a long sip of his coffee and reaches in his pocket for a cigar. —What we've got here is some office space that's deteriorating and very inefficient. Forty-five thousand square feet of it, and it costs us almost $400,000 dollars a year. Add inflation and the fact it produces no income for *us*, and it's not a very good investment. It's a lovely building, but . . . He shrugs.

—And the new building?

—We increase our office space 10 percent, it's modern, efficient, and the rent will be fixed for the next forty-five years. It's a lease-purchase deal that'll cost us about $200,000 per year.

The new address is only a block from the new American Medical Association building and two blocks from the new American Bar Association building. *Politics moves!* —Politics is where you're starting from now, isn't it?

The doctor gives him a quick look. —Sure. It wasn't that way for us always, though. Through the years we've relied heavily on federal government support, grants mainly.

The magazine writer knows the history. Psychiatry had it easy for a long time. The profession had its own federal agency, the only medical specialty that did—the National Institute of Mental

Health. It didn't have to slug in the trenches with the other special interests, it was an agency, not a bureau or department. Psychiatrists were separate, unique, special people. The grants flowed from the end of World War II, and no one in the federal government was going to take an ax to the funding. There were high hopes and very little accountability, until the money began to tighten up and other specialties began to say . . . we can do it better . . . and then began to prove it! Psychiatry just didn't produce, the promise never met the performance, and the federal government support that had been like a security blanket for a generation slid away.

—Of course, everything is so much more adversarial now, says the doctor, draining his coffee and moving to the side table for a refill. —We have to convince constructive and even less than constructive critics, and in order to do that we've joined the American political scene. Relying on federal government support is just not the same as getting active in the political process.

The writer notes how effectively and easily Blum has assumed the role of psychiatric advocate. His words are reasonable, his tone far from strident, and there is a persuasiveness in his manner, a subtle salesmanship. The writer recalls a conversation he had recently with a more iconoclastic psychiatrist, one who is very much up on the power skills of psychiatrists. —There is something in the training of a psychiatrist that makes him an expert on recognizing and using power, the psychiatrist had said. Most doctors don't even think of it, but psychiatrists deal with people whose conduct is out of control, whose behavior is deviant. Exercising power, using the art of persuasion, are endemic to the practice of psychiatry. Why wouldn't they be skillful in the political game?

The doctor rejoins him at the coffee table. —We recognize that hopes and prayers will no longer support psychiatry just because it's good. . . .

It will take political action.

The big battle was fought in Virginia. Blue Shield of Virginia had a problem with costs of coverage for mental and nervous disorders. Things were getting out of control, and something had to be done.

Ideas poured in from around the state, especially from psychol-ogists' and psychiatrists' groups involved with psychotherapy. The general consensus was . . . you've got to limit the whole procedure somehow, you've got to make it harder on the practitioners. Limit the field. Limit it to professionals, those who are licensed by the state, was the most acceptable thought. . . .

Yes, indeed, nodded the psychologists and psychiatrists, both of whom were licensed by the state.

But during the deliberations the Neuropsychiatric Society of Virginia had their own deliberations with Blue Shield. Listen, they said, if you *really* want to control those costs, we have a better way. . . .

The better way turned out to be not so good for the psycholo-gists. Let us, the psychiatrists, run this thing, the medical society said. We'll decide if a person needs psychotherapy, we'll supervise psychologists, and they can bill *through us*.

That's bullshit, countered the psychologists. We do psychother-apy as well as you, we're even better trained for it considering the negative effect medical education has on your capacity for em-pathy. There is no rationale in your continuing control.

The psychiatrists responded that many emotional problems in psychotherapy mask an underlying physical problem. *The medical model was dusted off.*

We know enough to refer someone when we see physical prob-lems.

Only *medically* trained people know enough . . . only we are trained to deal with physical as well as emotional problems, they retorted, and turned to Blue Shield, the *doctor's plan*, for confirma-tion.

Would Blue Shield go against its own? Couching their decision in terms of responsibility to their subscribers, they went the mile with the psychiatrists and ruled that henceforth outpatient psycho-therapy would be reimbursed only if delivered by a psychiatrist or a psychologist *supervised by a psychiatrist*. All billings would be made through the psychiatrist.

The psychologists were incensed and directly filed suit. They claimed that the medical society and Blue Shield engaged in a restraint of trade and cited them for violation of the Sherman Anti-

trust Act. Further, they had conspired to promote an illegal boycott of psychologists' services. It was a breathtakingly severe
lawsuit because the damages, if the psychologists won, could have
been trebled.

But the psychiatrists fought hard. No, they argued, this was no
conspiracy. They had simply been consulted by Blue Shield of Virginia (the doctor's plan) and had provided them with their ideas in
the spirit of cooperation.

The court agreed. They found no conspiracy . . . and furthermore psychiatrists and psychologists don't compete with each
other. Diagnosing nervous and mental disorders is something *psychiatrists* do; providing the full range of psychiatric treatment
including medication and not limited to psychotherapy is something *psychiatrists* do.

Round one in Virginia to the psychiatrists.

But the psychologists appealed.

—These new Blue Shield policies were intended to stop the en-
croachment of nonphysicians into psychotherapy, the psychologists
argued. —But they've also crippled psychologists as independent
practitioners.

—Blue Shield doesn't pay for unrestricted psychotherapy, the
psychiatrists responded. —Blue Shield pays for *medically* necessary services . . . a physician may be able to prescribe medication
which can be much faster and less costly than psychotherapy.

We and only we are the medical people around here, the psychiatrists implied, only we can interpret what is *medically* necessary. . . .

Still the psychologists insisted, —There *is* actual exclusion here.
Clinical psychologists *are* denied access to patients. They lose patients and they lose revenue. People must go elsewhere if they want
reimbursement for these services. . . .

In June 1980 the Court of Appeals decided . . . more in favor of
the psychologists than the psychiatrists. *Yes*, the psychologists and
psychiatrists compete with each other, *yes*, psychologists should
be able to bill directly for their services . . . *no*, there wasn't an
antitrust violation and conspiracy or an illegal boycott by the medical society and Blue Shield of Virginia . . . *yes*, there could be
valid reasons for Blue Shield to require some form of examination

and consultation with a physician so that there are no physical ailments undercutting the psychotherapy. But on the whole . . . *yes,* psychologists are independent practitioners and *must* be allowed to bill directly for their services. They are not under the control and supervision of psychiatrists.

Round two to the psychologists.

But at a recent psychiatric meeting the psychiatrists are hardly reconciled. A young attorney from a congressional committee stands before them, a convenient target for their irritation and indignation.

—What do you say to a psychologist who says, "I'm doing the same thing as you are?" the attorney asks.

—They aren't, a psychiatrist from New Jersey says. —We know it better than anyone else. You look at a psychologist's training, it's nothing like what a psychiatrist goes through during residency.

A Connecticut psychiatrist joins in. —Many of the courses we go to for continuing medical education deal with chemistry, things psychologists never get trained in.

The young attorney nods. —Psychologists feel, though, that there is a wide area of duplication.

—Are you just taking their word for it? the New Jersey psychiatrist asks, annoyed.

—Have you really *read* the Virginia decision? the Connecticut psychiatrist asks.

He does not answer. Instead, he smiles and invites other comments. . . .

—There is a sense of outrage that we were brought into this case! comes from another part of the room.

Donald Langsley, M.D., is a thickset man in his middle fifties with a round face. He has been described as genial and skillful at psychiatric politics. At the time of the Virginia case, he is President-elect of the American Psychiatric Association, and there are many psychiatrists who sleep better because of it.

He's former Chairman of Psychiatry at the University of Cincinnati Hospital, and from the time he took over in 1976, psychologists in the department saw their powers and privileges chipped away. One psychologist who ran a psychosomatic ward in concert with two internists and psychiatric residents claimed to have been relegated to seeing outpatients, even though the ward's patient load had increased 30 percent. . . . Another psychologist, who worked in the hospital's Clinic for Eating Disorders, a nationally known and respected program, was assigned elsewhere when a portion of the funding ran out, even though the clinic had generated hundreds of thousands of dollars for the department. . . . Psychologists who worked in the hospital emergency room diagnosing incoming patients, giving psychotherapy, or recommending hospitalization could no longer work independently: They had to be supervised by an M.D., *even if the M.D. was a first-year resident and the psychologist had years and years of clinical work.*

Donald Langsley does not strike you as a militant, and he's no unsmiling zealot. Wouldn't it be better if we could all work together, he seems to say. It's the patient's mental health we're interested in.

He doesn't really want to get mixed up in all of this, he says. Until very recently there was no problem, no warfare. He thinks the most intense feelings occurred when psychologists and social workers and psychiatric nurses decided they wanted to become autonomous private practitioners in hospitals and *assume some of the medical responsibilities.* . . . He believes there is no substitute for the medical skills of the psychiatrist. Psychiatrists and psychologists are *not* the same.

So Langsley comes to Virginia to testify. . . .

—I have seen patients who had severe psychotic conditions purportedly treated by psychologists with psychotherapy where drug or hospital treatment would have saved significant suffering and expense, he says.

He implies that control over drug or hospital treatment should be the psychiatrist's monopoly. Psychologists should not prescribe drugs; psychologists should not admit or discharge patients from a hospital without a physician's okay.

But . . . doesn't a good clinician know when psychotherapy isn't working? The psychologists think there is too much drugging going on, that more patients are overdrugged than underdrugged.

Langsley is well acquainted with the drug story. He believes his own general-practice colleagues better shape up and get their medical house in order, too. But, he argues, psychiatrists don't over-drug that much: They're more responsible about prescribing than primary-care physicians, the family doctors, internists, obstetricians, gynecologists. He is not alone in this view. Other psychiatrists believe some primary-care doctors prescribe pills as if they're lollipops. These doctors are living proof that pill power can be dangerous to your health!

Yet Langsley will not give in to the psychologists. All of this is a *medical* issue, sickness and health, mind and body. Blue Shield is a *health* plan; doctors treat sickness and preserve health!

—I have seen numerous patients who were treated for long periods by psychologists who did not detect thyroid conditions, brain tumors, etc., Langsley tells the Virginia court. —The delay in diagnosis in these situations causes a worsening of the condition and, of course, a significant added expense in treatment.

Donald Langsley landed some telling blows in round one, but the fight didn't end there. By the end of round two the psychologists emerged with the better of it. They could now bill directly and were considered competitors, in effect validating their nonmedical skills as on a par with the medical model of psychiatry.

Then Langsley became president of the American Psychiatric Association, and he worked his constituents in classic political style during the five-day annual meeting in San Francisco that saw him installed. How are *you?* . . . hello, Walter, how's Boston . . . shake hands . . . nice paper, Harry . . . shake hands . . . How's that study coming? . . . how are *you?* . . . shoulder pat . . . it's so good of you . . . great job, Bob . . . shoulder pat . . . thank you, thank you, my love to Helen . . . how are *you?* . . .

He made it evident that he planned to be an activist president, voicing opinions and reaching the colleagues who will help him. He begins a bimonthly column in the APA's newspaper, *Psychiatric News*, a commentary called "Viewpoint." He is still bothered by the psychologist's growing power and the threat to psychiatric control over the treatment of mental illness.

He finds psychologists driven "by economic gain and financial

rewards," looking to take advantage of the expanding psychotherapy benefits that would come about if and when national health
insurance is passed. Their techniques are most "interesting," as
they play not by the traditional rules where education and practical
competence is examined and judged, but by . . . "politics, lawsuits,
and Madison Avenue techniques to influence decisions that should
be scientifically based."

The power game that psychiatry has played so well for so long
suddenly has new rules now and a larger field to play. It is no
longer confined to the medical societies, medical schools, federal
agencies, the Alcohol, Drug Abuse and Mental Health Administration, the state legislatures, the hospitals, and the insurance
carriers. It's out in the commercial world where price and accountability and cost effectiveness and salesmanship reign supreme.

Psychologists are increasing the number of practicing psychologists, and herein lies another threat.

Psychologists are expanding their roles in medical centers outside departments of psychiatry, offering behavioral services to
other medical specialties such as pediatrics, neurology, anesthesiology.

Psychologists are making alliances with consumer and citizen
groups and becoming patient advocates. Sometimes the advocacy is
directed against . . . *psychiatry!*

Psychologists seek employment in government, and in all likelihood they'll be sliding into decision-making positions . . . and what
will happen to government funding of psychiatry?

Langsley suggests that there's *enough work to go around.* The
two disciplines should be working together. But in some instances
when psychiatry has encouraged standards that would best protect
patients, the only thanks was a rebuff.

The magazine writer feels the interview is going nicely. The
doctor is relaxed and talking easily, not seemingly perturbed about
the pressures that have been coming from the psychologists, although he recognizes that others take the challenge a bit more
seriously. Nevertheless there is a determination not to be pushed
into situations that are, well . . . expedient. Psychiatry has too

distinguished a history to act rashly, and it has the gift of . . . aplomb.

—But we're prepared, he says, leaning back and letting the cigar smoke curl at his cheeks. —If it's going to get adversarial, we're prepared.

—How?

—We've joined the political stream. We now have a large government office with very sophisticated people who write legislation and work with certain congressmen.

—Lobbying.

—Right. It's more crass, but legal, and a shift from a kind of adolescent expectation when dealing with the real world.

The greening of psychiatric politics, that's the angle the writer is looking for! Somehow you don't think of these people out there, pressing the goods, pitching their point of view like . . . the Teamsters, the construction trades . . . the *oil interests*.

—It costs, doesn't it.

—We spend several hundred thousand a year now.

The doctor gets up and makes for the side table for another cup of coffee. He motions, but the writer has had enough. While he pours he answers. —Generally what we're looking for is to liberalize mental health legislation. Money for more psychiatric training, research. Better reimbursement.

—How about the drug companies.

He smiles. —What about them?

—Aren't they a source of training, research?

—Well, they supply *some* funding. They can be helpful.

—The drug ads that fill up your publications and their funding for your meetings and conventions.

—Here's a journal that has no drug ads. The doctor lays a magazine on the table. —That's the Soviet journal. It has no drug ads.

His smile is swift, and he drums fingers along the back of the couch. —To get back to, um . . .

—Political action, the writer supplies.

—Yes. I think we're more powerful than many people realize. Some of the challenges facing us are the result of being part of the American establishment. People are more aware of who we are now, and when we put support behind legislation there's bound to be a reaction.

—Then why the gloom and doom about psychiatry being under siege?

—A false myth. A misperception. Psychiatrists are not used to adversarial interaction. Take that incident on the talk show you might have seen. The president of the Association appeared and wasn't aware that antipsychiatry groups had packed the studio! It was pretty awful. The conditions were very difficult for him and he couldn't say much. That was a good lesson. Next time we know enough to pack the studio with our people.

Round three of psychologists versus psychiatrists comes to Ohio. It is a lawsuit brought by the Attorney General of Ohio against the Joint Commission on Accreditation of Hospitals, the Ohio State Medical Association, the Ohio Psychiatric Association. The suit alleges that there has been a conspiracy to prevent psychologists from competing with psychiatrists in various hospitals and hospital programs throughout the state.

All we want, say the psychologists, is to be able to practice our profession to the full extent of our licenses in the State of Ohio. Under the rules of the Joint Commission, once one of our patients goes to the hospital, we're put in a subservient role to a psychiatrist. We don't like that, we don't think it's fair to ourselves or our patients, and it deprives us of the right to practice.

The Joint Commission, which sets standards for most of the hospitals in Ohio as well as across the country, requires that only doctors can admit, diagnose, and discharge patients from hospitals. If the hospital should *on its own* allow non-M.D.'s to admit and diagnose, it would lose its accreditation. *A psychologist in a hospital setting must work under the supervision of a psychiatrist.*

The Joint Commission has a board of twenty-one members, *thirteen of whom are medical doctors.* The brethren control the show.

Psychiatry argues that medicine and hospitals go together like a horse and buggy.

The psychologists say, you're afraid of the competition. We both do psychotherapy. You want us to work with one hand tied.

You can still *see* your patients, the psychiatrists cajole.

Only if you deem it proper, the psychologists counter. *You* have the final authority.

We have legal responsibility, say the psychiatrists.

We'll take that off your shoulders, gladly. (The psychologists know chess moves when they see them.)

Traditionally, say the psychiatrists, we always had responsibility for the care and management of patients.

Let's call them clients, say the psychologists. You're muddying the waters.

The psychologists regroup and try to put together for juries and lawyers the simple essence of psychotherapy. It comes out something like this . . .

Psychotherapy depends on a close, trusting working relationship between client and therapist. The strength of the relationship often has crucial consequences for the success of therapy. If a client must be hospitalized and a psychiatrist takes over where the psychologist left off, there could be unnecessary pain. And it is not as simple as starting from square one. That would be regrettable enough. But this could be like playing football with rugby rules.

Beyond that comes that crucial issue of *hospital costs*. Supervision demands its own payment. And the patient gets stung twice.

Both sides believe their arguments are sensible. But in round three there is a lot of slugging yet to be done. Turf, after all, is turf.

"There shall be a single organized professional staff that has the overall responsibility for the quality of all clinical care provided to patients . . ." is Section 3.1 of the Consolidated Standards of the Joint Commission on Accreditation of Hospitals. The use of the word "professional" before the word "staff" is new, an amendment that supercedes the word "clinical." Those clinical boys with their nonmedical degrees are going to get theirs!

The American Psychiatric Association are not about to let that word "clinical" stand, not when it refers to *"staff."* "Clinical" means psychologists, social workers, nurse practitioners. "Professional" means tradition, ancestry, the medical family tree.

The APA has learned its political lessons well. What are friends for but to help in times like these? The National Association of Private Psychiatric Hospitals . . . check. The American Hospital Association . . . check. Others, too, gave the Joint Commission a little nudge. Dr. Langsley is happy to say that they were able to encourage the Joint Commission to see it their way.

Big Leagues. The American Psychiatric Association has formed a Political Action Committee, PAC to the trade. It's been just a few short years since that day in June 1976 when they decided they had had enough of being Mr. Nice Guy. A political action committee is the most sophisticated step they can take.

PAC was organized with a kitty of at least $1 million.

PAC will be run by psychiatrists from every geographical division of the Association.

The staff of PAC will be highly skilled in lobbying and promotional techniques. Psychiatrists' political aims will be furthered, and there will be effort and contributions made for suitable and sympathetic candidates.

We've joined the political process, they say.

High time, they say, hanging tough and hanging in.

Eight

SEDUCTION AND SUPERBUCKS

Pamela, Daniel, and Peter live barely off Commonwealth Avenue in Brookline, Massachusetts. Daniel and Peter share a four-room flat on the second floor of a post–Civil War house. Pamela rents the top front. She has a bedroom, kitchen and a small living room crammed with medical books, works of Kant, Thomas Mann, Krafft-Ebing, and Reich.

On good days the three bike to Harvard Medical School. On bad days they hitch rides with other students. Occasionally they feel that half of their productive waking hours are spent in the logistics of getting from here to there, just surviving. Keeping warm enough in Brookline's damp, wind-chilling cold is a big thing. Fixing bike flats, broken sprockets, taping handlebars is another. They have learned to avoid the junk-food section of the grocery stores (cost per gram of food value is outrageous). Instead they eat a few good meals a week in one of the kosher dairy delis or in a Greek spot farther out the avenue. They try not to think of food except as a necessity. Their lives for the next few years will continue to be dictated by necessities.

That's why it comes so hard to say "no" when Roche or Ciba or Lederle or other big drug companies lay nice little "tokens" on them.

That first gift-day, as new medical students, caused them unexpected difficulties. . . .

Daniel is amazed because Pamela says she won't touch the manuals or stethoscopes left as gifts in the student affairs office. . . . Has a detail man come up to you even once? he asks. . . . Have they tried to pressure you in any way? They aren't even allowed around here.

That's not the point, Pamela says. We aren't in a position to prescribe drugs now, anyway. They're trying to influence us about their products, it's subliminal. . . . Pamela feels she knows the line between influence and independence.

Peter jollies her . . . What kind of bribe is a stethoscope? Would you sell a patient down the drain for a stethoscope?

Of course not! She hates this ganging up, but she's determined to convince them. . . . I wouldn't sell a patient for any price. But there has to be a reason why they give us these things, right?

It's about time somebody helped the poor medical student. And what kind of shitty money are we going to get as interns?

Why don't you make up a birthday list! Pamela bites.

Daniel thrusts his jaw in her face. I've got a *down jacket* on my birthday list. I'm close to pneumonia from your Yankee winters as it is. . . .

So go back to Virginia and study. . . .

Peter elbows in. Pam, why don't you take a flying . . .

She ignores him and jeers at Daniel. You think the lovely pictures in the manual are going to help you understand pathology better? Is that drug company slide rule sexy? It's a matter of principle. You start here, and where do you stop?

Daniel will sink with the equipment if he has to. Use what you can, he thinks. . . . I'm not asked to do a *single* thing in return. This isn't bribery. Harvard wouldn't *allow* bribery!

This place is no better or worse than any other medical school. And we're no better or worse than other people. But we're going to be *doctors*. And gifts are a piss-poor reason to be in this profession. . . .

Daniel wants to ease out of the shouting match. If it makes life easier, and liberates some cash . . . I mean, if everybody else is going to do it, then what the hell . . .

We should have a meeting and talk about it, Pamela says, knowing she's expecting a lot from her classmates. Even living as cheaply as they can, medical school costs over $13,000 a year. It's a damn tight life, and anything that can ease things, well . . .

Still, she *is* determined. Lederle and the others have a problem if they think they can tempt her with electrocardiogram guides. She has been in *training* against temptation. It's been over a year since she had a hot fudge chocolate sundae. Compared to that, this is penny ante. . . .

Okay, she says, let's have a meeting. It'll be interesting to hear what the rest of the class thinks.

Both men are glad she has calmed down. She cooks a mean lasagna, and they wouldn't want this argument to reach ridiculous proportions.

. . . We're going to be *doctors* . . . Pamela emphasizes at the class meeting. . . . And this influence is like pregnancy. There's no such thing as a little bit.

A laconic voice from the rear. Have you checked out research grants? Where would we be without the drug companies?

Another voice, agreeing. It's part of saving lives. Making people better. These companies do good in the best sense of the word.

They sure *do* good . . . Someone sides with Pamela . . . They do so good, in fact, their promotional budgets are in the millions.

Another voice . . . You'll be singing a different tune when it comes to practicing. . . .

Pamela has not sat down throughout the meeting. . . . I'm going to be a psychiatrist, and it makes me very uncomfortable to think judgments could be compromised by the influence of drug companies.

A voice from the side . . . Shrinks use drugs!

I *know* shrinks use drugs, she says. And that's what I mean! I don't want to feel obligated to any drug company, just because they've given me a gift. . . .

After half an hour Pamela isn't sure whom she's convinced, but when they take a vote the majority agree they won't accept gifts from the pharmaceutical companies. Pamela leaves, elated.

But the vote is *nonbinding*. And little by little the meeting is forgotten. "Tokens" continue to be dropped off at the student affairs office and gradually find their way into use throughout the student body. The little handy things that make medical life cheaper and easier. Freeing up a few dollars for something else.

Pamela stays clean, however. She solicits relatives for the equipment she needs. If she notices a Sandoz pen or a Pfizer pad poking from Daniel's pocket or from Peter's briefcase, she says nothing. She made her pitch. And maybe they're half right . . . maybe it's a seduction not worthy of note. So far she's seen no one asking for a quid pro quo. So far.

Drug companies are working hard to be the Big Daddies of the medical profession. It starts in medical school and continues as the young doctor builds up a private practice.

Hoffmann-La Roche is one of those involved in teaching the novitiate how to build up his bucks. It's all there on a tape cassette, provided free and played on the company-supplied tape recorder. The tape is called *Practice Management Mistakes and How to Avoid Them—The Roche Practice Plan—Getting Started in Psychiatry*. Actors, portraying psychiatrists, tell how to make it and what to avoid . . . stay away from alcoholics and schizoids, they make your practice look bad! You'll build your practice almost completely through *referrals* . . . but remember, general practitioners are often suspicious of young psychiatrists, especially if they are *female*.

Move to suburbia, that's where the bucks are. Get to know the cops, they'll refer people, it's a good patient base. Get board certified, your prestige will rise, and you'll be in a better position for insurance reimbursement. Join the PTA, become visible with the Chamber of Commerce. *But* avoid treating old people, it makes other patients uncomfortable and there's little money. Be selective . . . and you'll build up a nice paying carriage trade. . . .

Good advice? Yes, for making bucks, maybe even superbucks. Subliminally Dr. Shrink and Mr. Drug have created a symbiotic relationship: you need me, I need you . . . we're in this medical thing together. Shrinking, like drugging, is a business . . . enjoy the nice radio we sent? See, it gives twenty-four-hour-a-day programming, our own special station, you get *all* the drug and medical information you can use . . . drug companies only want to help . . . your friendly detail man will be in touch. . . .

Money for psychiatric training rained down in sheets from the federal government after World War II. William Menninger and others in the Surgeon General's office were the golden gods of the 1940s, and as with their psychoanalytic colleagues, they were clever in the ways of maneuvering state and federal bureaucracies. They *were* the feds, in fact. Psychiatry belonged to government. Money was available, and hungry medical schools filed grant applications to get as much of the meal as they could chow down. It was the beginning of separate departments of psychiatry in the medical schools and teaching hospitals.

Drug companies had a long way to go in those days. Big research discoveries and big bucks would not show up until the 1950s.

And when the money *did* start moving in from the drug companies, it was in the name of science . . . promoting health . . . doing good! A tender seduction, a subtle touch. In the right places.

The direct cost of mental illness in the United States in the late 1950s was estimated at more than one and one-half billion dollars. Twenty years later that figure would rise fourteen times, almost all of it under psychiatric or medical supervision. A tempting lode to tap . . . if you knew where to look.

Independent research was the key. Underwrite the research, get in on the ground floor, literally, then . . . sell . . . sell . . . sell! Promoting health . . . doing good . . .

Independent, the research must be! Scientifically accurate and reliable. Credible, no corporate strings.

But how independent can it *really* be? Are you constrained to give the drug company the results it *wants* rather than the results it should have? Are you tempted to prolong the experiments so there will be more grant money? Are you influenced in thinking that the drug, if marketable, could provide you with lecture and publishing fees?

And what are your research responsibilities, anyway? Finding out that the drug has side effects but going along with company pressure because the risk/benefit factor isn't too far out of balance? *I'm not in a position to judge*, you say, I just do the testing, I'm not *there* when the doctor decides on treatment.

It costs well over $100,000 to become a psychiatrist, and even during internship and residency the pay is lousy and the hours long. And there's small compensation from those iffy years in early practice, while you smile at the Chamber of Commerce types, butter up the internists and general practitioners for referrals. A person could use a little backup dough.

—If you think hanky-panky is part of drug development and research, you're very wrong, says the young psychiatrist who devotes many hours a month to drug research and edits a biological therapy newsletter. —It's simply much, much harder now to get federal money for research support than it once was. Today a lion's share of the money in pharmacology comes from industry. To bring a drug out on the market can involve anywhere from hundreds of thousands of dollars to many millions.

How likely would it be that a drug company is going to scratch a program after investing *millions*?

—I don't think any reputable drug company would like to be caught with egg on its face by coming out with studies that in some way have been bluffed or have had the data fudged. Sooner or later these findings would be challenged in subsequent studies. And if a company wanted to suppress toxic problems, then they would be liable for suit once the product got on the market.

One of the big worries in the drug company boardrooms is dollar investment divided by seventeen years. The patent clock is ticking, and there has to be a fast hustle to make it worthwhile for a drug to be researched, manufactured, marketed, and promoted.

Trading aerospace jargon, company executives huddle over the latest briefing reports on a new antidepressant . . . It looks like we've got a go–no-go decision here . . .

How's that, Andy?

Here are the prelims on the VA hospital studies, and the side effects look a little chancy.

That's a surprise.

We may recommend an abort. Look . . . there's Parkinsonian tremor effect on the elderly . . .

Last month you told me we were into countdown.

I'm not saying the mission is blown. But we've got to decide . . . go–no-go for more tests on dosage regulations.

What are expenses to date?

Including independent lab work . . . close to half a million . . .

No problem. This drug could hit the stratosphere. I'm for speeding up the tests. Let's get *moving* . . . and I want a report on those prison studies too. *That* could give us lift-off . . .

Roger.

—What's the bottom line? the young psychiatric editor repeats.
—Normal return on the dollar. I suppose. We live in a capitalist system, he says. In other words . . . drug companies are not in business for their health.

No great surprise that . . . *but* are they in business for *our* health?

—Remember their research is not really the research of any specific company. They farm out. In the last analysis it's the investigator who needs to know things like patient safety and informed consent. The drug companies know it's advantageous to be associated with prestigious journals, and publications like the *New England Journal of Medicine* aren't going to run articles unless they are impressed by an excellent trial. They know that the practitioner is going to be impressed by articles in these journals and will be more inclined to prescribe the drug.

Loxapine is the generic name for a potent drug that can quiet and sedate. It is commonly used for the rapid management of excitement and agitation, especially in acute schizophrenic episodes. Lederle Laboratories, a division of American Cyanamid Company, produces loxapine under its own trademark Loxitane. The market for hustling antipsychotic drugs for "rapid management" is highly competitive. Roerig, a division of Pfizer Pharmaceuticals, puts out a product called Navane, and McNeil Laboratories peddles its "rapid management" drug under the name Haldol. There are others, too . . .

Harold S. Feldman, M.D., Ph.D., is chief of the forensic unit at the Essex County jail in New Jersey. He is acquainted with Lederle and *New Improved* Loxitane. As an associate professor of the Department of Psychiatry and Mental Health Science at the New Jersey Medical School, he has nice credentials. He also has access to eminently "testable" people.

Loxitane works! Harold Feldman believes. He's tested it and he knows; he's tested it on the *real* hard cases, the toughies behind bars.

According to Lederle, Feldman concluded —Hostile and aggressive criminal offenders who are also schizophrenic require immediate, potent treatment . . . Because loxapine [Loxitane] has shown efficacy in the treatment of schizophrenia, a trial of its usefulness in schizophrenic criminal defenders was conducted. . . . A secondary aim was to discover whether treatment with loxapine [Loxitane] would be rapid enough to allow the offenders to progress from solitary confinement to a regular cell within a day or two of their admission and to recover sufficiently within ten days to cooperate with their attorneys and understand the procedures of the court.

Seventeen males and one female, thirteen of whom were black and five white, all deemed hostile and aggressive and slated for solitary confinement, were given injections or oral amounts for ten days. Of the eighteen, four developed exaggerated tremors and facial distortions, and treatment was discontinued in two cases. Nevertheless Harold Feldman concluded that Loxitane is safe and quite effective . . . —The rapidity of action was particularly useful in this unique treatment-setting.

Jail, of course. Thirteen inmates "completing the study" were deemed competent to stand trial.

Lederle was smiling and unbuttoning the pocketbook. A media blitz was underway. Feldman's report in tandem with media advertising will give Loxitane a lot of mileage. Full-page back cover ads in *Psychiatric News* and other medical publications depict a smashed section of a plate-glass window . . . then a pair of capable male hands shown filling a 3 cc syringe with *Loxitane IM*, "New Improved Loxitane IM," *Loxapine Hydrochloride Intramuscular for rapid intervention in the psychiatric emergency* . . . is the message.

It is noteworthy that the trade name Loxitane appears only *once* in Feldman's published report. The drug is called loxapine throughout, in keeping with the demands of scientific detachment. But the message is there . . . he was testing for Lederle, and at this point it is definitely a *go!*

Roger.

"It's called subtle money, and it works like this: A psychiatrist is asked to serve on a symposium or a round table and is offered compensation. A drug company has come out with a *new improved* antidepressant. Five or six psychiatrists who have shown interest in or have special competence in depression will be brought in. Now, it's not specifically a testimonial about *this* new antidepressant, it's kept more general than that. And it's called a *continuing education program* . . .

But most of the people there *know* there are selling overtones, it's obviously a pitch . . . because the drug company is underwriting the whole thing! And from this forum new promotions are developed . . . *Dr. So-and-So says* . . . *A ballroom full of physicians wants to know* . . . *Six out of seven doctors at a recent psychiatric meeting stated they use* . . .

Few drug-dispensing psychiatrists see anything wrong with taking compensation from the drug companies and serving on these panels. It's their professional duty to educate their colleagues . . . or it's a chance to learn something new . . . or it's only right they be compensated for the loss of income from canceling a day's patient load . . . But many doctors ignore the fact that drug companies' special interests are in the bottom line. Their profits run into the hundreds of millions, their prime purpose is to make money for their shareholders. Doing good.

Says one psychiatrist, —The honorariums come to hundreds of dollars plus expenses, and I've been involved in many sessions. I've been requested by a certain drug company to teach primary care physicians about depression, and I welcome the opportunity to get the information out. Since it's not being done elsewhere, of course, I'll do it for the drug companies. It's a nice supplement to my practice, but I can justify it by saying my time is worth *something*, and I had to give up treatment of patients and forgo their fees in order to help the drug companies.

Depression. Some people have it. Other people study it. Depression and psychotropic drugs . . . and superbucks. Sometimes they all go together.

The head of a private outpatient psychiatric clinic knows. —I think almost 90 percent of psychiatrists accept the fact that depression has a biochemical basis, and now we are on the threshold of proving it scientifically. And the drug companies are quite interested in drug efficacy studies. It stands to reason they aren't interested in any other kind of research. The studies we get involved with are paid for by the drug companies. One of my collaborators is studying two antidepressants . . . each owned by a different company. . . . We're using patients at the VA hospital, and although they don't know it, they're supplying us with information for the drug companies while they are being treated.

Is this really independent research, then? The response is quick and clear. —Of course. The studies are done double blind. We don't know which drug is which.

But you know who's paying, and you know thousands of dollars have changed hands. How independent can you *really* be?

Scotching the snake isn't so easy. Dr. George A. Schumacher is a well-known specialist on headaches. In 1972, while Professor of Neurology at the University of Vermont's College of Medicine, he found himself propositioned, and "pacified," rejected, all in the space of two years. The seduction scenario began with a letter from *Modern Medicine*, a promotional medical magazine sent free to more than 200,000 doctors. The letter, dated July 31, 1972, was from John H. Rosenow, M.D., the Executive Medical Director of Modern Medical Publications, publisher of *Modern Medicine*.

The letter asked Dr. Schumacher to take part in a forum based on an abstract published in *Modern Medicine*. The discussion would deal with the question "What are the best prophylactic and therapeutic medications for the treatment of migraine?" He was to draft an essay of about three hundred words and submit it within a month so it could be edited and returned for final approval. He was told he could either condemn or praise the abstract—whatever he believed it deserved. The letter went on to say that for every forum, the magazine asked for the reactions of physicians who had distinguished themselves in the field with which the abstract was concerned and who represented many points of view. It was the magazine's wish to expose its readers to all sides of various problems about which there might well be an honest difference of opinion among men of integrity.

Dr. Schumacher read the abstract and was concerned that its premise relied on drug treatment for migraine, in particular on a drug that Schumacher recognized as not having the specific or unique superiority claimed . . . Fiorinal . . . manufactured by Sandoz. He prepared his comments and submitted them. And he took strong exception to the recommendation of Fiorinal. But after all, he had been told he could reply with *condemnation or praise*.

The people at *Modern Medicine* were in a quandary. What to do about Dr. Schumacher? Maybe he could be steered in the right direction. So correspondence flowed back and forth. Rosenow edited and *deleted* the paragraph that questioned the specific value of Fiorinal . . . he also *deleted* a paragraph that criticized Sandoz's claim that Fiorinal was useful for "tension headache."

Dr. Schumacher replied and insisted his criticisms of Fiorinal be reinserted. Rosenow finally agreed to a compromise, and plans for publication of the manuscript went ahead.

But the drug company snake had *not* been scotched. And Sylvia Covet of Modern Medical Publications didn't see that it should have been. Acting on behalf of her employer, whose healthy profits came from drug company advertisements, she rejected Dr. Schumacher's contribution out of hand. And she rejected it at the point of publication . . . even after a picture had been solicited. She gave a simple explanation—Dr. Schumacher's comments did not meet the standards set up for the series. Period!

It was six months after his contribution was first solicited and three revisions later. Now, that's a lot of doctor time to dump down the well. At this point Schumacher had an investment of time and money in the project. His sleuthing, deductions, and neurological experience over the years had him angry and determined. He fired off a letter to . . . Sylvia Covet . . . editorial director . . .

> It has become apparent now that even a journal such as *Modern Medicine*, as well as drug manufacturers themselves, can have a biasing influence upon readers. . . . In view of this I believe FDA should bring a journal such as yours under its scrutiny . . . and it is my intention to bring this matter to the notice of the FDA in complete detail. To reject the manuscript because it was too "incendiary" is a ludicrous comment in view of the strong differences of opinion that sometimes exist between critical scientists.

And hadn't the first letter from these people said he could write a condemnation or paean of praise?

Dr. Schumacher was working up a head of steam. He pointed out that Sandoz now had full-page ads for Fiorinal on the back covers of the *Archives of Neurology*, another heavily distributed medical journal, even while the FDA was showing concern about the manufacturer's claims for the drug.

He let fly another salvo.

> Your action is furthermore understandable in view of the decision by Sandoz, following the FDA's scrutiny, to recruit physicians in the headache field . . . to carry out therapeutic trials of the drug (paying the physician $200 for each patient included in the study) *after the drug had been on the market for twenty years.* [emphasis added] This also tends to explain why *Modern Medicine* has decided to publish a Forum on the medical treatment of migraine. It would seem that it may have been suggested by Sandoz, probably in consultation with and the approval of Dr. F., who put Fiorinal on the market, enabling Sandoz to make millions. It is obvious that both

Dr F. professionally and Sandoz financially have a large stake in what appears in the Forum.

In whatever way Dr. F. was tied in with Sandoz, Dr. Schumacher saw this as an insult to the ethics of medical practice. He himself had seen the snake's seductive eyes, but he had withstood seduction. With righteous indignation he continued:

> Though you may have had other reviewers, I suspect the dampers were put on the publication of my views by Dr. F. I cannot conceive of any other clinical scientist in the headache field objecting to any aspect of the content of my statement. . . . To request the opinions of four different physicians . . . and then to turn the views of one down because of the negative comments of a reviewer with whose opinions my views did not coincide, is a grossly dishonest statement.

Dr. Schumacher bundled up the correspondence with the people at *Modern Medicine* and sent it to the Federal Drug Agency's Bureau of Drugs. It became part of a mountain of damning material now on file against drug monopoly and superbucks and the incestuous relationship between these companies and the physicians or their organizations who are part of the snake-oil scene. On September 17, 1975, Dr. Schumacher's file was sent to the Senate Select Committee on Small Business, for the attention of the Subcommittee on Monopoly. Hearings on the pharmaceutical industry began April 28, 1976, and letters in this file were published by the government, and the message is clear . . . Beware the Medical-Pharmaceutical Complex! . . .

The con.

Soft carpets in the foyer of the luxury hotel. Palms circling a step-down court. The sound of a small waterfall and the magic of pink lighting. Mantovani strings piped into the Oak Room and the Empire Room and the Grecian Room . . . a regular oasis of opulence, perfect for a cold winter's night. Perfect for a medical man who has been invited for a nice evening of *soft sell*.

It's January, a perfect time to gather the medical people from the icy and wet city streets, the cold out-of-doors, and bring them into some *warmth*.

The drug company has been having a little trouble lately with reduced interest for its oral tranquilizer. The sales figures show a drop of almost a percentage point. It's not good news, though there is hope. The research people have come up with a one-a-day tranquilizer, perfect for maintenance. If the new product can get off with a bang . . . if it can be tied to the older product too . . . if the new one can hype the older one . . .

It's just 150 milligrams of time-release drug. Easier for nursing homes, for clinics, for the rank-and-file patient who can't be counted on to take regular dosage. One a day is all, who could forget or be inconvenienced by that!

Now this should be an evening to remember for the drug company. They've got a closed-circuit television hookup, they've got that prestigious university where shrinks have been testing the one-a-day beauty, they've booked the best ballrooms in twenty-three of the best hotels across the country. They're going to *present* the new drug in gala fashion.

Every three-piece-suited detail man working this drug is on hand, introducing, glad-handing, pitching . . . But it's *soft* sell, it's education, it's promoting health. *We're here to help* . . .

Tie-in will include full-page ads in a dozen distributed-free journals and *Psychiatric News*. The cream of shrinkdom is turning out, each ballroom has its own panel of experts.

The advance man in Boston is elated. He's certain he rounded up the best psychiatrist available for master of ceremonies. A tweedy, honest-looking Dartmouth man, worked at McLean Hospital, the best credentials. If this doesn't impress them nothing will. He'll be so earnest on the tube, so believable . . .

The advance man and two detail men from the company had taken the master of ceremonies out to dinner before the session. They had been discussing program procedures, and the shrink had just asked whether there would be questions allowed from the floor after the presentation.

The advance man . . . Nice ones, we hope . . . He laughs . . .

There's a planted question for each city. Leclerc has the one for Boston. When the hands go up, you call on *him*. Ignore the others. After he's done, and we're off the screen, the sky's the limit. Give them five, ten minutes each, then move to the next. Otherwise, we'll be there all night. And I think we deserve a little serious drinking after the show's over, right?

The psychiatrist realizes he doesn't have to drive. They're sending him home to Newton by limousine. A little serious drinking. Not bad . . . He waves the waiter for another Gibson.

The advance man nurses his Perrier. He wishes dinner would get there soon. Sop up the booze. Got to keep the shrink in line for the next two hours. He kicks the detail man in the ankle. The detail man excuses himself unobtrusively. It's his job to hurry the menu along and tell them to water the Gibson. Just a touch.

The symposium at the Copley Plaza in Boston on this January night is one of hundreds that are repeated throughout the year. Sponsored by the drug companies, they help account for an average of a billion dollars spent each year for drug promotion. Every modification of a drug makes it worth a symposium. Every symposium puts the drug company in direct contact with the prescribing source . . . the medical doctor. The drug companies book the hotel ballrooms, pay for the refreshments, and in the case of any doctor participating in the program, be it through research or by appearing on a panel, there are ample rewards.

A group called Health Learning Systems specializes in setting up symposiums. They state that some of their closed-circuit presentations reach up to *eight thousand* physicians at one time! That's a pretty good audience when you're doing the selling!

And the drug companies? They're doing *good* . . . by *doing* good.

Nine

AT THE PLEASURE
OF THE KING

In medieval England there was a tradition of what to do with someone who commits a crime and then claims a defense of insanity. There were no psychiatrists then, no expert witnesses, no sophisticated testing, no great body of psychiatric-legal thought and theory. But there was a procedure.

Very simple. A mad person who committed a crime went to prison. He stayed in prison *at the pleasure of the king* until he "recovered" his senses. Then he stood trial.

A group of psychiatrists gather to talk about testifying in court. Most have had substantial experience in the courtroom, some more than thirty years. Mainly they have testified when someone has plead insanity or when an application has been filed to commit a person to a psychiatric hospital. The law calls these psychiatrists *expert witnesses.* . . .

—I think the American Civil Liberties Union and the courts have caused much harm to psychotics, says a psychiatrist who works in a state hospital. —They keep pushing for and recognizing patient rights, including the right not to be hospitalized. These patients need help, no matter what the ACLU says. . . .

—Right, right, adds a well-known forensic psychiatrist, who almost always testifies for the prosecution. —More and more law is interfering with the treatment process. Remember that court in Boston saying people whose decision-making was based on fantasy, completely disorganized, not in touch with reality, could make decisions about their own treatment?

A young New York psychiatrist asks, —You mean if somebody believes he is a tree and stands for thirty-six hours on a cold street corner in a catatonic state, he can theoretically decide he doesn't want his rump punctured by a needle? He can make *that* stick? He can reject the one thing that will bring him down to normal?

—Nonsense, isn't it? says a white-haired, dignified-looking psychiatrist. He is by far the most formally dressed, dark pinstriped suit and vest, silk tie and matching pocket handkerchief. His voice is rich. —Lawyers just don't understand the way we think, how we're trained. The kinds of questions they ask when we're on the witness stand demand answers even when there aren't any answers. Over and over I've told them psychiatry is *not* an exact science. . . .

—You're damn right it's not! a California psychiatrist breaks in. There is minor muttering because he is not a favorite. —None of us is an expert on the state of someone's mind in a court of law. I don't believe that any of the questions the law is interested in can be answered in an expert way by a psychiatrist. For us to be called experts, we're supposed to be able to reach opinions in ways lay people aren't trained to do. But really there isn't anything we can do that a lay person can't do. . . .

—But *you* testify, reminds the forensic psychiatrist. —You give opinions, too.

—Sure. But I testify on why psychiatrists are *not* experts on anyone's mind. I don't testify about how sick people are or what their future behavior might be. I testify about the state of the art of psychiatry. I *do* give opinions on why judge or jury should ignore all previous psychiatric testimony. Forget the so-called experts, I say. . . .

—Ridiculous! If we aren't the experts, who are?

* * *

—Maybe it's an elitist way of thinking, but a psychiatrist is a medical person, and for some reason—not especially rational, I guess—I would have more faith in an expert witness who has had medical training than someone who hasn't . . . says *a well-known Boston trial attorney.*

On the morning of November 27, 1978, his last day on earth, George Moscone, the Mayor of San Francisco, sits for a moment behind his big desk. The slaughter of almost one thousand people in Jonestown, Guyana, was just thirteen days before. Many of those dead had been his people . . . voters, acquaintances, former residents of the city. A monstrous act, the mind of a madman, surely.

On that same November morning a seemingly harmless snack-foods truck plies its route through the rabbit warren of hills and streets that is the North Beach section of San Francisco. Among the truck's goodies are plastic-wrapped tubes of cake. People will be told these cakes provided George Moscone's death warrant.

The truck pulls up to a small tobacco and snack shop on Lombard Street. It will be the usual order, the driver thinks . . . candy, crackers, some packaged bakery products.

But out of habit he asks the owner, You need to bump the order? I got the stock.

The owner looks down his list. Maybe next time. We'll need a larger inventory for Christmas. He begins putting the boxes away as the driver makes out the sales slip. Glancing down, the owner spies an empty space inside the glass-enclosed counter.

I almost forgot, they cleaned me out this morning before school. The kids. You got some Twinkies in the truck?

The driver stops writing. You want a full order?

Yeah. The kids around here sure go for them.

George Moscone could not dwell too long on the horrors of Jonestown, because local politics is swirling about him. In less than an hour he is to name Dan White's successor as a city supervisor. It's all set.

Dan White. When he had resigned his city supervisor's job two weeks before, Moscone had been surprised. White had been one of the hardest working of the supervisors, young, aggressive, ambitious. He had come a long way from his days as a beat cop.

I can't make it on my salary, Mayor. Ninety-six hundred a year. My wife and baby need more.

Moscone had accepted the resignation with genuine regret. I'm really sorry to see him go, the mayor had told others, I think he's a good guy.

But soon afterward White had come again. You haven't appointed anyone to my old position. I've changed my mind. I want the job back. Would you reappoint me?

Strange. But Moscone was inclined to go along. White *had* been doing a good job. It's going to make us both look a bit foolish, though.

I just want my old job back, Mayor.

Then, before anything could be announced, the pressure came. Especially from Harvey Milk, another supervisor and an avowed homosexual. We are *definitely* against his reappointment, Mayor. He's the one supervisor who's been antihomosexual from the beginning. Need I remind you he voted against the homosexual rights ordinance, the only supervisor to do that?

The pressure mounted until Moscone found himself in the classic politician's dilemma . . . Whose support do I want more, whose support can I afford to lose?

Finally he decided not to reappoint Dan White, and this morning at an 11:30 A.M. press conference he would announce his choice—Don Horanzy, a real estate loan officer with the U.S. Department of Housing and Urban Development, a man adept at working with grass-roots citizens' organizations.

The choice pleased Moscone mightily, and in spite of the lingering sorrow over Jonestown, he is in good spirits. Dan White . . . too bad. Don Horanzy . . . welcome!

At the same moment but several floors below, a man crouches beside the city hall basement window. He sees shadows inside and taps the glass.

The window is opened cautiously. A startled city hall employee sees ex-Supervisor Dan White and hears him ask to be let in through the window. It seems, White says, he forgot his keys to the double-locked doors that lead in from the parking lot. Though it may have occurred to him, the employee never asks why Dan White just didn't go around to the front of the building and enter through the front door.

Of course, that would have meant going through the electric-eye screening. Any hidden metallic weapon would have registered.

So Dan White crawls through the basement window, thanks the employee, and disappears into the bowels of the building.

A few moments later Moscone's secretary quietly lets herself into his office. Dan White's outside. He wants to see you.

Moscone figures it's a last-moment plea for the old job. Futile to hear him, of course. But what's the harm in listening?

I'll see him in the rear sitting room. Moscone then follows his secretary to the outer office where White is waiting.

Smiling and in shirt sleeves Moscone greets White . . . *I'm really sorry to see him go . . . I think he's a good guy* . . . and beckons him to the rear office.

Do you want anyone to sit in on the meeting? His secretary asks, knowing the mayor usually likes someone else there.

No, he responds, I'll see him alone. And they move off together.

Within minutes George Moscone is facing a Dan White he doesn't know. In his hand the former policeman holds a snub-nosed five-shot Smith & Wesson Chiefs Special Revolver. He squeezes the trigger.

One shot catches Moscone in the right lung.

Another destroys his liver.

The mayor falls to the floor.

Still breathing.

White moves over him, and in classic warrior tradition he places the Smith & Wesson to Moscone's head. . . .

Two more shots, a coup de grace, and George Moscone is no more.

I'm really sorry to see him go . . . I think he's a good guy.

* * *

Moving quickly now, White goes out a side door into a public corridor. No one has seen him leave. He reaches the supervisors' offices on the other side of city hall. Through the main reception area he goes directly to Harvey Milk's office. He has reloaded his five-shot Smith & Wesson Chiefs Special Revolver.

Harvey, can I see you a minute?

Milk assents and White leads the way to the office he had used when he had been a supervisor.

Inside it is Harvey Milk's turn. A Dan White he doesn't know.

The first three shots tear into Milk's body . . . and then, two more in the head, delivered warrior-style.

Harvey Milk is dead.

Thirty-five minutes later Dan White is four blocks from city hall. The police station is familiar, he used to work there when he was a cop. His wife is beside him as he makes his way into the building.

The whirlwind begins . . . and he remembers to turn in a Smith & Wesson Chiefs Special Revolver, nine expended shell casings and eight unexpended rounds of hollow-point ammunition.

First-degree murder is the charge. There is little dispute about how the killings were done, but people ask why. A nice-looking, hard-working young man . . . why?

The trial becomes an expert witness turkey shoot. Doctor, the prosecutor asks *his* psychiatrist, was Dan White suffering from mental illness at the time of the crime?

—I don't believe so, no.

—Doctor, the defense attorney asks his psychiatrist, —was Dan White suffering from mental illness at the time of the crime?

—Yes, I believe so, he replies. A fairly steep depression and a compulsive personality. A workaholic . . . uptight . . . overly conscientious . . . contributing to his depression . . .

The defense lines up its psychiatrists, four of them, as well as two psychologists, "experts" capable of dissecting and measuring the whys. They know their witness.—Doctor, could Dan White have premeditated these killings?

—He not only did not premeditate or deliberate these killings, but as a result of his mental condition he was not capable of any kind of mature meaningful reflection.

Could he have felt malice toward the people he killed? the witness is asked.

—At the time of these killings, White was not thinking about the effect of his behavior on human life, the value of human life.

Malice and premeditation, the ingredients for first-degree murder, they never existed as far as Dan White was concerned?

You enter a basement window to avoid detection, you carry a well-hidden revolver with plenty of extra ammunition, you go to see the one man who can give you your job back, you shoot him, and then do the same to another, delivering a coup de grace, reloading your weapon at least once . . . and there's no malice or premeditation?

—The last thing he was doing, capable of doing, was thinking clearly about his obligations to society, other people, the law, and so on.

Now the trial is held, six months after the killings. Dan White's psychiatrists weren't there when it happened, and much of what they are told comes from people with a certain point of view to protect or advance . . . such as Dan White himself. But they *know* . . . they *know* . . .

What went on in White's mind at the time of the killings!

How about *those* for experts!

There's more.

—Doctor, when he shot George Moscone in the head twice, after Mr. Moscone had fallen to the floor disabled, did he have the capacity at that time to know that those two shots delivered to the head would, in all likelihood, finally kill George Moscone?

—I don't think so. He was literally not focusing. I'm not sure he was capable physically of focusing his eyes on the mayor.

—Doctor, how did you understand the reloading of the gun after he shot George Moscone?

—As a police officer, he had been trained to automatically reload a gun once you [sic] have fired, and that it was something that was done basically as a matter of reflex.

And not . . . certainly not . . . because he planned to kill again. A reflex action . . .

Still, the whys persist. Why is he depressed, why can't he focus, why does he ignore the value of human life?

Expert Martin Blinder is ready with an opinion. Dr. Blinder, serene in his certainty, a young man with a future, on the medical school faculty at the University of California at San Francisco, a psychiatrist in tune with modern trends.

This man, he testifies, was mentally ill not only when he shot George Moscone and Harvey Milk, but throughout his adult life. He has a manic depressive syndrome dating back to his adolescence.

This little event here, not getting reappointed, isn't the culprit. *It's his whole adult life.* That's what's wrong with Dan White. Adulthood.

It's based partly on a biochemical defect in his body, a sugar imbalance, Dr. Blinder announces. This brings on frequent episodes of depression.

But if this condition had persisted all these years, why would it cause him to kill two people now?

Dr. Blinder's been waiting for *this* question. He knows how stressful modern life can be. You've got to think of everything. Psychiatrists are trained to do that, of course.

Well, Blinder reasons, let's take a look at the way Dan White eats. What kind of diet does he follow?

He's a modern-day food junkie . . . junk food . . . almost exclusively. There you *are*, Blinder suggests. That's what set him off.

Dan White's depression, he testifies, was escalated by excessive sugar from an exclusive diet of junk food . . . Twinkies cupcakes and Cokes. . . .

Twinkies?

It's a lethal weapon?

Twinkies . . . sugar, enriched flour, niacin (a B vitamin), reduced iron, thiamine mononitrate, B_1, riboflavin, B_2, water, corn syrup, partially hydrogenated animal and vegetable shortening;

may contain: beef fat and/or lard, soybean and/or cotton seed, and/or palm oil, eggs, dextrose, skim milk, leavening (sodium acid pyrophosphate, baking soda, monocalcium phosphate), whey, modified food starch, salt, corn flour, mono- and diglycerides, sodium caseinate, polysorbate 60, lecithin, artificial color and flavor, sorbic acid.

Dan White's essential defense is on the grounds of "diminished capacity" in that when he committed the murders, he just didn't have all his marbles. Blame it on the adult-long manic depression and on the weird sugar imbalance that was aggravated by eating too many Twinkies and drinking too many colas.

He just couldn't have known what he was doing, the psychiatric experts say.

The jury agrees. *Guilty of voluntary manslaughter.*

Seven years and eight months in prison, the judge decrees.

It could be less than five years with time off for good behavior.

Dr. Blinder and the Twinkies defense have prevailed. *Junk food could be dangerous to your mental health . . . and his,* a warning label may have to say.

Blinder isn't above a little finger-wagging. After all, when you've come up with a theory that partially justifies killing two people in cold blood, and the reverberations are heard throughout America, you're entitled.

The press has even given your theory instant recognition . . . *Twinkies defense.*

—Judges and juries should determine issues of guilt and innocence, sanity and insanity, Blinder tells a reporter two weeks after the Dan White case. —Psychiatrists are often pushed into making that decision for them.

There goes Blinder, speaking his mind. . . .

—There is a tendency for psychiatrists to find mental illness in every instance of emotional stress. I personally resist this.

Six months after he was sentenced to prison, Dan White had *not* received any psychiatric treatment. The tests he took when he first entered prison showed he had no apparent symptoms of mental disorder.

He definitely was in touch with reality.

But Dr. Blinder, he goes right on. Now it's to Arkansas, a case where five women are suing the United Steelworkers for $500,000 because of emotional distress they allegedly incurred from harassment for crossing picket lines.

The National Right to Work League, with an antiunion bias as long as your arm, would *love* to humble the Steelworkers. The League represents the five women, and they need an expert to talk about emotional distress.

Psychiatrist Blinder's available . . . and he will be paid $900 a day.

He examines the women. *Psychic trauma*, he says, lingering from the strike of two years before. No one touched them, but never mind. There were verbal threats, obscenities, dirty names such as . . . *scab* . . . property marked up and defaced, general antagonism.

Psychic trauma. Unreasonable fears, sleeplessness, loss of appetite, increased smoking, diminution of sexual function, disturbance of bowel habits, anxiousness, crying spells, heightened irritability, nightmares, even suicidal thoughts.

In his expert view all of these unhappy symptoms came because the women crossed the picket lines and tried to work in defiance of a strike.

Sure it was a tense situation, Blinder says, the women probably magnified out of proportion what was going on. Nevertheless the union should pay, even if a large part of the emotional distress was caused by the women's *perception that they had been injured*. They don't really have to be injured.

Doesn't that open the door to all sorts of abuses?

Some of these women are suffering from *traumatic neuroses*; others are suffering from *adult situational stress reaction*. —These women were relatively symptom-free prior to this event, he says.— I have medical records to prove that.

Can't that apply to anyone who finds himself or herself in a tense situation?

—The presence of problems in one's life is not the same as a psychiatric disorder.

Dr. Blinder, do you remember the Dan White case?

You said . . . *There is a tendency for psychiatrists to find mental illness in every instance of emotional stress. I personally resist this.*

The United Steelworkers' attorney knows his man. In the courtroom, in full view, he hands Martin Blinder a package.

Twinkies!

—Dirty pool! Blinder complains to a reporter. —Bringing that up in Arkansas . . . it's not relevant.

Another attorney is speaking to a group of psychiatrists in an ornate city hotel ballroom. Every seat is taken, and there are people standing along the sides. The speaker is well known to the audience, he's written numerous briefs for their Association over the past few years, and they know him to be articulate, reasonable . . . and in their corner.

He is talking to them about one of the most pervasive powers they have: the power to commit someone to a state hospital *involuntarily*, to deprive a person of liberty, not because they have committed a crime or caused damage, but because of their mental condition.

The psychiatrists are concerned because lawsuits have been coming thick and fast lately, spurred by advocates of due process and other constitutional guarantees. Why *should* patients get involved in treatment decisions, some mutter, we know better than anyone when a person should be committed. . . .

—It used to be that your only role in society was as a care provider, the attorney says. —But now you have another role, you've become society's policemen, responsible for putting people away, for committing them.

Policemen? Have we really come to that?

The attorney strokes them . . . —Of course, you have tremendous power, but you didn't ask for it, you've never asked for it. And really you don't want it . . .

You mean, untrained people might make these decisions if we didn't? Ridiculous!

—Society is looking for someone, and—let's face it—you're elected.

We can live with it.

Now the attorney earns his pay. —Increasingly, there is a trend to use psychiatrists as a means to identify dangerous people and commit them. *This is a role psychiatrists are ill equipped to meet.* [Authors' emphasis] If you people keep talking about dangerous personalities the courts are going to say, "then you had better tell us when they can become violent" . . .

We can't do that. Predictions? They must think we're magicians. . . . and of course the science hasn't progressed to that point.

—To the lay person and even to some physicians, certain psychiatric symptoms are very frightening and intolerable, and their first reaction is to go straight for the institution, when in fact the delusions or hallucinations may be long-standing and totally harmless to the person or to others. I think psychiatrists are better able than anyone else to weed out who needs hospitalization and who doesn't, says *a well-known East Coast trial judge.*

Objection, your honor!

The courtroom stills, as if a photographer has just snapped a time-lapse picture. The witness, a psychiatrist, sits upright, at attention, eyes riveted on the young attorney who has just spoken. The attorney, standing, waits for a reaction from the judge.

There is a brief silence before the judge glances at the witness and offers the briefest smile . . . perhaps an apology for the interruption.

He looks at both lawyers. Counsel will approach the bench.

Once both lawyers are in front of him the judge leans forward. He asks, Are you objecting because the witness has been asked for a prediction on how dangerous the defendant's behavior might become?

Yessir. Predicting dangerous behavior. Psychiatrists are clearly not qualified. They have no special training or innate ability in this area. This witness is certainly qualified in psychiatry, but not in rendering an opinion about danger.

I don't think I agree, the judge says. Society has put them in this position, regardless of whether they, or you, like it. Society wants them to give opinions, and I'm inclined to go along. He turns to the other lawyer, an older, less intense man. Will your witness be able to give us a prediction?

The lawyer shrugs. He wanted to check the file first.

Back to the young lawyer. Any chance of your withdrawing the objection?

No sir, your honor.

All right. The judge leans back, nodding a brief dismissal to the lawyers. He raises his voice. Objection is overruled.

The older lawyer addresses the psychiatrist. Now, Doctor, let me repeat the question. On the basis of your examination of the defendant and of all other relevant interviews, documents, and files, do you have an opinion on whether this defendant would be likely to commit one or more dangerous felonious acts at some point in the future?

The psychiatrist looks down and wets his lips. He glances briefly at the judge, then takes a quick breath. Now look. We're no better than the street-corner butcher in making decisions about dangerousness, because the same information we get could be given to any citizen and we're not much more clever in analyzing such things. Our crystal ball is no better than a well-informed citizen's. . . .

The courtroom is not an easy arena for the psychiatrist. Lawyers and psychiatrists just don't think alike. The psychiatrist, trained with the medical model, is just not used to having opinions and conclusions challenged or questioned, especially by nonmedical people. Cross-examinations? Many psychiatrists feel it is cruel and disgraceful. Yet lawyers, trained to the adversary system, believe that the truth will emerge from a combative process that hones the basic issues.

Certain psychiatrists keep their cool by thinking of their time in the courtroom as a contest: —My intellectual powers against yours; they stay detached, above the fray, and thus disdain that their opinions could be attacked.

—I tell all my residents to think of it as a game, one highly regarded forensic psychiatrist says.

Sure. Game playing. It avoids getting emotionally involved in issues of life, death, freedom, and human rights. To play the game psychiatrists turn to the jargon of their profession. It is easy to intimidate juries and even judges.

Lithium responsive aggression . . . total parenteral nutrition in anorexia nervosa . . . advanced tardive dyskinesia . . . schizophrenal hemodialysis . . . psychendocrinology . . .

Yet pomposity can affect the outcome of a case. There is a fine line in the game. A psychiatrist who makes an overbearing, obnoxious appearance can bring out the resentment of the jury. The jury can't take it out on the psychiatrist, but they can take it out on whomever the psychiatrist was testifying for . . . and they do.

Medical jargon can be avoided. It requires a willingness to enlighten rather than influence or coerce.

How about Martin Blinder? *Traumatic neurosis, adult situational stress reaction*, that's what he diagnosed in the women scabs in Arkansas. Any doubt about what he means? Doesn't it sound bad? Of course. Despite the fact that their "condition" might be as common and no more serious than a summer cold.

The custody battle. Another arena for psychiatrists and lawyers. The key is the best interests of the child. The weighty questions rarely have to do with sanity or insanity, mental competence or incompetence, but have to do with who is the better parent.

—In every custody case, says a Boston psychiatrist, —when I see the first parent I come away thinking the other must be an absolute lunatic, a terrible parent . . . then three hours later I see the other parent and I just throw up my hands. How can I tell which one is more fit?

—I think we have allowed ourselves to be *used* in the custody process, echoes a Texas psychiatrist. —It's a horror. The lawyer says "protect the client," and sometimes nothing could be worse for the family. I'm really disturbed by the ease with which we allow ourselves to be bought by the legal system.

—If I had a choice of an expert in a child custody case, I'd take the psychiatrist before I'd take the psychologist or other nonmedical person. I think psychiatrists are trained to make a more thorough evaluation of the situation, they make a better presentation, says *a family court judge*.

It wasn't as if he and Famous Psychiatrist were strangers. They had known each other for years, though he couldn't remember having seen him testify in court.

But others had told him, He puts on a regular show, he's so good. He is so well known he has the judges eating out of his hand.

Judges, he knew, were just as celebrity-conscious as gas station attendants and Woolworth salesgirls. A celebrity in their courtroom? It marked them, gave them identity.

And the lawyers whose witness the celebrity was? Judges were not above remembering that, too.

Ridiculous, he scolds himself. It's just a simple custody case, nothing more. My client wants her kids, we have a psychiatrist who's been involved with the family—and who *just happens* to be a celebrity. It's what he says that counts, not who he is.

The lawyer picks up the telephone book and searches for Famous Psychiatrist's number. He half expects it to be unlisted but realizes that he does, after all, have a public psychiatric practice.

Famous Psychiatrist. Author, lecturer, television personality, a European, trained in psychoanalysis, who has reduced some of the more esoteric concepts to simply daily-living rules and games. His books have sold in the millions, and he is in constant demand.

Famous Psychiatrist is in, he is between patients.

The lawyer identifies himself and his client. I understand you have examined my client.

Yes, he says in his clipped accent. I know her case.

As you recall, the lawyer goes on, she gave up her children several years ago . . .

Very manic, then, Famous Psychiatrist says, shaky, most unreliable. *I could not have supported her continuing with mothering responsibilities.*

But now she's remarried, and she wants her children back.

Yes. She's made fine progress. I've been able to help her.

The lawyer listens to the well-known voice, picturing the well-known face blandly reassuring, calmly assessing. What I'd like to know is whether she is not able to take on the mothering role again.

Oh, yes, Famous Psychiatrist says, she's certainly ready for *that*.

Good. I'd like you to testify for us.

There is a brief pause. Then the voice, more clipped than usual. No, I'd rather not.

But you know her. Your opinion would be most valuable.

I don't *like* to testify.

He is firm, and the lawyer finally tells him that he won't call him to the witness stand unless he has to.

Why don't you have someone else see her? he suggests.

But the lawyer knows that in the short time remaining before trial, no one else could gain the insight into his client that Famous Psychiatrist already has. He is cool now, almost angry. *He doesn't want to go to court.*

We'll see what happens, the lawyer says.

On the afternoon of the first trial day, the judge has both lawyers in chambers discussing a matter of procedure. He asks them whether there will be any expert witnesses.

Yes, of course, says the father's lawyer. I have a child psychiatrist waiting to testify.

The mother's lawyer hesitates. I have an expert who is very familiar with the case. But I promised not to call him unless it was absolutely essential. He is so busy.

Well, the judge says, we have testimony already in on your client's emotional state. It seems to me you'd want to show that in the best possible light . . . if you can.

The mother's lawyer knows what he has to do. The judge is telling him he can't hope to win his case unless there is supportive psychiatric testimony.

He telephones Famous Psychiatrist. I need you tomorrow morning, he says.

I don't *want* to testify.

We'll lose the case otherwise.

I don't *want* to testify.

The lawyer is exasperated. Then I will have to subpoena you. You *must* testify.

Really! he says, most annoyed.

But the next morning he is there, and the lawyer calls him to the witness stand. There is an excited buzz around the courtroom as Famous Psychiatrist rises and makes his way. The well-known face looks as if he has stepped in something quite malodorous, and there is an uncharacteristic swagger in his bearing.

The first few questions are innocuous, establishing only that Famous Psychiatrist has indeed treated the mother over a period of time. The first hint of trouble comes as the lawyer attempts to get more specific.

How would you characterize the mother's emotional state when she gave up custody of her children? the lawyer asks.

Why, that's a difficult question to answer . . . and no matter how the lawyer rephrases, Famous Psychiatrist refuses to provide a satisfactory response.

The lawyer tries a different approach. Is the mother's emotional state improved from what it was when you first saw her?

Well, I *suppose* you could say that . . .

Good. In what ways?

That's a difficult question to answer, I'm afraid . . . and Famous Psychiatrist proceeds *not* to answer it.

The fencing continues, with Famous Psychiatrist refusing to say anything of substance, yet providing bland reassurances that *something* indeed had happened to the mother years before and that somehow there has been improvement, though to what degree and in what areas it is impossible to pin down.

The lawyer is exceedingly frustrated, but the most important question remains. It *has* to be asked.

Is this mother now a fit parent to have custody of her children?

Well . . . perhaps yes, perhaps no . . .

The lawyer is disgusted. Famous Psychiatrist is playing a game with him *and he can't win*! With a jerk of his head he signifies that the other side may cross-examine. But the other lawyer knows to leave well enough alone and declines.

Famous Psychiatrist, his face a model of aplomb, leaves the witness stand. As he walks by the mother's lawyer, he reaches in his pocket and throws a folded sheet on the counsel table.

It is his bill.

About the Psychiatrist in the Courtroom

For many years the courts have wrestled with finding the proper test for deciding a person's sanity. The most widely accepted modern standard came out of M'Naghten's case in England in 1843, the so-called *right and wrong test*: a person was considered not to be responsible for his criminal acts if he could *not* tell the difference between right and wrong. It was inevitable that psychiatrists would be called upon to apply the test in particular cases, and when they testified, they were considered expert witnesses. They could offer opinions and conclusions, things that nonexpert witnesses were not permitted to do. The M'Naghten Rule, as it came to be known, has been modified or supplanted in many states by other tests more directly relating to whether a person had a mental disease at the time of the criminal act. But the psychiatrist continues to testify as the expert, often participating in a courtroom farce known as the "battle of the experts," where each side has its own psychiatrist and where the jury has to decide which one they believe. The psychiatric profession usually bemoans such a confrontation because it dilutes the value of psychiatric testimony, but lawyers see it as a natural extension of the adversary system, and they say that psychiatrists have generally been quite willing to testify.

There is dispute within the psychiatric profession over just how much of an expert a psychiatrist should be. Some feel there is no such thing as impartial opinion, that a psychiatrist, even as an expert, cannot be above the fray. He *must* be an advocate for his views and for the side he represents, he *must* use the witness stand as a platform for his concern for his position. He must *educate*.

Others feel they are truly not qualified to be expert witnesses, especially in criminal cases. Arguments against the psychiatrist's role in the courtroom include the biases that accumulate after years of testifying for just one side or the other. Some are seen as "hanging shrinks," others as "bleeding hearts," and one judge has gone so far as to accuse psychiatrists of "benign perjury" for couching testimony to encourage the removal of criminal defendants from the prison system so they can be treated with therapy in the hospitals.

Yet the use of expert psychiatric testimony will continue because there is formidable intertwining of the roles of lawyer and psychiatrist within the adversary system. Most major law schools, for instance, have a psychiatrist as a faculty member, and most major medical schools provide courses in forensic psychiatry. Psychiatrists, like their brethren in psychology, probably *do* have a role to play in pointing out criminal responsibility and in diagnosing mental instability. The problems arise when they reach beyond their expertise, such as in custody matters or in conjecture about potential for dangerous behavior, and the courts let them do it.

Ten

THE PENILE SYSTEM

There is so much contained anger among the women psychiatrists that it stirs the air. Here it is a sunny, beautiful first week in May in San Francisco, and this anger bleeds into all the good times. It's practically taking over the psychiatric convention.

You can see it rising, like decomposing matter from a spring thaw rises from the river bottom. Ready to explode. Ready to soil the nice business suits and wing tips. Ready to fleck the trimmed Vandykes. Ready to muck up the cellophane-covered badges that read *delegate*.

It's a crime, what with so many important things to consider, such as *confidentiality* and the latest challenges by the *insurance companies* . . . what with the third edition of the *Diagnostic and Statistical Manual* that throws old psychiatric symptoms and terminology into a cocked hat. Yet here are these angry women . . . they're only 15 percent of the profession, *15 percent* . . . and they claim the Association is acting sexist! Just because next year's convention choice is New Orleans, which happens to be in Louisiana, which happens not to have ratified the Equal Rights Amendment.

Female hysteria. Predictable female hysteria.

Outside the Civic Center, the convention's headquarters, teacup-sized clouds scud in the blue sky. Pink rhododendron blooms nod around the reflecting pool where kids have shucked their sneakers and are dangling bare feet. In front of the guarded doors that can only be broached by badge, groups of former mental patients chant diatribes against all psychiatry.

At this moment the angry women see none of this. They're holed up at the Hilton. For days they have gathered in small groups in tucked-away corners. Chairs are drawn into semicircles. Some of the younger and thinner ones sit on the floor, others on tables. It is purposefully casual. The boardroom atmosphere with water glasses, sharpened pencils, and carefully arranged seating belongs to the male species.

A local science reporter slides into a corner of one of the meeting rooms, where a tactical planning session is under way. There are about forty lady doctors, some young enough to wear their hair straight and swinging; some older, in two-piece print dresses. One woman in a denim skirt is nursing a boy who looks old enough to walk. She sits him up from time to time, but he'd rather get down. She strokes his head. —Shhh, she says. The reporter runs a look at her brown nipple with the rough bumps around the aureole. It's the first time he has been in a room full of women shrinks. There is something different about it.

The reporter feels he knows from nothing. The city desk called him to cover these ERA meetings and the proposed boycott of the convention in New Orleans, but he can't figure why it should be him when he's a *science* writer. He was planning on sailing over to Sausalito, and now he has to cover something political. He already did the column for tomorrow. It was based on some new data about shock treatments.

It's no big deal, the editor tells him. But it has to do with shrinks and it was on television last night, and if you watched the news shows you'd have caught it. Get me thirty inches of type.

It's more a woman's angle. Put one of them on it.

It's a psy-chi-a-tric problem, the editor enunciates. That's your territory.

It's not science, it's political, the reporter objects again.

If it's about shrinks, it's science, the editor answers. Thirty inches.

Thirty inches. That takes care of Sausalito.

The lady doctor with the squirming baby looks uncomfortable. Her eyes flit as if to test what effect the child's mild disturbance has on the others. No one gives her a glance, so it must be in her imagination. Yet she scoops up two shoulder bags and the boy and aims for an unmarked door.

The reporter touches her arm. Could I talk to you out in the hall for a minute? He tips his shoulder so she can see his orange press badge. He follows her to the door. I'm going to the bathroom, she tells him.

So the door is a toilet and not an exit. He recovers. Maybe later?

She shrugs. I'll see you in the hall in a minute.

Unisex johns. It's good enough for the Hilton conference rooms. So why is it still a weapon of the anti-ERAs? He'll ask her.

In the hall she says, Can you wait until I drop him off at the day-care room? The boy runs down the corridor at top speed, and her shoulder bag sways as she keeps up with him. In a couple of minutes she returns, breathless. He has more stamina than I do.

Yeah. He remembers psychological tests that had a normal adult male follow a two-year-old around for hours imitating movements. He reminds her, mostly to show that he's up on scientific tests and data. It blew the guy away, he says. They laugh.

He pulls out his notebook. I was thinking about unisex bathrooms. We get all this anti-ERA stuff, and that's one of their fetishes.

Wrong word, fetish, but I know what you mean. Have you seen our slide show at the women's booth? She's referring to the basement of the civic center, where drug companies, scientific publishers, electronic manufacturers with their biofeedback apparatus and scientific exhibits, rest elbow to elbow.

I haven't seen it, but of course I've seen some of the other exhibits. Of course. That's where he got most of his information to write about shock treatments.

How come your paper didn't send a woman reporter? She looks him up and down.

I do the science. I told them this was political, but . . . He spreads his hands.

It *is* science, it's mental health.

Can you give me a rundown?

You haven't seen the slide show. There is no smile.

He returns the serious look. I'm afraid I haven't done much homework on this.

But she doesn't seem to mind. She tells him the Chairman of Physicians for ERA has created a slide show to demonstrate the scare tactics used by the anti-ERAs. It focuses on how the Amendment will change the laws that affect health and the practice of medicine. She smiles for the first time, but it is brief. There's a segment on the unisex toilet fantasy. You'll enjoy it.

One of the women *should* have covered this, he thinks. Then mentally erases the thought. He fears she can read his mind. But it's just an old rumor, right? Alienists, mind readers, and the rest of it? Can you give me some background on how you and the other . . . women psychiatrists have reached this impasse?

Impasse? I wouldn't use that word.

What then?

It goes like this. The majority of male psychiatrists, especially in the political and educational power structure, have figured out a treatment of choice for us.

Us?

The women psychiatrists. Me and the rest.

A treatment?

Right . . . they're using benign neglect.

I've heard the phrase.

So have we.

She digs in one of the diaper bags and comes up with a gray and red pamphlet. It's a public relations piece called *What Is a Psychiatrist?* Published by the American Psychiatric Association.

A notation on the back offers them for order at $7.50 per hundred.

She has underlined a part . . . *The psychiatrist comes to know that human development and behavior are influenced by biological factors such as heredity, hormones, nutrition and physical illness: psychological factors such as childhood experiences, family relationships and social factors including cultural differences, deprivation and prejudice.*

You wonder, she says to the reporter, if they're so smart, how come they say this and still don't believe it.

I'm glad *you* said that.

I guess I have a special point of view.

What do you . . . he waves his hand toward the meeting room, . . . intend to do about this?

Try to persuade the board to reconsider the membership vote to go to New Orleans. And if that doesn't work, total boycott of their meeting there.

This all started in 1974?

Lively voices are being raised beyond the door. She looks impatient to return. Look, do you want a cup of coffee? There's a hospitality room on the lobby floor. I really want to get back inside. But I could meet you downstairs in a while, and that would give you a chance to go through some of our literature.

She was managing him. He didn't like it.

I think I'll go back inside too.

She raises her eyebrows at his set mouth. Suit yourself.

I will.

He picks up a chair and carries it closer to the speaker. A few women glance in his direction. Only one gives him what he would call a searching look. There is a tingling in his neck and he recognizes it as discomfort. He feels like a . . . what? . . . a *minority!* Not even in Chinatown off the main streets has he felt this . . . aloneness. No, separateness. He wiggles his fingers at the doctor he has been speaking with. He wants to pass her a note . . . *I report objectively, but I want you to know I'm on your side.* But why does he feel this separateness if he has such empathy? It isn't guilt. He didn't make the lousy laws. He isn't responsible for the chauvinist attitudes of the big chunk of the male medical profession.

He wants to pass her another note . . . *Some of my best friends
are women*.

Thirty inches. He whips open the spiral notebook and untops his
Flair pen. He wants to lean forward to catch what the speaker is
saying. She is soft-spoken. But leaning forward would not look in
character, so he slumps down and hikes his right ankle over his left
knee. He wishes he had an empty chair next to him so he could
drape his leather-patched tweed-jacketed arm over the back. It
seems stupid to balance his notebook against one knee and use just
one hand to write and balance the pad while the left arm just
dangles uselessly with no chair to rest it on.

What's going on with him? He's covered science symposia and
done interviews for years and never worried about *image*.

Up *this*!

The speaker is authoritative but not strident, certainly an attractive woman, confident . . . It is interesting, as you may have already
noticed from our various confrontations, that many of our male
counterparts cannot deal with a woman's anger. They see it as a
throwback to mother's anger when she said, "I am displeased, you
are naughty, you'll have to be punished." They can't argue with the
anger, and they can't respond in a logical way. Their thought pro-
cesses go askew, and they don't see the legitimacy of the argument
or the anger. All they sense is the anger. And it dredges up childhood.

There's a question from the floor, a woman who brushes her
long hair back with the palm of her left hand. The reporter notices
she wears no ring. The woman says, There must be a nonthreaten-
ing way to show them inequality hurts . . . both for doctors and for
patients.

Another stern voice behind her mutters, The anger is *their* problem, not ours.

The woman turns halfway, saying to the room, I mean, perhaps
we're polarizing . . .

The speaker interrupts. We have a legitimate right to be angry
and frustrated. Medically educated men do not perceive this inequality as having anything to do with women's mental health. But

it does, it does! All the major mental health organizations see it our way. All, that is, except *this* organization and the American Psychoanalytic Association. Both are so myopic they don't see a problem in holding meetings in states where our right to equity under the law isn't recognized.

There is a loud burst of applause, and the speaker offers a faint smile.

The reporter notices the woman without a ring is nodding vigorously.

The speaker continues, But you asked for a review of our efforts to get women into positions of authority. Let me get into that . . . it's not for fun or mental gymnastics that we asked you to submit scientific papers for this convention. Especially papers that deal with issues concerning women. It's been a long road for us. . . .

The joke started making the rounds of the predominantly WASP medical profession as early as the 1930s:

Q.— What is a psychiatrist?
A.— A Jewish doctor who can't stand the sight of blood!

In the 1930s, with a few exceptions, clean-cut Anglos and Saxons did not jump into psychiatry. America was a country of *doers*. Psychiatry was a talking and intellectual business, its hero the Jewish physician from Vienna, Sigmund Freud. Psychiatry dissected *dreams*, it dissected *childhood*, it probed the *unconscious*. What kind of business was this for a red-blooded American Anglo-Saxon doctor?

Psychiatrists were called alienists, mesmerizers, hypnotizers, *analysts*. They analyzed guilt, anger, aggression, depression, catatonia, agitation, withdrawal, and illnesses suspected of being psychosomatic.

But analysis in the care of the horrendously mentally ill had no place in most treatment at that time. Instead, quick and energetic modalities were employed to handle major distress . . . injections to induce massive seizures that left the patient disoriented but calmer, those grand mal convulsions that caused compression fractures and left in their fearsome wake terrified inmates who would rather claw through sandstone than be subjected to any more "cure" . . . the water treatment . . . high-pressure hoses jarring him back to the present . . . wet sheets, the "treatment of choice" of the more compassionate, which bound the patient like a mummy, and thus secured, the patient assuredly would calm down.

It was scarcely a place for a woman. As doctor.

But why would any psychiatrist in the 1930s want to go into these state-run hellholes anyway? There was no money. They were usually gruesomely filthy. They were as graft-ridden as the state prison systems. The food was starch for breakfast, starch for lunch, starch for supper. They were lonesome places. Nobody to talk medicine or philosophy or *anything* with.

The private hospitals. That's where the money was. But still no place for a woman except as a zaftig matron or stocky nurse. Anyway, there were enough incompetent doctors to fill the positions in the insane asylums and psycho wards. The alcoholic, the misfit, or the foreign-born doctor who couldn't make it anyplace else could find a berth and at least be guaranteed three squares and salary.

Psychiatry remained, at the nub, a man's world for two very good reasons. It was part of medicine . . . its role model was Freud.

(A Jewish doctor who can't stand the sight of blood?)

Freud's philosophies as well as his psychoanalytic mode were imported lock, stock, and barrel to the United States in the mid- and late 1930s. We were handed a legacy. The Nazis assured this.

World War II witnessed the mass drafting and enlistment of doctors, especially those fresh from medical school. Women doctors were left to take care of civilian service.

Battle casualties of a mental nature came in droves. Battle shock, battle fatigue, Section Eight, nervous disorder, slid into military jargon. Those that General George S. Patton couldn't smarten up with a good slap in the face or threat of court-martial were sent to bivouac behind lines. Some were screamers, some were sweaters, some were catatonic. Others were just plain down-to-the-gut-all-out-exhausted.

The newly drafted doctors were told . . . we've got to get these men back on their feet and in their boots. It's up to you. . . . And the doctors were shipped to Texas for a three-month course in psychoanalysis, a once-over-quickly in how to be a psychiatrist. And it wasn't long before the military had set up the most extensive psychiatric training and treatment program in its history.

A man's world. Definitely a man's world protecting the little woman back home and getting these good buddies back in their boots.

The course of treatment? It proceeded from the analytic model, what is sometimes called the *defect model* . . . there must have been some *defect* in the soldier or sailor to make him break down and conk out. *So let's find it and analyze it and get rid of it and get this man back in those boots!*

Well, the ninety-day wonders were excited about this. It was *feasible.* They could take the battle casualties through hypnosis, back through screaming nightmares, inject them with sodium amytal and look for the latent *defect* (mother fixation? castration complex? birth trauma? childhood deprivation?).

The generals and the admirals waited for the return of these physically able men in whom thousands of boot camp dollars had been invested. Only a dribble came back.

Patton sneered. Is *this* any way to fight a war? Diddling with the psyche? I want *fighting* men. . . .

Letters went off in triplicate to the War Department, and they were sent down to the gull-gray asphalt-shingled prefab buildings that had been thrown up along the Potomac. The letters accused, they demanded . . . how much time do you need to get these men back in the lines?

The administrators did what they do best. They checked the files. The *old* files.

The World War I records. The administrators blanched when they saw . . . the return rate for battle casualties was no better than *now.* Something around 10 percent.

And there it was. *The defect model* had been pursued in that war, too. Find the defect, talk it out, sublimate it, correct it. *Why don't you like the trenches . . . let's look at your subconscious.*

But . . . Florence Nightingale had a better average than 10 percent.

Florence Nightingale?

Get these men back in their boots. Forget the defect model for the time being. Let's try . . .

Nurturing and sodium amytal to help the patient relive his battle experiences. Moving the psychiatric units close to the battlefield. Warm showers, soap that lathers, clean sheets, good food. And that means fresh food. Fresh fruit. Meat. Vegetables. *Compassion.*

Recognize that anyone can have an acute upset, and you can deal with it by giving immediate support. O mothers, could you have told them this from the start? O women doctors, would you have suggested this decades before if you had been part of the team?

The word got out . . . most mental-trauma battle casualties were going back to duty in seventy-two hours. An estimated 70 percent of battle fatigue casualties were not requiring evacuation for further mental treatment.

It was a lesson to be learned. Nurturing. Encouraging support. Immediate therapy intervention . . . with care.

But was this *scientific?* Medicine was *scientific,* psychiatry was *scientific.* Now, aversion therapy with its beatings and shocks, *that* was scientific. And probing the id for latent defects, *that* was acceptable methodology. But nurturing? This Florence Nightingale stuff? Hardly scientific. Surely not chemistry. Not medical. It was . . . *nursing.*

But nobody let on. And, anyway, the war was just about over.

Back at the Hilton the speaker stands up and paces for a moment, collecting her thoughts. Suddenly she smiles sweetly and cocks her head. With an exaggerated shrug of the shoulders and an outsplaying of hands she affects long suffering, bewilderment. But tell me so I can understand, she says, *what is it you women want?*

Applause and laughter.

Then she grows serious, and she lays out a capsulated history of indignities. Twisted logic. Convoluted defenses for the male diagnosis and treatment of women's problems.

I find it alarming that any competent psychiatrist could believe that the oppression of women or any other group member could be seen as "nonpsychiatric" and therefore irrelevant to identity, quality of life, and mental health.

The Pitts paper! someone behind the reporter calls out.

Right. A perfect example of what I'm talking about. The speaker leans on the back of a chair. You all know the Pitts paper?

A few women shake their heads, others yell "yeeesss."

Okay. The Pitts paper comes from work supported by *our* Association. Published in *our* journal. It seems the quote researchers unquote studied suicide rates within the profession and decided that two thirds of women medical students and graduates who were suicides had "primary affective disorders."

The reporter knows that the term "affective disorder" was new nomenclature for bonkers . . . around the bend . . . off the rocker . . . nuts.

She continues. They also concluded that "affective disordered" women are more likely to choose a medical career.

There are boos in the room. She smiles. Yet male and female physicians have identical suicide rates. Make sense?

Nooo.

There is a set to the mouths of those who have not heard of this report. *More women doctors have emotional problems than men?*

The reporter listens to the muttered comments. He jots . . . *equal rights tip of iceberg . . . most male-female shrinks divided on cause and effect of mental pathologies . . . conspiracy to play up instability of women?* Maybe he could do a Sunday mag piece. Maybe even a national supplement. *Check* Ms., he scrawls.

The speaker turns to a colleague. Would you recount our experience with the board of the APA Journal?

A small, beautiful woman with almond eyes and soft jet-black hair swivels in her chair. She stays seated. Naturally we were furious about that article. But it was only one of many that we documented. We wondered how many of the fifteen to twenty thousand psychiatrists who read this would question the conclusions. It was reminiscent of racist theories . . . incompetence of blacks, greed of Jews, wiliness of the Asian. . . . In the past we had decried the

Journal ads that again and again had depicted women as neurotic, in need of Valium . . . to be *sustained* on Valium. And it finally took the federal authorities to make any dent in that one.

The reporter is chagrined. He has seen these ads for years. He never thought of them as *sexist*. Weren't most middle-aged women depressed? Weren't most young girls neurotic? And old women querulous? Well, hell.

He notes on the page: *Two thirds of mental patients are women. Medicated b'cse sick? or sick b'cse medicated?*

The speaker has been going on and he swings his attention back to her. We complained to the Journal that articles were not representative of women. And we asked for fair representation on the editorial board. Fourteen percent of the Association members are women, but that percentage has never been visible in the power structure. Well, we were *invited* to attend an open meeting of the board to discuss this. They couldn't have been more accommodating. But this is what happened. They had already talked *informally* before we even got there, by phone, by grabbing each other at meetings . . . you know the way they do it.

And we didn't know that until later. So we went in with smiles and handshakes and determination. And they sat around the table and doodled notes and nodded as we asked for things.

We asked for blind reviewing. We asked that Dr. So-and-So's name be kept off the piece that had to be peer-reviewed. That would assure independent reviewing. But no way. Struck down. Nicely. But struck down.

We asked for a special issue of the Journal that would deal with women and mental health. You would think we had asked for the keys to the kingdom. Impossible. Adamant, this time. No.

We asked for more women on the editorial board and they sat back and tapped their pencils and said the editorial board was composed of people with certain talents and it was not chosen on the basis of sex or race. Do I have to go further? And their broad excuse was *if the editorial board of the APA Journal acceded to these requests it would compromise their intellectual integrity.*

She pauses as the first speaker stands up. Can I add something? I think it's important to get this bit of information into the events we're talking about. While we were tackling the Journal we were also trying to get women placed on various committees. We had finally figured out that having a women's committee was a good way for the Old Boy network to slough off on us all women's issues. We had minority status. And there shouldn't be any minorities in this profession. To have female issues dumped on the women's committee was reinforcing this business.

The reporter had gone through the free-speech movement in Berkeley, had listened to Reagan the governor talk about task forces and then shove them back in the closet, had heard his own parents, in frustration and anger, incomprehensible to the end, ask, "These kids . . . what do they *want*?" When he said, "A voice, man, a voice," they looked at him as if he came from Mars.

Now he was having difficulty taking notes that would have some relevance later. It was a jumble. What the hell was the *bottom line*?

The speaker pulls a sweater on. The air conditioning is dumping cold, smoke-rancid air into the room. If you look at these committees, she says, you'll find a token woman here and there. And if there are more than one, they're considered "safe." They're inclined to accept health care and the psychiatric profession as is. But since all appointments are made by the president-elect, we went to him. We even . . . God forbid . . . suggested that a woman should be considered for president.

And with a straight face, she says, in all bouncy earnestness, He nodded and pondered. She imitates the president elect. He is all politician . . . pumping hands and grasping shoulders. He asked, Did we really think there was such a qualified person within the profession? Such a woman? Show me an Anna Freud, or Helene Deutsch, he said. He put his arm on my shoulder.

Deutsch? Freud? Was the president-elect simple? The reporter writes *Arrng intv'w with p-e.*

The group breaks for lunch. The woman who had talked to him in the hall brushes past. He grabs her arm. You suggested we could talk a bit after the meeting. You said something about your residency and what it's like being a woman psychiatric resident.

Are you going to be around this afternoon?

He looks at his watch. Until three. I need to write up my notes for the story.

Then this is just a news item for tomorrow? Maybe you don't want to get into more than this. Her hand sweeps the air.

His assignment is to keep it narrow . . . confine the story to these specific events. His reporter's instinct tells him he is on to something bigger. And who else is covering this?

I do. There's an angle that's troubling me. I want to find out what a profession that's mostly male and that treats mostly women *thinks of women.*

The doctor in the denim skirt smiles. If you were a Jew, would you go to a Nazi for help?

No. And I am.

Then you get my point.

In 1974 the Board of Trustees of the American Psychiatric Association, at the urging of thousands of women and men within the profession, passed a resolution supporting the ratification of the Equal Rights Amendment. At that time the idea of equality for women seemed to be the wave of the future. Even the Republican party, after some bloodletting and howls, decided they could expect higher grades by agreeing rather than by dissenting.

By 1977 the assembly of the district branches had gone even further. They urged the board to support passage of ERA by taking their convention business only to those states that had ratified it. The precedent for this action went back twenty years, when the Association had agreed to avoid meeting in those states that discriminated against blacks. The board agreed with the districts' recommendation and put it to a vote of the membership.

The membership said no.

So the Association convened in nonratified Georgia in 1978. The women and men psychiatrists who believed in equality swallowed their anger long enough to attend and appeal to the board to withdraw from the 1981 meeting in New Orleans. Most sincerely believed it was better to work from within.

You can't legislate love.

And the board agreed to withdraw.

A second referendum was sent to the membership. Again they voted no.

In 1979 the Association met in nonratified Illinois.

In 1980 a third referendum was sent to the membership. Of the 44 percent who voted, the majority said no.

How many cheeks were there left to turn? How much aversion therapy does it take to make the message clear?

The women psychiatrists for the most part decided finally to use muscle. Boycott New Orleans, where the '81 convention was to be held, if it finally came down to that. No papers. No attendance. No money for the new political action committee.

And there are other tactics, when push comes to shove, that won't be so dainty. *Do you want your women patients to know how you stand on equality? That they're referred to as hysterics? Crocks? Little Old Ladies With No Apparent Distress? Depressed dolls who need a little shock therapy? Do you want us to tell them that their psychiatrist's views about women may be dangerous to their mental health?*

Penis envy, is it? Hold on to your socks!

In the newsroom the editor looks over at his reporter, who is staring into space. I don't like to rush you but I could use your copy in an hour.

You'll get it.

Thirty inches.

Yes.

What's up?

The reporter laughs without parting his lips. You've read my electroshock copy, haven't you?

Sure.

Can you juxtapose it to the equal rights story?

That's up to composition. But what gives? You're not getting a by-line on the rights story.

That's not the point. The subtleties here are beautiful and I didn't get it until now. He fishes out his copy of the ECT story. I summarize this report, see, which challenges the antishrink attacks on ECT as a coercive mechanism for the behavioral control of the poor and ethnic minorities in state hospitals. Look, the reason I did this story is because the cuckoo's nest is the way most people think that things are still going down. I felt the antishrinks were doing a number. And the shrinks now have data to prove that ECT is used mainly in *private* hospitals. And guess what?

Just tell me.

Data from New York, which has the largest network of psychiatric facilities anywhere, show that people who generally get zapped with ECT are *white middle-aged middle-class females.*

In private facilities?

In private offices, private hospitals, private clinics. Generally used for *depression.*

What about the public hospitals?

Still mostly females, but they aren't necessarily white, middle-aged, or middle-class. Many are very young. And many are very old.

You could lift some of it for a sidebar, but that's almost editorializing. I'll talk to composition.

He catches up with her on the third floor of the San Francisco Civic Center. You mentioned you'd talk to me about your residency.

Residency? She looks at her watch. She's due at a symposium on community mental health care. About what? Remind me.

We were talking about the profession. Chauvinism, if you will.

That word has lost its sting. Overworked.

He wonders, does she always challenge the definition of words?

She capitulates. I'll meet you in forty-five minutes. Out here. A promise.

You, ah, don't have to go back to the Hilton to feed your baby?

Her eyes flash. I'm not tied to him. No. He also drinks out of a cup.

Forty-five minutes. I'll be here.

She stretches out on the couch in the press room. Feels good to get my feet up. He sits in a straight chair next to her. Role reversal.

How come you decided to become a psychiatrist? He isn't sure the question is relevant, but he's never dealt with a woman shrink. In fifteen years of science reporting. Well, that's natural. Men tend to talk to men.

I was already a doctor. Almost. And I was married. Frankly I thought psychiatry would give me a greater sense of support and equality. But there were no women with whom I could discuss this.

You see, academic and hospital positions are discussed within the Old Boy network. Gossip and openings and recommendations go on up here. She points to somewhere above her head. Women are scarcely if ever privy to this. It's simple. Men golf together, share drinks together, exchange residency or service camaraderie together. It's a club still closed to women. John tells Ira and Ira recommends Sy.

The reporter says, So the system, as a gastroenterologist once put it, repeats on itself.

She approves of his humor. Smiles. Which reminds me; when I went into my residency I wasn't pregnant. Only married. I was the first female resident in practice. There was a sense of deviance. But I denied this at first.

When did you get pregnant? It couldn't have been long ago.

My last year. My supervisor must have felt many emotions, not the least of which was anger. Of course I felt tired, as you do early in pregnancy. As a medical man he should have known this. But he put me on extra duty, so I was working at least one third harder than before. This was to "compensate," he said, for the future time off I would be taking to deliver and recuperate.

He whistles. Nice guy. Sensitive shrink.

She nods. The devilish thing about this is that I felt caught in a bind. If I complained I would be termed hysteric. And I found this frustration and exhaustion coming out in the treatment of my patients. Not only that, but my extreme fatigue was a great disadvantage. My attention span shortened and my concentration drifted.

But I got through it. Then I signed on for a year at a state hospital. There I made two important discoveries. In the year that I served with five other women psychiatrists, there wasn't one incidence of patient violence against us. This made history as far as we were concerned. The other thing I found out was that the salary of the average woman resident is still two fifths that of a man.

She makes no move to continue, but then looks up with the quickness of a rabbit or a hunting dog. You ought to talk to Dr. Cone. I wish you would. She's a psychiatric supervisor. Fantastic person. When . . . where will your piece appear?

I'm not sure. But I'll let you know.

She reaches over and shakes his hand. It's been nice. Not always nice to remember, but good to talk. Her face breaks into a young grin.

When he sits down with Dr. Cone he says the perfunctory things. You're an important psychiatric supervisor, you're regarded as a role model for women.

Her smile is cool. Suspicious? When there are scarcely any women supervisors, each one is important. And we become role models for the same reason.

He splits a can of cola with her and clears the press room sofa of the afternoon editions.

Like many psychiatrists she doesn't wait for specific questions but gets into a free flow. It is a way of controlling the encounter. My expectations for women residents are much greater than they are for men. I seem to demand that they be supergreat, to perform better, work harder, prepare more papers. And this is tough on them. Yet it follows a pattern. Minorities always have to outperform the regulars, swimming against the undertow just to stay even. I give male residents much more latitude.

Yet, as meager as our progress sometimes appears, we are accomplishing changes. We're supporting innovations in the residency programs, bringing up issues of maternity leave, day care, and flexibility of training. And we see women's practices growing while those of many males are slacking off.

I know there are plenty of male colleagues who feel guilty about the short shrift dealt to women, but there are still thousands who ignore us.

The reporter wrote *shift* instead of *shrift*, and wondered if it was an unconscious slip. Being around these shrinks was enough to . . . He realized he had missed some of her monologue. What? Sorry.

I said, such pettifoggery. The ones who explain us away by say-ing we're strident or feminist. If that attitude weren't so inexorably tied in with mental health and mental illness, it would be . . . she searches for the word.

Ludicrous?

Yes. That'll do nicely.

A woman of perhaps fifty-five or sixty paces between the coffee urn and the couch in the press room. The reporter had seen her once at one of the symposia on women and had been intrigued by her fleeting injunctions to her colleagues . . . "Forget about writing memos . . . speak out . . . conserve your energy and your emo-tions."

He asks, How did you come to your philosophy? Unlike Dr. Cone you say that women shouldn't be tough on other women. Who helped you? Don't you have to drive yourself harder?

It's too easy to feel that way, like Dr. Cone. Almost all of us have the good-girl syndrome that means perform, perform, per-form. It's a killer. I was lucky. I got into child psychiatry and had other women to work with. My supervisor was a woman who taught me how to place limits on my time, how much work I could do in a single day. There are no celestial prizes for such an out-pouring of energy as Cone demands. But setting limits on the in-vestment of emotion is hard for most women, especially good Janes. I had to go through conscious restraint.

Self-hypnotism?

No. I had help from my supervisor. She would say, "Monica . . ." then space each word with the force of a ball bouncing against the wall . . . "you . . . must . . . learn . . . not . . . to . . . accept . . . unlimited work . . . and . . . responsibility."

How many are lucky enough to hear that from a boss? "Look at Klaberg," she would say. Klaberg was a third-year resident. "He writes blanket prescriptions, tucks his knees into an afghan, and reads mysteries all afternoon."

Well, I could not stomach Klaberg, who walked through the wards with his head averted, glancing at charts, smiling enigmati-cally as he scribbled *continue drugs* or *medicate as required*.

I asked her, "Are you saying to be like Klaberg?"

My supervisor snorted. "Ridiculous. Of course not. He is putting in time here for only one reason. That Fifth Avenue practice he talks about. But you could do worse than mimic Klaberg a couple hours a day. *You could read a mystery*."

I felt betrayed. I was a *doctor* . . . a *healer*. If I were even a little bit like that schmuck and didn't invest emotions and unlimited work, then I wasn't living up to my best.

The reporter likes this well-padded, contented, cheerful lady who has worked with children for thirty years or more. Apparently at one of the subway stops you changed trains.

I did. And I changed without bitterness. I became part of a network of psychiatric women who hear about each other, who speak out on the issues, who fight for changes in ward and staff treatment for patients.

Has it made you lose respect for your male counterpart? *Male counterpart?* What kind of stuffy piece of jargon was *that*? The pseudoscientific jargon must be rotting his brain.

She rescues him. The men I work with?

Or come in contact with.

There are thousands, I guess, who think as I do, who overinvest energy and time, who don't play god. And thousands of others . . . She waves her hand in dismissal.

He looks at his watch. One last question. He grins. A conjecture. How do you think your fellow resident . . . Klaberg? Yeah, Klaberg, would feel about women and their rights to equality? An educated guess.

No guess. He is opposed.

How do you know?

I met him in Cleveland at a symposium. He wanted to buy me a drink. He said, "The drink's on a nice fat lady from Central Park West."

"And what's *she* on?" I asked. "Diazapam," he said. He says he's big in the Ladies Aid society . . . the Valium circuit. I know what he means. It pays very well.

Gloria Steinem is at the Hilton in a small suite used by the Psychiatric Association for restricted media events and small receptions. She exchanges information with leaders of the equal rights group and makes notes for her speech. Within an hour she will address an overflow audience in the main ballroom.

With her loose hair, soft blouse, and engaging smile the forty-six-year-old Steinem still looks like an earnest Smith College senior. She has been brought to San Francisco as the rallying figure for the five-year battle to convince psychiatrists that equal rights and mental health go hand in hand. The message has been long in the telling, loud and clear . . . but the majority of psychiatrists don't want to listen. *Politics and mental health do not mix. We will not be dictated to by a shrill minority. Nobody tells me where I can and cannot go. A doctor's philosophy is his own business.*

You bet.

When Steinem speaks, the college girl look is gone. She says that your psychiatrist's view about equal rights could be dangerous to your mental health. What we're trying to do here, she says, is overthrow the caste system where sex and race determine the human future. We're trying to redefine politics, the power relationship in our daily lives. . . .

There are cheers and applause. Steinem nods imperceptibly, she knows her audience. . . . It is not possible for a psychiatrist who does not believe in a client's full humanity to help that client achieve it.

The women psychiatrists want action. Steinem is ready. We are prepared to help in any way we can, she says. And it would be socially irresponsible not to publish a list of those psychiatrists who refuse to boycott meetings held in nonratifying equal rights states. Every woman across the country can then know which psychiatrists believe women are inferior to men. It can be done. It will be done. . . .

Outside the hotel there are pro-ERA demonstrators. Steinem makes a quick appearance. She grabs a bullhorn and calls for public support. Some of the male psychiatrists getting out of the shuttle buses from the civic center look quizzically at her. *Politics and mental health do not mix* . . . There are some enigmatic smiles. Aplomb.

The reporter has followed Steinem out into the street. He turns

to a man in his thirties. The badge says he is a delegate from
Connecticut. She's suggesting the women prepare a list of all psy-
chiatrists who refuse to boycott next year's convention in New
Orleans. How do you feel about that?

The delegate slowly shakes his head. Anger makes his smile
measured. I like publicity. Any free publicity *they* want to give me,
fine. It'll help my practice.

You bet.

It is the day after Steinem's appearance in San Francisco. On a
motion introduced by Dr. Elissa Benedek to hold next year's convention in an ERA-ratifying state, the board has voted twelve to
two to do so.

To hell with that bare majority that thinks it can keep psychiatry
in the nineteenth century. Views on equal rights are part and parcel of psychoses, neuroses.

Donald Langsley, the new president of the APA, is excited. We
did it! he says. Even with threats of a lawsuit by the New Orleans
convention bureau. We did it! Even after clear warnings from Association lawyers that what they were doing might not stand up. In
the excitement of the moment the new president wants to hug every
woman. He savors their approval. He reaches into his pocket *as if
searching for his own money* and announces a nice hunk of cash is
going to be donated from APA to the cause of equal rights.

The editor asks the reporter, What do you feel about things? Is
there any more story?

The reporter has a gut reaction. It's not over. This is dandy
excitement, and the icing makes the cake look good. But there's
mold inside.

The editor disagrees. I think we're finished. A happy ending.

The reporter drums on his desk, he has this *damn* feeling . . . So
they're not going to New Orleans. . . . There are still thousands of
psychiatrists out there who don't give a damn about women as
people. Nothing has changed that.

The editor knows the feeling of coming down from a story.

You've got time coming. Wrap it up and go home. Take tomorrow.

What can he say? It's a good deal.

By a month after the convention the reporter's notes are curling. He has had four rejections on his article idea about the male psychiatric attitude. *Freud's been attacked enough,* one editor writes . . . *since so many more women than men get treatment from shrinks, maybe there is something wrong with them.*

The phone rings. The lady says, You're the person who wrote those newspaper stories about equal rights and mental health. During the convention. It is a statement.

Yes.

I called your paper. You didn't talk to me during the convention, but I was there.

He reaches for a pencil. Automatic reflex. Very exciting. The board showed . . .

It didn't mean a thing. Her voice is flat, angry.

Pardon?

Not a thing. The board's vote, all that talking and congratulating ourselves. It didn't mean a *damn* thing.

I don't understand . . .

They just *revoted* to go to New Orleans. Only Elissa Benedek and two others voted not to go.

He had had that gut feeling. Everything had seemed too easy, somehow. Why? How?

Threats of a lawsuit by the convention bureau, pressure from Louisiana psychiatrists, letters from psychiatrists across the country, our Association attorneys . . . we just weren't *ready* for all that, I guess.

I suppose I could update the whole story, he says.

Anything, she says. I really just wanted you to know. Those of us who have no stomach for what's been decided are going to Houston.

You said your own attorneys had something to do with this final decision.

The *association* attorneys, she corrected. *We* had an opinion from a George Washington University constitutional law professor who said the board has the sole authority to decide the site of the annual meeting. They didn't pay much attention to *that*.

He could imagine the American Psychiatric Association in court on something like this. Our lawyer says *this* . . . your lawyer says *that*. Psychiatrists against psychiatrists. Image would certainly suffer.

Could I read you a letter? she asks.

Sure.

It's snide, but fairly typical. It was published in *Psychiatric News* after the convention. It's from a psychiatrist, of course . . .

Politics and mental health don't mix, the reporter jots . . .

The lady begins to read . . . *The very persuasive argument that ERA is a mental health issue needs to be extended. Inflation and the economic policy also affect mental health. . . . The gas crisis and traffic problems are further problems . . . and any state that does not impose the 55 mph speed limit should also be boycotted!* . . .

The reporter writes faster now. So this is what it has come to.

Would a Jew go to a Nazi for help?

About Women in Therapy

The medical establishment has a history of giving short shrift to women. Psychiatry itself did not welcome women to its ranks much before the latter part of the nineteenth century, when a very few, mostly single, did some private practice or went to work in the large state and psychiatric hospitals under the protection and tutelage of the male superintendents. There the women psychiatrists were part of the family and protected, reinforcing the concept of the weaker sex.

The first bid for recognition from male colleagues came in 1876 when a female delegate, Dr. S. H. Stevenson, requested to be seated at the American Medical Association convention. The big stall was on, the matter shuffled to a committee, and the matter remained closed for the next fifty years. The American Medical *Women's* Association was formed in 1920, and two years later the powerful male-oriented AMA allowed women physicians to join.

Fifty years after this the American Psychiatric Association voted to form a task force on women, and three years later they created a Committee on Women. But not until the beginning of the decade of the 1980s was a woman named to a top position in the APA, when Elissa Benedek was elected trustee-at-large.

But the battle is hardly won. A 1979 study of women psychiatrists shows that although they have the same number of years of postgraduate training as men, those in private practice still have lower incomes than their male counterparts.

Serious questions are being raised about the appropriate *type* of psychiatrist to conduct therapy with women. Where do the biases lie? What does the psychiatrist feel about women's history as a minority? How does the therapist view behavior? Equality in the marketplace? Self-assertiveness? Intellectual ability?

Dr. Nancy C. A. Roeske, coordinator of medical education in the department of psychiatry at the Indiana School of Medicine, is perhaps the profession's leading spokesperson for women's rights . . . whether as therapist or as client. She believes there is a growing tendency for women patients to question how male psychiatrists can understand women's conflicts, since the conflict is unique to them and not shared by men. And she submits that the changing role of women may be threatening to the male therapist, both as an individual and as a representative of a patriarchal culture. Furthermore she challenges the male therapist's perceptions of the abnormality of a woman patient's behavior. Behavior, she believes, is a subjective concept based on societal mores. So if a psychiatrist accepts a male-dominated society's definition of abnormality without using criteria other than those in fashion, then the therapist may become little more than an agent for society. Is this helpful for women? Scores of women do not believe so.

In a society that offers more opportunity for self-realization than heretofore, there is still the burr of sex-role designation. Of course, there are conflicts, and some very harsh conflicts, to be resolved by women. And the choice of a therapist under these conditions becomes critical.

Amelioration of the problem is what the client is seeking. Reinforcement or exacerbation of the pain is the last thing she needs.

The warning to women in general from women doctors in psychiatry is clear. Look well into whose hands you hand yourself.

Eleven

GOOD-BYE, PEPSI GENERATION

Handsome young doctor Peter pitches his gold-tassled mortarboard onto the bed of the cramped apartment. His penny loafers do a quickstep as he sings . . . youth, glorious youth . . . spring skiing in Aspen, wind surfing the coast . . . skydiving in Jackson . . . *Whoooey!* . . .

Daniel stands in the door, twirling his mortarboard on a finger. . . . Your talents will be wasted in psychiatry, he says.

How's your foramen lacerum? Peter recalls words, now easy, that baffled them in first-year anatomy.

Fine. How's your psyche?

Nursing a castration uncertainty. Time to reaffirm the old sex drive . . . want to go in town?

Yeah. But first a joint . . . Daniel aims for the bureau where he keeps his stash.

Riiiight . . .

It was time to do something about the parents. They had both reached eighty, but one was mentally fit and the other was, well, slipping. The woman, Agnes, was becoming exhausted with the care of her husband. His tempers and moods filled every twenty-four hours. It was no longer possible to get a good night's sleep, what with his nighttime perambulations.

He would wander out of his bedroom carrying a pillow as his drawstring pajamas slid over his shrunken hips, murmuring that he had to fill buckets of water. But more than once she would find him not at the sink but standing before the gas range trying to turn on the jets.

It was hard for her not to talk to him in the old, normal way. After fifty-five years it is expected that one acts in set patterns. Now the patterns were breaking down and she was getting confused and upset. When she tried to lead him back to bed, he shrugged her off and stood in front of the toilet, trying to void. He could stand there for an hour, trying to void.

Afraid that he would set the house on fire, she tied a string from his wrist to hers, so she could feel the tug when he got up to wander. He tugged all night long and became furious when she tagged after him.

It became increasingly chancy to leave him at home alone, and there was nowhere to turn to get someone to sit with him. Baby-sitters were in school. The neighbors were almost equally old. But Agnes still had to shop for food, and she would rush for all she was worth.

One day, she thought, I should get someone to come regularly and watch him, but her pride was such that she couldn't admit that her once intelligent, competent husband had lost a few links in the brain chain.

She tried to get out in the morning because he seemed brighter before noon. But one day he fooled her. When she returned from her errands, he was not passively watching the Bugs Bunny cartoons that were now his entertainment staple. Instead, he had the cuckoo clock apart, all over the dining room table. It needs reworking, he said.

She looked long and hard at him. It was not the first time he had dismantled and oiled clocks. Twenty years before, he had cleaned the grandfather clock with its hundreds of springs and wheels and made it work again, just so. Had he regained competence?

He sat at the table fingering and turning each wheel, lifting and setting down the weights. —If I had my magnifying glass, I could fix this.

She ran to his workbench to find the discarded magnifying glass that fit over his glasses. When she handed it to him, he looked at her quizzically. —What is this for?

—George . . . ? and she started to berate him.

He flung back the chair, trembling with rage. —Do you think I'm a fool? What are you bringing me?

—The magnifying glass, she said placatingly, —It's all right, George. Let it be.

He was still in his pajamas, and they were damp.

The two children had a consultation and compared notes. —He has taken apart every lamp in the house. The only light he can't reach is the ceiling fixture in the kitchen, the daughter says.

—He can't go on like this. She looks ready for a breakdown, the son says.

—His doctor thinks it's time to institutionalize him.

—Where will he go?

—The county hospital . . . The daughter blinks away tears. They both know it used to be called the insane asylum.

—What do we have to do?

—A psychiatrist must declare him mentally incompetent.

—Is that what he is?

—He's old . . . *confused* . . . His doctor said that they couldn't keep him in the regular hospital for more than a quick checkup. He seems to be having these little strokes.

—Can you take care of it?

The daughter nods. —I guess . . . I have to go to the court and get commitment papers and find two psychiatrists to examine him and sign the papers.

—What about her?

—She can live alone for a while, I guess.

Senility . . . the inevitability of old age? . . . is that the way they, too, would go?

Good-bye, Pepsi generation.

They say . . . we have seen the future and it is us. Medical people have special names for the future us. "Crock" is one, "turkey," "toad," and "dirtball" are others. Some say these are defense words to deal with an unpleasant reality . . . that the aged are not as attractive as the young. Others say these words represent a pervasive and prevalent attitude toward old age. After all, what's the *future* in dealing with people like the future us?

From that first cadaver . . . diseased, atrophied, shrunken, sagging . . . to the "gomers" lying on gurneys in emergency rooms, the medical person is *schooled* to lose respect for the body. The body is a thing . . . in the case of the old person still alive, a creature to be shunted elsewhere. Medicate, ameliorate . . . and out the door!

But after all, what's nice about this end of the life spectrum? Babies are cute and kissable and huggable. Gomers? Out the door.

The future us should be especially interested in removing the aura of legitimacy from treatment that is denigrating and cruel. The attitude of the medical profession in general and of psychiatrists in particular has a well-documented history of such treatment towards the elderly.

For starters, the big lie that senility and old age are synonymous still has the endorsement of doctors. The big lie has taken such hold that most of the future us have irrational terrors about growing senile and incompetent . . . *I want to die before I get that old. . . . My greatest fear is losing my wits. . . .*

Peter finds it hard to face the geriatric wards again after the month in Hawaii. Turmoil, pressure, stress, overdoses, infarcts, Parkinsonian tremors, Alzheimer-type senility, confusion . . . keratosis, papery skin, bone degeneration. It's all his.

Pamela meets him for lunch. She's going into pediatric psychiatry. Her hospital is wealthy. The week previous, three-quarters of a million dollars was raised by friends of the hospital to buy a piece of cancer-detection equipment.

Peter envies her, he says.

But you've got *action*, she retorts.

Listen, I've got bowel retention, not action.

Do you drug much?

The rule is sedate, sedate, sedate. Give this for anxiety, that for agitation, this for depression, that for heart arrhythmia, this to remove water . . . He leans into her face . . . Do you think drug prescribing is habit-forming?

She blows away the lock of his hair that touches her nose. . . . Yes.

He becomes earnest. I'm reading more. I'm scratching the surface, anyway. I know that most of the old people I see have a depletion of biogenic amines.

She nods. Of course. Amines have been connected to mood changes . . . can cause euphoria or depression . . .

I think most cry easier and laugh quicker, Peter continues. I see a challenge in connecting this to memory. I want to know why my patients' memories come and go . . . mostly go.

It's caused by old age, isn't it?

He bangs the table. . . . There you go! The term "old age" is nothing but a big basket. There are hundreds of things masquerading in that term.

Pamela looks puzzled.

My old patients who are confused because they've had cerebral infarcts have a different type of problem than old people who are confused because they're depressed. I'm seeing that old age is not a disease. . . . I'm seeing there are more different kinds of old people than there are different kinds of kids. . . .

Really? She acts amused. . . . You talk like you've discovered a new country, a new culture.

Maybe I have, Pam. . . .

In 1978 a conservative estimate of patients misdiagnosed for severe brain disorders was listed at 10 percent. *Ten percent* of those showing brain-disorder symptoms did *not* have brain disorder, even though doctors diagnosed them as if they did! The prime cause of their confusion came *not* from mental illness but from drug-induced toxic states and undetected infection.

A leader in geriatric research, Dr. Robert Butler, has laid it out clearly, insisting that all symptoms of brain dysfunction in advanced age are not inevitable and irreversible and that the cost of a missed diagnosis that results in permanent brain damage is high indeed.

Aging, which really begins at birth, is a changing process of the multielements of the body. True aging can creep on cat's feet or come with a rush. It is accelerated by disease, neglect, nutritional deprivation, obesity, lack of interest, genetic faults. It can be slowed by good health, longevity diets, exercise, genetic factors, and a general love of life.

Senility is a catchall convenience of easy diagnosis. It connotes a finality, an irrevocability that stigmatizes and shoves an elderly person into the category of the living dead. Because medicine, and, of course, psychiatry, consider themselves science rather than art, narrow diagnosis is preferred. For this, men and women of medicine cannot be entirely to blame. Society clamors for definitions, rational prognosis, and *treatment*. "Sophisticated" people believe there must not only be terminology but also constructive, easy-to-obtain solutions. Even with dread diseases we are anxious to hear a definite diagnosis. After the first shock it seems easier to live with.

Ambivalence can be an unbearable cross for a diagnostician. Having made a decision about labeling and course of action, doctors are much relieved. Rightly or wrongly they have nevertheless *decided*. This is infinitely easier to live with than doubts, trial-and-error treatment, or no medical treatment at all.

The psychiatrist examines George for brain capability. —Who's the President of the United States?

George chews his lips. —He's doing a good job considering the condition of the country.

—Do you know his name?

George smiles. —Why? Don't you know?

The psychiatrist asks George if he knows what year this is.

George rubs his hands together. He can't seem to get them warm. —It hasn't been a good year, although not as bad as last.

—Do you know the month?

—The month of what? George looks puzzled. What is this man driving at?

—Do you read the newspaper?

George's eyes turn to the television set. He would like to watch some cartoons. —I gave it up. Everything is the same as it always was. Nothing improves. The cartoons make more sense. Do you watch the one with the bird that solves everything?

—Road Runner, Agnes supplies.

—Ah, yes, Road Runner, the psychiatrist says. —Is that now on television?

George offers to turn the set on, but Agnes shushes him. He has cut the plastic-covered antenna wires into sections and tried to solder them back together. Reception is just about nil.

The psychiatrist stands up. He's heard enough. Senile dementia. Definitely commitable.

He says to Agnes, —I'll sign the form when your daughter gets it from the court.

—He'll only get worse? Agnes has worried this question for weeks. It must be asked.

—Yes. Organic brain syndrome. Global impairment of the intellectual functions. . . .

Agnes asks her daughter,—Are we doing the right thing?

—He needs round-the-clock care, the daughter says.

—If I could get some home nursing care . . . Agnes's voice trails off.

—How can you afford that? They are barely hanging on in the old house. The daughter and her brother are barely hanging on too. Every bedroom in either house is filled, and both couples have jobs.

The daughter sets about doing the necessary things . . . getting the court papers signed, visiting the funeral home to talk about the inevitable. It makes her feel ghoulish, but her life seems to go from crisis to crisis anyway. . . .

—The psychiatrist's bill is fifty dollars, the daughter tells her mother. She will pay it out of her next salary check. —The county home wants seven hundred dollars a month. They will take the amount from his Social Security for now, but they'll want the balance when he gets out.

—He won't get out, Agnes says.

—You know what I mean.

—Oh, God, will I have to sell this house?

—They will put an automatic lien on it. But don't worry about that now. Do you want to go with me when I take Daddy up there?

Agnes looks at her daughter as if she's crazy. —Of course.

There is this about aging: the kidneys become greatly smaller, the filtration rate of wastes decreases by half. The wastes are absorbed into the bloodstream, causing myriad problems, from fatigue to erratic gait. The urine becomes increasingly watery as wastes are left behind, the body structure itself appears to become more simian as hands often reach past the knees. The breasts sag, the spine no longer has a nice curve, hair thins and falls out, the skin develops keratoses. There is a major loss of beauty and normal functioning.

George and Agnes's doctor comes to the house and sits for a while with Agnes. She talks about George and his wanderings, taking the clocks apart, the lamps apart. Half the time he refuses to eat and sits staring at his oatmeal. When she tries to feed him, he turns his face away and says it's poison. Agnes says her shoulders ache, she's losing weight, there's no family within three hundred miles, and their money is low.

The doctor examines George, and George becomes affable. He strains to be normal. He stands up for the doctor.

—Is he taking his nitroglycerine?

George has a history of angina.

Agnes nods. —I watch his medication. He gets vitamins, she says. Medication! Watch his diet! Anyone else in George's shoes should be so lucky! Didn't she pull him back from the brink of death six years before, after he had had an intestinal cancer operation and his body was skin and bones? And didn't she pump six, seven eggs into him in glasses of rich Guernsey milk? She got him fat again.

But Agnes is ashamed to tell the doctor that George stands in front of the toilet for hours, trying to dribble, feeling as if he has to, afraid he will wet his pants. George's temperature seems almost normal . . . 99 degrees. The doctor does not remember that George has been running 97 degrees for a year, so he does not suspect an infection. Anyway, everything seems to shut down sooner or later with these old people.

At the community mental health center a seventy-five-year-old woman has been brought to the admitting room. The secretary takes down the medicaid number and asks the companion what her relationship is to the woman. . . . She's my mother, the young woman answers in Spanish.

Do you speak English? the aide asks.

Sí . . . she smiles ingratiatingly . . . Mi modd-er, she is confus-ed . . . need to be in nursing home . . .

This is the fourth admittance of the day, and the aide is growing weary. . . . Has she Social Security?

The daughter shakes her head. Worked as maid . . . no card . . .

Here we go again, thought the aide. Another ninety-day drop-off. Ninety days of medicaid benefits, then zoom, out the door. She is frustrated and short with the daughter. . . . You can't leave her here for more than ninety days, if that. There are no nursing home openings right now. . . . Are you able to take her back at the end of the ninety days?

There are tears in the daughter's eyes, and she nods her head. . . . *Mi madre es muy confuso* . . .

I understand, says the aide. But do *you* understand? There is no place for her on a permanent basis, you will probably have to take her back . . . until a bed opens up . . .

Every day the aide prays for more deaths . . . and more beds.

The daughter nods. She would certainly never tell this lady that her husband is sitting out in their car ready to go back to their apartment to pick up the U-Haul trailer with their possessions. They're on their way to Oregon to find work. There's no way they could take the old lady. No way to keep her. The daughter and her children will never see her again, and the mental health center will never track them down. *Muy confuso. Pobre madre.*

The psychiatrist at the community mental health center has asked for a complete physical work-up on the seventy-five-year-old Mexican woman. She finds her, unlike many of the street drop-offs, in pretty good health. She's anemic, but every one of the drop-offs seems to be anemic, victims of poor nutrition if not outright starvation. The doctor suspects most of the confusion may come from a low red-cell count that would mean less oxygen carried to the brain.

This woman is shy to the point of withdrawal, but this is not unusual for new patients at the center. The woman is moved into the geriatric section of the hospital complex and soon is the center of cheerful attention. There are others who speak Spanish, and within days she has been accepted.

The psychiatrist visits the elderly once a day, and they become trusting and friendly. It is heaven compared to the threadbare lives they left, although they are depressed about not seeing friends or family. But new friends compensate. And so do clean sheets, warm baths, the good meals, material and wool for handiwork, medicine that makes them feel lively and well.

But each one has a countdown chart. Twenty days in, seventy to go. Thirty days in, sixty to go.

Where will they go? The state hospitals have been closed down one after another, and the ones that are left are overcrowded. But that's the end of the line. No Social Security, most of them, to pay for a nursing home. Ninety days is the limit for treatment at the center.

The ballroom has been booked for a psychiatric symposium on nursing home and outpatient care. Question: Is the quality of life better in small, scattered nursing homes than it was in the larger institutions?

There is no consensus. One psychiatrist says that in his personal view it is better today. State and county hospitals were the pits.

Not at all, counters another psychiatrist from the Deep South.

To say that is to slough off responsibility. In the institutions there were movies, walks, therapy, socialization. What is the incentive to provide this in community-based homes? There isn't enough money or room in the facilities to have physical therapy and recreation. Shoving the elderly into smaller and inadequate community facilities was a cheap trick. Money was cut off to the institutions, and now it's up to each area to seek its own funding. Institutionalized elderly can't survive on medicaid. At least before, there was enough food.

The shrinks on the panel look uncomfortable. What sort of nonsense is this, suggesting we go *backward* . . . or that yesterday was better than today?

It's our job as advocates of mental health to speak up for the elderly, the southern psychiatrist says. There must be more mental health services, better nutrition, better treatment.

Eyes are glazed. It's an hour past lunch. Sleepy time.

The woman psychiatrist who has no beds for her ninety-day-then-out-the-door-elderly grabs two colleagues. What are we going to do besides sending them to the jails and overcrowded wards? How can I do this to them? They're dumped at our center for ninety days. Then nothing. Where does the buck stop?

It's political, one of the doctors answers.

Bullshit, says the other. We are talking cost effectiveness. Everything has to be cost effective, and it's getting worse. Elderly can't be returned to usefulness in the eyes of our society. Measuring cost effectiveness in terms of humanity is hard to do.

Prove to me that it isn't political, the first psychiatrist retorts. The conservatives hate mental health, public health, decrepit, poor, handicapped, and elderly. They almost wiped out California and will do it to the nation next

How long are you going to stay in that community mental health facility, the other psychiatrist asks the woman.

She rubs her forehead. I don't know. It breaks my heart. We watch them become happy and trusting and better equipped than they have been for years. What can you suggest? I believe we have a social mandate.

If we're so smart, how come we can't be effective, the first psy-

chiatrist asks. Listen. He bangs his fingers into his palm. There
are four ways to go to get your rights. Cooperation, advocacy,
legislation, and the courts. Pick your route.

All I want now are some beds.

Then coopt the system.

The woman shakes her head. No wonder people keep us at arm's
length.

At one time it was thought that children were simply small editions of adults. It was believed that babies were born with a brain
already adult size, ready to be packed with information and experience. The subtleties of infant and child development eluded earlier
societies.

As ludicrous as this belief is today, we hold similar attitudes
toward the aged. They are considered by most to be simply older
editions of young adults.

Ironically, while we are now educated enough to realize that
drug dosages should be tailored to the size of a person, we still
neglect to take into consideration metabolic and physiological
differences. Since there are subtle differences in physiological measurements between youth and age, should we be medicating
equally? Two physiological measurements of body composition
that change with age are muscle and bone. Both decrease with
aging. Body fat as a proportion of body weight increases with age.
The volume of blood plasma decreases slightly with age.

What this means, for instance, is that the same dose of alcohol,
adjusted to body weight, will cause higher blood alcohol levels
among the elderly than among youth. There is, of course, less lean
body mass and body water in the elderly in which the alcohol can
distribute.

Kidney function will decrease about 35 percent between twenty
and eighty years of age. Drugs are removed from the body by
kidney excretion and liver metabolism. Drugs that are removed
through kidney function should be used with care in the elderly.
Lithium, for instance, in use since the 1970s, is commonly prescribed to create emotional balance. It is now suspected of causing
permanent kidney scarring and damage. Perfectly legitimate drugs

to help ailing heart or circulatory systems or prescribed for infections can accumulate in the elderly and cause side effects of confusion, staggering, dementia. A psychiatrist evaluating an elderly person with all the classic syndromes of brain disorders may diagnose Alzheimer's disease, or multi-infarct dementia, when in fact the blame falls squarely on the buildup of drugs.

The most common causes of *reversible* impaired intellectual function are therapeutic drug intoxication, depression, and metabolic or infectious disorders. Medications that do good and that are important to extending life can be lethal in unconservative dosage. These include diuretics, digitalis, oral antidiabetics, analgesics, antiinflammatory agents, sedatives, and psychopharmacologic (mood altering) drugs.

There is something the medical people call a *polypharmacy problem* . . . the overmedication of a patient, particularly an elderly patient, or the prescribing of a drug that interacts negatively with another drug, the use of drug B to counter the bad effect of drug A, which in turn can produce a new and worse side effect. But medical doctors, including psychiatrists, have training in this sort of thing, we believe. They are supposed to know better.

A Harvard University psychiatrist studied prescriptions used at a leading hospital, and published his findings. Time and time again he found polypharmacy problems, with some patients getting *seventeen drugs* at the same time, and he wonders, does it go on elsewhere? Everywhere?

Let's not draw national conclusions just because of this particular study, says the chief of medicine at the leading hospital. But . . .

A Harvard University psychiatrist, a leading hospital, a scientifically controlled and published study . . . you wonder . . .

Gerontologists write volumes about the need to sensitize doctors to the changes of age. Get them early, they say. Doctors need to visit elderly in nursing homes, they need to see them as outpatients, to see them ill, to see them well, to see them productive, to listen to them. Our fragmented society isolates medicine, including psychiatry, from this. . . . *But it's such a depressing way to practice*

*medicine . . . many elderly only have, at best, a few years to live,
you know they're going to get more and more depressed . . . if
they don't become senile first . . .*

Senility is a disease, it's not automatic just because you get older.
Many people never get senile. Depression is a disease too. But it
affects different people different ways. Just because you get older
doesn't mean you will get depressed. Forget the drug ads, depression and old age don't dance the two-step!

*Well . . . I never had a course on aging in medical school. It
didn't seem . . . important, somehow . . .*

Welcome to the great majority! Few medical schools even require a course on geriatrics, and until recently less than half the
medical schools had elective courses. How would *you* know what
was important?

Let's take a look at a forty-year-old heavy drinker and smoker.
Open him up . . . there's an *aging*, hardening liver, there are *aging*
lungs (with diminished capacity to hold oxygen), there's an *aging*
brain (with brain cells dying from the lack of oxygen) . . . it's old
age! Deterioration through abuse equals old age. . . .

Meanwhile, an extensive door-to-door drug and alcohol survey
in the late 1970s showed that our elders felt less need to use drugs
and alcohol of any kind to relieve stress and anxiety than did
young people or middle-aged people. . . .

*But everyone knows you heavily medicate older people, they
need it!*

It is Pamela on the phone for Peter. . . . How about coming
over for dinner?

My therapy night, he tells her.

Are you into psychoanalysis already?

No, no. . . . I'm working with a group of elderly. . . . *Group*
therapy, not personal analysis.

Well, Freud felt analysis wasn't worthwhile for old people. . . .

Peter sighs. . . . I've heard *that* before. He did his best work in
later life. . . . Anyway, this group therapy is really interesting. . . .

Can I come?

Sure . . . you really want to?

Oh, Peter, guess what? He can almost see her jumping up and down . . . We got a new scanner.

So you said.

This is another. We can do computed cranial tomography. How would you like *that* for your elderly?

Doubtful value, he says, knowing it sounds like he's putting her and that rich hospital down. But he pushes on. . . . *We* don't think it's helpful in measuring dementia, if that's what you're referring to. There are many patients with gross brain atrophy and no signs of dementia and others with dementia and no signs of atrophy. . . .

She is taken aback. So what are you into, psychological testing? . . . There is a curl to her voice.

We use tests, sure. But they aren't perfect.

Last time I saw you, you wanted to get more scientific. Now you tell me tests and scanners and computers aren't reliable. . . .

You need to observe. But *you* know this. Why are we arguing?

She sighs. Peter, I respect what you're doing . . .

You *really* want to go to my therapy group?

Sure. How old are they?

Up to ninety-five. Mostly women. The men are treated like movie stars. It's beautiful. The women love to mother them. Hey, we've got one eighty-year-old who's taking courses, has planned her own funeral and is taking therapy to work out her angers and fear of death. She's almost blind, and when she came, the report was that she was incompetent . . . he laughs . . . incompetent, my foot!

What do they talk about?

His laugh turns into a hoot. . . . Pam, you won't believe . . . the youngest is seventy-five, right?

She nods.

They talk about their . . . parents!

At the county hospital the daughter goes through the maze of corridors first, to find out where to take George and sign more papers. She is told to take his clothes to the laundry room. She protests, —The robe and pajamas are new, there are a dozen pairs of new socks, the sweaters are cashmere and fine worsted. They can't be washed.

They'll be boiled, she is informed. Regulations. Protection against infestation, germs . . .

Four hundred dollars she has just spent on clothes. They would be shrunk beyond use. Would he even get them back? At the laundry intake, a burly girl scrawls George's name in indelible ink on every garment. His favorite Egyptian cotton shirts are marked up the back. —These won't be ironed. You should take them with you.

—Keep them. The daughter is already feeling ugly. For $700 a month this is . . . an insult.

Agnes and the daughter walk on either side of George. —Who are we going to see? George is so trusting.

—You'll be staying here, Agnes says. —For a while. She swallows tears.

The staff psychiatrist meets them while George still shivers in his overcoat. He cannot get warm.

George tries to muster a bright look. —How do you do?

The psychiatrist leans against the wall and looks each of them up and down. —He's coming in today?

—Yes, says the daughter.

—I wasn't informed. He shrugs. —Never mind. It doesn't make any difference. He won't be here long.

My God, he's talking in front of my father, the daughter thinks. She feels faint. Does he think the man's totally senseless?

The psychiatrist reads the short report from the committing psychiatrist . . . *organic brain syndrome, Alzheimer's disease* . . . senile psychosis, obviously. Terminal. —Pop was giving you a little trouble, was he, Mother?

Agnes trembles. —I . . .

Her daughter interrupts. —Don't call her Mother, and for heaven's sake, don't call him Pop. He's not your Pop. Nobody's Pop . . .

The psychiatrist raises his eyebrows at the outburst. There is silence. The daughter looks at her feet, getting control. Then, almost beseechingly, asks, —Is it nice?

—Nice? The psychiatrist cocks his head.

—Yes. Is it *nice*? Is it pleasant here? Will this be best for him?

—Pleasant? Nice? No, it is not nice. He shows plain irritation. —Of course it is not nice. It's dreadful.

Agnes looks stricken. The daughter wishes she had never asked.

The psychiatrist busies himself with her father's file. —I have seen a lot like him. Hundreds. He will be gone soon. Two, three months. So *nice* is not a long-term worry, is it?

The daughter has to ignore this. —I have his pills. Nitroglycerine, digitalis, vitamins. He takes two vitamin tablets, and we've been giving him extra vitamin C to help his . . .

—No pills. Put them back in your bag. Nothing beyond this door.

—But he needs . . .

—We'll see to what he needs. You can take him to the ward and they'll change his clothes. Take his outer clothes home.

—His things are in the laundry.

—Everything is mixed up anyway. They'll find something to put on him.

Indignities. Would there be a limit? George stands passively, chewing his lips.

A clinic for impaired elderly and their families, set up by the University of Washington, is located in Seattle. It aims to combine the role of the family with outside support-systems. —The psychiatric needs of the elderly have not been adequately addressed, says a doctor connected with the clinic, —and the family has not been sufficiently supported.

The elderly person and the family are first evaluated by a psychiatrist. Then a social worker calls at the home to assess the environment, while an architect looks over the household to see what can be done to make life easier. A nurse and a physical therapist come on the scene to strengthen the activities of daily living.

Assessment is made at a conference, and recommendations are made in the following areas: the living arrangement, nutrition, self-care, physical health, emotional and mental factors, family stress, financial matters, interference with family members' work. Decisions on medication, counseling, or both, will follow. In industry they call something like this the systems approach. It has a tendency to be effective.

Of the ninety-four patients helped the year after the clinic opened, sixty-eight were found to have cognitive impairment. That is, they were slowly going downhill but could be helped to spend more worthwhile time outside of institutions. Twenty-six were judged to be *reversible*, and through better nutrition, therapy, certain medications, they came around remarkably well.

At the time of the first visit the family members were ready to send their elderly parents or close relatives to an institution. They were beset by guilt, confused about responsibility and the best course of action. There is no question but that the Seattle clinic gave them immeasurable help. Clinics like this are located all over Scandinavia, supported by the government, and offering services that the United States has not even contemplated.

When the daughter next visits George, she finds him tied in a wheelchair. The sleeves of his shrunken wool dressing gown are high off his wrists. He recognizes her at once. —I'm ready to go, he says. He beckons her to come close and whispers in her ear. —The doors are locked but I have figured it out. When they take out the trays I will follow. You run this place, so there is no problem. Are my clothes in the car?

She ignores this and asks what he had for lunch. She looks about and notices that although it is only three o'clock, all the supper plates have been brought to the ward. On each plate is a slice of curling white bread. There are dishes of something that looks like corn pudding and two slices of bologna. He doesn't answer, so she asks if he gets the ice cream she has ordered for his daily snack. He shakes his head.

—You must, she says. She is already impatient. Would he even remember?

He repeats how he could escape, and she again ignores him. Agnes is now in the hospital with pneumonia and exhaustion. The crises gallop. She tells him, —Your fishpond is fine.

He cocks his head. —There are no fish in the pond. He drained it four months ago. She doesn't know this. In fact she had not looked at the pond. She's lying. But how would he know. Humor him. —The fish are swimming around.

—No. He shakes his head, trying to remember. —How can that be?

—Well, they are, she says emphatically.

He won't argue. She is from the world of the living, out there.

He waves to an orderly. —Excuse me, the young man says. —He wants to go to the bathroom. He grabs the chair and wheels her father away double-time.

The daughter gets up and walks through the ward. There are ten beds in the room, five on each side. At one an elderly man sits half up, his lunch tray on the table next to him. It looks untouched. She wonders whether to offer the man some of the green gelatin or the cold soup. The man could never reach the tray by himself in a million years. His arms are frail as sticks as he lies staring at the ceiling.

A TV set with a rolling picture and no sound is attached to the wall in the adjoining dayroom. Four men in rattan chairs stare at it.

When the orderly comes out of the bathroom without her father, she asks how he is. —Doing fine, he says.

—Is the TV broken? she asks. She thinks about his Bugs Bunny cartoons.

—Yes, he answers.

—Can that man eat by himself? She motions to the bed across from her father's.

—Yes, says the orderly. —When he's ready he will. His eyes dart as if sensing trouble. —I'll make sure he gets supper.

—And my father's ice cream. Does he get it?

—Yes. He enjoys it.

Can she trust him? What else can she do? If she could come back every day and check, but she lives 350 miles away. Her frustration mounts to a scream inside her.

—You can go, if you want to, the orderly says. —He'll be in the bathroom for a while, and he has already forgotten you're here.

She reaches in her bag and thrust $10 at the orderly. Bribery. It has come down to this. —Please see that he gets his ice cream.

He pockets the money. —Your father's a nice man. We take care of him okay. He shrugs. —We'll all need care someday, I figure. Right?

She lays an oblong package on the table by the door. —I brought cigarettes. Would you share them with the others? They asked me to bring them when I first came here.

—Sure. His eyes light up.

When she gets to the waiting room, she fishes in her purse for some change and drops it in the soft-drink machine. She feels drained. A thirst that can't be quenched. She punches the perforated slot on the can and tips the Pepsi to her mouth.

About the Elderly . . .

Robert Butler, director of the National Institute on Aging, is himself a psychiatrist. He is without doubt our most important professional spokesman for the elderly and for his written work on the subject has been awarded the Pulitzer prize. He calls this the "century of the elderly" and reminds us that by the year 2020 one fifth of the population will be over sixty-five. Speaking as a psychiatrist as well as an advocate for the elderly, he has urged his profession to form a society of geratric psychiatrists. Such a model exists in the Boston Society for Gerontological Psychiatrists and The Group for Geriatric Psychiatry of New York. He identifies organic brain disorders as a prime research priority. One million Americans seem to be affected.

Yet Butler, in summing up the attitude of his colleagues, says "a period of negative countertransference toward the elderly has occurred in psychiatry." Negative countertransference. Negative feelings toward the elderly generated by the psychiatrist. It is a sad commentary by one of their own. But what does it mean for the future us, or those of us who must deal with the elderly today or tomorrow? What are the specific implications?

A survey conducted by the APA reveals that no more than 2 to 4 percent of patient time is devoted to the elderly. Why is this? There are many reasons, but the main ones seem to be these:

There is little financial reward in the treatment of elderly. They are mostly *not* in the higher income brackets. Beyond meager health insurance coverage, what can a doctor expect in terms of reimbursement?

Most psychiatrists believe that the elderly do not make good candidates for analysis or psychotherapy. This attitude stems from Freud himself, although the man disproved this point by producing some of his best work in his later years.

There is a prevailing attitude that the elderly are nonproductive and not worth much of a psychiatrist's time. This attitude undoubtedly is fostered by medical training. Only a handful of schools have mandatory courses in aging, and elective courses in the subject are meagerly scattered in other schools. Student contact with the elderly is hardly considered, let alone encouraged. Deprecation of the elderly is an *accepted model* all through medical school and clinical training.

Diagnosing mental problems of the elderly is generally quick and cursory. Most psychiatrists prescribe treatment without bringing into the mix the sociological, cultural, or physical factors that may account for depression, anxiety, confusion, hallucinations, dementia. Specific laboratory and clinical work-up is usually deemed too costly, too time-consuming. The cost/risk factor plays a huge role in determining who gets what diagnosis and treatment.

Preventive medicine, especially for the aging, has not caught on in the United States among the medical establishment. As a consequence, drugs that have been used in other countries to stay the aging process have not been supported here. One such drug is called DEM. According to research, it is a drug that seems to hold back deterioration of brain neurons involved in glucose metabolism. (Enzymes utilized in the burning of glucose undergo changes in the elderly and may result in cell shortages.) While this drug has been used sparingly and occasionally in the United States, in Europe it has been so widely prescribed over the past two decades that it outsells penicillin. Doctors there administer substantial dosages of DEM to stall mental decline. They also recommend its use as a preventative, often at the first signs of mental deterioration. In the United States many doctors are not convinced about its merit, but that may be because, according to researchers, results are not particularly spectacular with the low dosages used in the United States. Currently two international studies confirm DEM's ability to slow down aging as it regards neuron impairment.

Twelve

LOONY BINS
AND CITY STREETS

Hey, man, how are you?

Joe De Leo spins around to see who is yelling. Someone he knows? He is not sure. The voice is, well, familiar. A little high. Giggly. Joe De Leo shades his eyes. That penetrating California sun.

What are you doing in Salinas, man? De Leo, isn't it? Sure, I remember.

The man does jabber. De Leo has hazy recall. Napa, was it? The state hospital? Four, five years ago? He left Napa before De Leo.

I live here. De Leo feels as if he was enclosed in a heavy serape. He must look up through his eyebrows.

Riddle. It's me. The giggly laugh. Cornelius Riddle. Did I ever tell you my name was Cornelius?

How do you do, Cornelius. I'm pleased to see you again.

De Leo, you look together. You making it okay? I thought you'd go out in a box. You got no family, right? So where are you staying? Got an old lady? Who'd put up with a goat like you? Good times we had once in a while back at Napa, right? I mean, although it was a shithole, we had a laugh. But I was *glaaaad* to split. I'm down here working the avocados, then it's back to the Haight. On a high right now. Got to take advantage of *that*. You know about *that*, right? I got a shot before I left the Haight. They figure I got some time to make cash before I crash . . . the giggle . . . under the table, you understand. Beer money. Nothing great . . .

Jabber, jabber. De Leo would like to move on. Those manic highs scare the hell out of him. I'm on my way to . . . he swallows. This Riddle is a stranger. Why should he tell *him* where he is going? He has to live in this city. . . . I'm going to lunch . . . his eyebrows, like awnings, shade the mistrust he knows is in his eyes.

I'll join you, man. Saw a deli downtown, and it looks like you could get a beer. Not much in this place. Take the Haight, there's something every block, if you know where to look, but I see this highway here with fancy brick and stucco restaurants, expensive, you know? If they even *let* someone in with boots and all . . .

I don't know, De Leo says. That is the truth. He does not go to fancy places for meals. He is just beginning to work through his fears and find his way downtown, though he will sometimes sit quietly on a barstool and drink a beer with a couple of men from his rooming house.

So where are we going to eat? Cornelius persists.

The sun is unrelenting. The words of the psychologist circle De Leo's vision. You don't have to tell anything about yourself if you don't want to. You have civil rights. Your name is protected. Your rights are protected. No matter what happens. If you are jailed, we will protect you.

But Cornelius Riddle is not a policeman or a warden. He came out of Napa too. Yet De Leo can't bring him to lunch. If he could, then every bum off the streets could come. Cornelius is down to work avocados. De Leo turns his head away. You have to eat by yourself. I have a regular place I eat at, and there's only so many seats.

Riddle pulls himself up and jams his hands into his jean pockets. He is lanky and disjointed.

De Leo does not know whether to expect curses or threats. The invisible serape is pulled tighter.

Riddle toes the ground and does a shuffle. Man, don't let it get you. His voice is soft.

De Leo is more shocked by the response than if Riddle had belted him. You've got some good medication? he asks.

Yeeaaah! He slowly claps his hands. They give me these long-acting shots. I got it together.

Now De Leo wishes he could take him to the center. But that is impossible. Not without warning. Have you got a piece of paper? I got an address. You could come by and see me when you get into Salinas.

Cornelius tears open a near-empty cigarette pack, shucks the smokes into his shirt pocket, and fishes for a pencil stub. He starts to giggle, then is carried away in a belly laugh. He gasps, De Leo, you remember that son of a bitch used to eat *butts* in the dayroom? Stuff the butts into his face and chomp them down? You remember him?

The serape lifts off De Leo's shoulders and he, too, howls, remembering. He *stole* them after we all told him to knock it off. It could make you puke . . .

Did they let him out?

Sure . . . before me . . . De Leo is laughing so he can hardly get his breath.

Did he quit?

He came here for a while . . . they worked with him . . . he's gone now . . . he *was* coming around, though . . .

Filter tips and all! Cornelius cannot stop the reminiscence. . . . But he'd leave the ashes. The least he could've done was eat the goddamn ashes. He crams De Leo's address into his bulging shirt pocket. . . . It takes all kinds, right?

De Leo watches him go off, and then he, too, turns down a street of bungalows. The living skills center where he will soon be eating lunch looks no different from any of the neighboring houses.

The living skills house is part of what people call a community mental health *center*. There's no exact count of how many centers there are around the country. Some say three thousand, some say three hundred. It probably depends on how elaborate you envision a center. Perhaps a drug-dispensing counter for outpatient mental health problems could be called a center. Perhaps a bunch of rooms where volunteers and semiprofessionals treat suicide threats, alcohol and drug problems, could be called a center. Some store-front room with knocked-about furniture, a jar of instant coffee, and a fake copper plug-in hot water dispenser could be called a center. There are centers . . . *and* there are centers . . . One, at the Community Hospital of the Monterey Peninsula, south of San Francisco, is called the Garden Pavilion. It may be the most elegant community health center around.

But this center, bounded on the east by Carmel Valley and on the south by Big Sur, is not scheduled for a visit by Joe De Leo at this point in his life. He is trying to get it together a few miles away in Salinas.

Joe walks through the front door of the living skills house and goes into the living room. There's a clatter in the kitchen and some good-natured arguing among the table-serving detail. An upright piano with its back facing the living room has been draped in a sheet of garish crepe paper. Joe De Leo loves it. It makes him feel that good things are happening. One of the regulars is sprawled in a lounge chair. His eyes, which had been fused to the television set, now follow Joe around the room. There is no smile on his face. He refuses to do much of anything except watch TV and eat lunch. No softball or movies. He won't go out for a coffee with anyone. He may have been a state hospital regular too. Getting back into the world is no easy job. Walking from the board-and-care house to the living skills center is already a giant step to normalcy.

Joe manages a hello to the half-dozen others who are watching a card game in what was once a dining room, and goes back to the kitchen.

The kitchen is busy and full of light, and nobody notices the scuffed linoleum or the faded plastic tablecloth. He goes right to his chores, which are posted on a weekly schedule in front of the staff office. Set up glasses, pour juice, dish out dessert. In the old refrigerator is a large tray of rice custard. The food gets eaten up, that's for sure. It's far from fancy, but not as boring as the state hospital. And the cold stuff is cold and the hot stuff hot, the way it should be.

The staff people think Joe is the greatest. He's a success story in the making. After a dozen years away he's coming around, he's becoming one of the earth people. The drugs are the big thing that keep him stable and less paranoid. He has a skills sponsor and soon will start to work part time to supplement his lean subsidy. Right now almost every penny of his supplementary social security income goes to the rooming house for board-and-care, and he has virtually nothing left for clothes or an ice cream or a movie.

He would like to tell the staff about Cornelius Riddle, but his deep shyness and fearsome reticence keep his lips sealed. He answers nicely when spoken to, but one cannot expect volumes from Joe. He's just getting it together too. Slow and easy.

He's ready to go for softball after lunch, though. The first day he did that was like scaling a huge mountain. A little trembly at the bat, but that's the medication. Yet, given the choice between the hideous paranoia and a little tremble, he has no problem knowing which way to go.

That imagined serape sometimes lifts up with wings of its own, and lets him stretch. It's been months since he's had to demand to be let out of the center's bus because everyone was *staring* at him. Months since he hasn't had to duck under archways to avoid *them*.

No way does he want to go back to an institution. Those other guys and women at the center, some may be on a slower boat, but anything is better than the lockup wards. That's the way De Leo sees it, but there are plenty of others so off the wall they have to be hospitalized. And some have been locked up for so long there can be no tomorrow with the earth people for them. They could barely exist outside of some type of institutional protection. A lifetime of bars and dependency has fixed them for good.

So how did De Leo and the others get here? To Salinas, to the board-and-care homes, the hotels, the decrepit rooming houses, the halfway houses, the long-term convalescent houses, the *city streets* . . . archways, subways, bus stations? How did so many mentally disordered become so *visible* in such a short time?

The word was *deinstitutionalization*, and it was based on the correct premise that most mentally impaired people don't have to be shipped to outposts and locked up, except as a cosmetic convenience to society.

Large, depersonalized institutions provide a remarkably ugly way to care for any except the temporarily psychotic or chronically traumatized. As humanitarian concerns gained widened popular appeal during the Kennedy and Johnson administrations, as "community development," "citizen participation," "civil rights," fired the imagination of a generation of social planners and activists, it was not strange that attention would soon be turned to the loony bins. How many people *were* there who had been committed for years or a lifetime without necessity? How many indigent old people were being dumped because there was no place else to go? Why wasn't the federal government doing anything about the shame of the back wards, the neglect, the cruelty, intimidation, inadequate funding?

In truth, the federal government had nothing to do with the state and county asylums and work farms and other vacuum cleaner institutions that swept the countryside clean of the brain-damaged, brain-diminished, neurologically impaired citizens. St. Elizabeth's in Washington, D.C., with its resident population running well over twenty thousand, was a clear exception. As part of the federal district it came under the scrutiny and funding of Uncle Sam.

Emptying the loony bins had its genesis in the work of the federal Joint Commission on Mental Health and Illness, and when the report was published in 1961, things began to happen. They found that institutions were keeping people who could be *mainstreamed*, or at least returned to communities where they might lead happier and more productive lives. But the grabber was that *federal funding* was being recommended for states and cities that were interested in organizing community centers where preventive or even stabilizing treatment could be offered. Only the real gone cases might have to stay in hospitals.

That gorgeous word *money*, part of the Great Society tickle, had mayors and governors stumbling over themselves to see what could be done in getting some of the action for themselves and maybe *cutting back taxes*, which never hurts a pol, or providing showcase facilities that could be used by *middle-class voters*. The political implications were tantalizing.

Everyone's for health, and even mental health doesn't sound too bad if you're not talking about the crazies. And even the conservative psychiatrists on the Commission thought this was the way to go, because there was a whole new untapped reservoir of patients *out there,* including children in the schools who needed therapy or maybe drugging for hyperactivity or inappropriate behavior or whatever. The definition of mental illness could now be broadened, and the psychiatrists were going to be in charge of getting reimbursement and doing diagnosis. And this was not *socialized medicine* or *national health care,* which would drive the AMA and the American Psychiatric Association bonkers, because who wants to have fees set and the bureaucrats looking down your vest? This was simply taking advantage of federal money for the care of people in the local community, and state matching money perhaps for people in the local community, and insurance plan money for people in the local community. Money for mental health professionals.

So the states set out to cut back on budgets for their hospitals . . . getting rid of ward after ward, sending the patients to licensed and unlicensed temporary homes or foster care homes or wherever someone was willing to take them for the subsidy they brought with them. And at the same time there was some additional federal money to build community mental health centers . . . not the upward of thirteen billion it was estimated would be needed to do the job right, but *some.* And there was money for research grants in mental health.

Lyndon Johnson, at the vortex of the whole business, playing both Daddy War and Daddy Bucks, was dealing out a goodly share of the categorical grant money to help ease the burdens of mental health professionals; at the same time, wasting whole villages in Nam. There was a certain madness to the period.

New York and California went slightly mad also, and couldn't wait to close out the state facilities. The big dump was on.

And then came the federal double cross. And the state double cross. Conservatives in the White House and Congress entered the scene and piously put the lid on categorical grants for sustaining mental health facilities. Shrewdly they knew they couldn't take back from the state and local pols what had already been promised them, so they sweetened the move by changing categorical grants to "revenue" sharing. Decentralization of government, it was called. But pork-barreling is what it was, as lump sums were laid on governors, mayors, and town managers *to do with as they wish.* Fat chance, when streets need paving and the police departments need more men and the firemen are threatening to strike and people want tax relief, that more than a token, if that, of *these funds* was going to go to mental health.

Conservative politicians like Ronald Reagan when he was California's governor saw budget cuts in social services as a divine right of the moneyed, and cut he did. The state facilities were emptied as fast as hail melts in Alabama. California, which housed more than thirty thousand *chronically hospitalized* in 1960, now is down to around five thousand, give or take the number passing in and out of the back rooms of the jail facilities.

To add another element of madness, the mental health professionals became embroiled in internecine struggles. Who would be responsible for doling out pills and drugs? Who would sign the reports? Who was qualified to be director of a community center? How much psychoanalysis should there be? Who is a licensed practitioner? How do we staff the centers? Who's on call nights and weekends? What about preventative diagnosis and treatment?

It is predictable that the very people whom the humanistic dreamers determined to help when community mental health first became a reality, the chronically ill and impaired aged, are still left with the dregs of a back ward existence. It has been too tempting for everyone, including the psychiatrists, to serve the more attractive upwardly mobile person. And it is also tempting for the pols to ignore the chronics. For the chronics have no effective advocate, and they don't *contribute.* The conservative pols would even take away their pitiful supplementary federal allowance if they had a chance. The snakepit mentality flourishing.

The psychiatrists have gathered to discuss the accusation that jails have become the new back wards. They are sensitive to this criticism. Now, it was one thing to try to clean out the state institutions and get the patients into a community setting, but here comes the big problem of the 1980s: security from the mentally ill. Where do we go from here?

It's not true, says one psychiatrist, the facts don't bear out the accusation. Jails are still, well, *jails* where people who break the law are placed, and we simply don't see all these so-called mentally ill patients the media keeps talking about.

The media again. Troublemakers. Stir things up. Reporters like this Michael Harris who mucks around and finds that three men, obviously sick and wandering the streets of San Francisco . . . but not sick enough to cram into the city's already overstuffed mental wards . . . have committed crimes and are now in jail. One tried to rob a bank, one is acccused of smashing car windows and terrifying the occupants, one is hauled in for assault.

We don't find jails used as makeshift hospitals, says another psychiatrist. Our studies show that.

But Harris, like a bulldog, has a grip on mental-patient dumping and won't be stilled. He writes then that the San Francisco director of jail psychiatric services tells him the number of mentally ill prisoners accused of serious crimes has grown 70 percent in 1980, and on any given day one prisoner in twelve is classified as *mentally ill*. And the hospitals can't take them because they're full up, and Napa State Hospital is so crowded you have to wait for someone to go out in a box or be discharged before you can open up a bed, and people who need help are being turned away and sent back to the streets, where they become ripe for getting into criminal activity.

But what is happening in San Francisco is happening in counties all over the state. It's happening on other city streets. It's happening in New York.

The mayor of New York, exhausted by battles with the governor and the state legislature and the idiots in Washington who would like Manhattan and the boroughs to sink like a lead apple into the East River, is yelling about this too. Since the safety and general happiness of tourists and taxpaying, *voting* normals is his primary concern, he wants the chronically or recovering mentally sick off the streets. They create a climate of fear, he says. And besides that, in 1980 New York City had to ante up $47 million just to take care of new Medicaid payments! Money the State of New York would have paid before deinstitutionalization.

They know very well what they're doing up in Albany. They're doing a form of budget cutting, *just as California* did, and they're following mandates that say *deinstitutionalize.* More than that, they're saying let's put the problem back to those grass-roots communities where it belongs. *The least government is the best government.* When it comes to funding for the halt and the ill and the aged, naturally.

The big double cross is beginning to be felt, and felt strongly. No matter what the psychiatrists say in defending their role as advocates of the mentally ill, they're no match for the jugglers who said *build community mental health centers,* and then welshed on categorical grants, who said *we'll save millions by closing down the state hospitals* and then did not pass that "saved" money to the communities, who said *mental patients can do better in a community setting* and then provided scant funds to make recovery or stabilization possible.

In San Francisco the mentally ill who frequently are picked up on weekends or after office hours are taken to the Hall of Justice and put into stripped-down cells on the seventh floor, if distraught enough. And, if distraught enough, left naked so they can't hurt themselves, and left without medication (because it's illegal to administer even a mild sedative without prisoner consent).

The Health Department knows they shouldn't be there, they know it's illegal, but . . . *there's no other place to put them!* And what happens in San Francisco is duplicated in many other counties. Jails, of course, do not turn people away, and when the cells get too crowded, everybody makes do. The mentally ill end up on the floor, in the corners, out in the hallways, corralled by a system that was supposed to liberate them!

The psychiatrists are baffled. It wasn't supposed to work this way. What happened?

A case of too much theory, too little practice. Psychiatrists don't usually hang out in jails or use subways or frequent bus terminals, they are less apt to be in those areas where indigent mentally ill shuffle through their days. You won't find the psychiatrists in tenements, fleabag hotels, the 1980s edition of skid row. They don't *know* the fear and the degradation of marginal life, they didn't foresee the misery of survival. The community mental health center is supposed to be the salvation for the deinstitutionalized mentally ill, but in many places it has become the excuse for budget cutting, and it has been victimized by political aspirations.

But it's a fine idea, the psychiatrists say. The dream is too good to lose.

Sure, if you get enough money and support, if people are *really* convinced.

Look at Monterey, the psychiatrists say, now, there's a program that's working. . . .

You wonder, who could get sick living on California's Monterey peninsula? Who could get depressed or feel murderous or be agitated or have delusions? Can there be any place in the world more tranquil, more benign, more *moneyed?*

Well, society doesn't create all our mental and physical ills, and the people of the Monterey peninsula also suffer. But let's face it, they suffer in nicer circumstances.

And the Community Hospital, the *center* for physical and mental health, is one of the nicer circumstances.

It's about the best that money can buy.

By 1971 inpatient psychiatric services were started in a special wing with twenty beds. Monterey residents no longer had to trek to Salinas or Agnews or the state hospital for psychiatric treatment. And a staffing grant from the Alcohol, Drug Abuse and Mental Health Administration meant that in 1972 twenty-four-hour crisis intervention, day treatment, outpatient, consultation, and education programs became available to everyone, regardless of ability to pay.

The Garden Pavilion was the name given to the mental health center, and it is appropriate. Fit for a king or maharaja. Seventeen gardeners tend the beds that ring the building, precious gems of fire and color. In the mental health center itself a five-foot Snoopy dog lolls in an oversize chair, making it seem that mental problems can almost be . . . fun! Indoor palms and pots overflowing with daisies. Occupational therapy rooms, group and individual counseling rooms, bright light everywhere. Pacific sunshine duplicated in planned lighting control. And soft chairs, lush pillows, stereo and billiards; game tables and arts and crafts and twenty rooms where guests can stay and be treated. And each room with its own balcony.

There are no locked units.

And for a patient to get admitted the psychiatrist on the hospital staff must say aye or nay. It is a psychiatrist's dream hospital, where humane treatment can flourish, where the really desperately ill can be sent elsewhere. Because on the Monterey peninsula no one who needs to be chronically hospitalized for mental illness stays there.

Monterey is, in essence, the culmination of the mental health dream. Not one of your store-front centers with trash swirling against the doorway, where the bag ladies come in for an injection of some long-acting tranquilizer, where confused elderly are steered to be processed into hotel or rooming house, where the closest contact the psychiatrists have with patients is signing a sheaf of forms already prepared by a staff social worker. Monterey is living proof that some communities can make community mental health programs work . . . even without federal money, even with state cutbacks on other money sources. And when detractors of community mental health centers say they won't work, that it was better when the state institutions were *full*, just have them look at Monterey. All it takes is money.

Big money . . . from the community . . . from private insurance . . . from Medi-Cal and Medicare. And volunteers to man the gift shops and serve up soft drinks around the tropical fish indoor pool, and to transport the elderly to occupational or group therapy. And it takes coordination within the community, with alcohol and drug counseling services, with halfway houses, with juvenile services. It takes staffing of neighborhood clinics . . . it takes money!

There is no substitute for community care of the unnerved sick person, says a psychiatrist who has lived with and worked in institutional settings all his life. This psychiatrist is also an anthropologist, a student of divergent customs and mores. He knows that mental stress exists in every milieu, from the most primitive to the most convoluted. Age is no exception, either.

People heal when they are among supportive family, friends, and professionals. On no account do children belong in state institutions. Nor do adolescents. They belong in manageable settings within the community, if not altogether at home. When are we going to learn this, he asks?

The moral treatment of patients started in the mid-1860s. *Moral treatment?* The idea of being basically *kind.* Pious people would visit the asylums and pray with the inmates. And many people got better.

Faith and Christian goodness were vaulted in importance . . . though we now know that major psychosis is in and of itself often inherently limiting. It is self-remitting, and many suffering with major psychosis become spontaneously improved within six months to two years. Only about 15 percent never make it, they become the chronics who require ongoing and sometimes regular medication.

Of course, back in the 1860s the praying probably did help; it soothed, and it gave the message that someone *cares.*

Now in most societies healers try to mobilize family and community support systems for their patients. In many nonwestern societies the ceremonies may go on for days. The family gathers around, the shaman or witch doctor or voodoo priest performs the ritual, and the patient sees *helping* hands. At some level he knows, he *knows* that money has been put up *on his behalf* to hire the shaman or witch doctor or voodoo priest. Time is being donated by family and friend and neighbors, *on his behalf* . . . they are concentrating on *him.* People *care.*

And that is the essence of the way community mental health systems should work, says the psychiatrist. The ideal centers are geared to give immediate treatment, are set up for crisis intervention. And people who are well enough to function with the support of medication and psychotherapy are ideal for community mental health centers. They were created with the idea of giving caring help. Without caring, there is only that jailhouse mentality that treats those who are different as troublemakers and puts them in the nearest available institution—and today that's probably the local prison.

Back in Salinas, Joe De Leo goes out the kitchen door and stretches his arms. The serape whose warp is tension and whose woof is anxiety lifts by the strength of angel wings. He yells to one of the group members to throw him the softball. It goes over his head but he laughs as he fetches it from the clump of bird-of-paradise. I missed, he admits freely. The man who threw the ball smiles. My aim is no good.

Neither man would be here if it were not for the ameliorating effect of specific drugs. Yet neither is on the doses thrust at them in the state hospital. And neither would be here if those drugs, since 1955, hadn't been made available *even to those who couldn't afford them.* And neither would be here if there weren't some backup funds like medical insurance or state insurance or local budgets to rent this house that is now a learning skills center. And neither would be here if low-paid mental health paraprofessionals weren't here to help them. And neither would be here if the community had raised hell about having mental health care right in its midst.

The word is out. The *psychiatrist* in charge of the mental health community center is coming over for a visit. The air is charged. This is the big man coming. This man represents power, and even the lowliest mentally dysfunctional recognize this. After all the trips in and out of institutions there is only one Big Daddy in the whole system . . . the *psychiatrist.* He decides who's sick or well, how much and what kind of medications, who's chronic, who's acute, who's educable, who's safe, able to be viable within the community. That kind of person deserves respect. That kind of person makes the walls reverberate.

The psychiatrist in this case is not a fearsome person. He knows what institutions are like, having worked with them for years, and he's all for the system that believes in getting people on their feet and back to the land of the living. He also knows how institutions suck the lifeblood out of a patient, make him vulnerable, self-doubt-ing, dependent. Enough time in an institution and you become a basket case.

Yet to the people of the learning skills center he is still THE MAN. And the agitation in anticipation of his visit is palpable.

Joe De Leo is calmer than most. He's going to play softball no matter what. Tomorrow he goes to job training. The next day he will have a half-hour session with a psychiatrist whom he sees every other month. The shrink will look over the reports on De Leo and smile and say, well, this is okay. Keep up the good work. And De Leo will feel good about it. He knows he would have to be pretty bad to be *sent back*. The grapevine tells him there aren't even beds enough for the acute psychotics at this point, and they would be in no hurry to reprocess De Leo.

One of the women on clean-up detail in the kitchen has been sweeping the floor slowly and randomly for half an hour. She sweeps a little dust and some crumbs against the doorjamb, and a few flakes fly onto the sidewalk. Most of the crumbs stay lodged against the jamb.

The psychiatrist drives an old gas-economy-size car. He has a dozen places to visit, meetings to attend, some media people to meet. He can only spare a wave for the people at the learning skills center, but he knows them by face and name. Community acceptance, funding, and support are high on the list of his priorities. And with it all there's a private practice to keep up. The mixed bag of his role as administrator and doctor are traditional, but they seem incongruous today. He is playing out the game whose rules say you have to be a psychiatrist to be in charge of mental health functions in the community. So be it. He does his job with the best of them.

It's back to the streets where John Steinbeck drove, where Steinbeck walked into the meager town under that unrelenting Salinas sun, where the stores were so poorly stocked that Steinbeck couldn't find proper pencils or appropriate writing tablets and had to rely instead on his editor for supply.

The psychiatrist is a man of Steinbeck compassions. He knows it isn't good for the thousands of people who still can't make it to sit dummylike in front of television sets in the boardinghouses that are now the drop-off spots for thousands of former inmates. But nevertheless there's always that opportunity to get up and go out the door and go downtown for a beer or pick up a date. No locks. There is nothing that can beat that. *No locks. No steel doors. No barred windows.*

But he lacks Steinbeck's fury and so is not stirred to anger at a mental health system that in most places closes up nights and weekends, a system where you can't find a psychiatrist in those off-hours to take a sick person out of jail and medicate him or find a hospital bed for him, a system where city streets and archways are a substitute for occupational and physical therapy, a system where psychiatrists can't be bothered with these "crazies" any more than they could when they were locked up in the asylums. And to keep the system working and effective inject long-lasting tranquilizers to keep the "crazies" manageable and at arm's length.

And he has no fury at a system that says let psychiatry be in charge when in fact most psychiatrists wouldn't be caught dead working this beat, and most of those who do only like the room at the top.

Joe De Leo, his serape floating on wings over his head, is organizing the equipment for the game. The bus is waiting to take them. Mitts in the box, count the bats. There's going to be rain, someone shouts, and the first spray comes with the steel cloud that blurs the sun. Play ball anyway. And Joe De Leo thinks ahead enough to get a rag from the kitchen for wiping mud from the ball. He is first on the bus.

About Community Mental Health

The hundreds of thousands of former institutionalized mental patients who now mingle with the rest of us present a fiscal and social problem of untold dimension. New York City, undoubtedly the hardest hit in the nation, received an influx of 40,000 mental patients when New York State reduced its psychiatric hospital population from 84,000 in 1963 to the current level of 23,000. The difficulties for New York City as it tries to provide adequately for these ex-inmates are almost insurmountable.

The city pleads for the state to increase support, to take over the burden of Medicaid (which is now funded 50 percent by the federal government, 25 percent by cities, and 25 percent by states). In New York the governor argues that the federal government should take over all Medicaid responsibility. Sadly, this does little to help beleaguered neighborhoods and the mentally ill.

Most housing for these released patients is at its best less than modest, at its worst a filthy disgrace. By 1980 half of the low-priced New York City hotels that patients used either had closed or had jacked up rates to the point where they were no longer affordable. The homeless wander the streets, report for medication, get fed and bedded in "shelters" once used for alcoholic derelicts. The clients, as they are called, are easy prey for assault and harassment. Those who are not able to get attention and lodging sometimes become violent themselves.

As new mental patients appear on the scene, or as drug and alcohol-precipitated disorders occur, the meager facilities are strained to the limit. There are not enough social workers, not enough doctors or psychologists, not enough counseling, not enough beds, not enough living skills centers to help ex-inmates to learn to help themselves or even work again, not enough job skill centers, not enough jobs. Not from any sector, private or public.

Joel Fort, M.D., a psychiatrist who was in the vanguard of providing community health care to the impoverished and mentally unstable young people of San Francisco's Haight-Ashbury district in the 1960s, comments that he has long fought the traditional psychiatric organization, which, he believes, finds reasons to exclude people from treatment. *And this includes the community mental health centers.* —The hours of service and regulations are designed to drastically limit the number of people served, you have a clinic that works with this problem and not that, with just this geographical area and not that, money wasted on memo production, accountability.

In New York City the only financial support the Human Resources Administration can expect from the state to help with services is limited *to those who have spent at least five consecutive years in a state institution and who had been discharged since 1974.* This, estimates a city spokesperson, accounts for less than 5 percent of all dischargees.

Thanks to long-acting psychotropic drugs, ex-inmates walk around for days and even weeks without checking in. Some stagger from side effects, some make facial grimaces or have erratic tics from side effects. Some are able to work at menial jobs when they can get them. Some can't find employment because of stigma. Some have no permanent place to live. Some never see a decent meal. Many get held up, ripped off, molested. Many spend their days in doorways and subways.

Under circumstances like these, are they any better off than before?

Thirteen

THE MOTHER LODE

The late-afternoon sun breaks through his window just as Dr.
Harry Tweedy's last patient has left the office. The sudden warmth
streaming across his shoulder infuses him with quick energy, and
he springs to his feet.

He stretches his sinewy body, ready for some isometrics against
the desk. But just as he begins, there is the buzz of the intercom.

He stares with some annoyance at the plastic bank of buttons
with the single blinking light. A hell of a time for *that*, he thinks,
but out of reflex he responds.

Yes?

It is his secretary. Dr. McKay is here.

Dr. McKay? He doesn't remember any Dr. McKay. . . .

Dr. *Alex* McKay, his secretary prods, from Blue Shield.

That Dr. McKay. Right, he says, and slowly slumps back in his
chair.

In a moment a rather lumpy middle-aged man walks into his
office with hand outstretched. I'm glad we could get together.

The voice and the man are not overly impressive. McKay's suit appears a bit rumpled, and he has obviously gone to fat. Probably happier being a bureaucrat than seeing patients, Tweedy decides.

He offers him the chair across the desk, noting that McKay has brought along a thick, zippered case.

I'm a bit intrigued by some of your work, McKay says.

Tweedy smiles. He's been through this with other doctors. A combination of hesitant curiosity and prurient wonder. I don't suppose you approve of my treating transsexuals.

McKay shrugs. I guess my question is . . . does it work?

Tweedy leans back. The transsexual technique? For some, I suppose. Those that have the determination and the patience.

Yes, of course. It's not easy for them, is it?

No, it's not easy. Tweedy clasps his hands behind his head and waits. He knows why McKay has come, and he wishes he'd get to it. C'mon, man, Tweedy thinks, I've got a cocktail party. . . .

Is there a usual psychotherapy period for your—ah—transsexual patients?

About a year, I figure. I see them once a month usually.

McKay's eyebrows shoot up. Only a dozen sessions?

It's just exploratory therapy, doctor. I'm not looking to change them or cure them. I don't care how anal retentive they are! Can they handle a sex change, that's what I want to know.

Yes, of course, McKay mumbles as he fishes in his case and withdraws a bundle of papers.

Tweedy wonders whether to pull out the file folder sitting in his desk drawer. He has read it through twice today, and somehow keeping it out of sight makes him feel more confident. Would it intimidate McKay if he were to put it in front of him on the desk? Probably not. McKay has been through review sessions like this many times, he's been around for years.

I have a copy of your Blue Shield contract here, McKay says, laying out the papers on the desk. He looks up with the trace of a smile. Usually we try to resolve these things by phone or letter. It's so much easier.

Tweedy nods but says nothing. They both know why McKay is there. The matter *couldn't* be resolved by phone or letter.

McKay thumbs through a few pages. The patient is . . . Hershorn, Virgil Hershorn?

Right . . . age twenty-eight, white male, scenic designer, unmar-
ried, highly intelligent . . .

McKay pauses to read one of his documents. Yes . . . well . . . as
I mentioned over the phone, Mr. Hershorn has filed a claim for
reimbursement for his psychotherapy with you . . .

I suggested he do so, Tweedy says.

McKay nods, keeping his eyes on the document. Yes, he refers
to that.

It's not the usual kind of therapy, you know, the exploratory
kind. It's a hell of a lot more complicated than that.

Doctor . . . McKay says quietly, is Mr. Hershorn preparing for
transsexual surgery?

Eventually, I suppose. But right now . . .

Would he be seeing you if he weren't looking for a sex change?

Sure. The guy *needs* a psychiatrist. Tweedy notices that the
lumpiness in McKay's face has somehow firmed up, that his eyes
have taken on a sharpness. . . . The guy's got problems, he adds.

Look, Doctor, problems aren't enough to pay insurance claims.
What we want to know is . . . are you providing psychotherapy for
a recognized mental disorder? Now, our contract with you and
with the public specifically excludes any reimbursement for cosmetic surgery . . . and we also have serious doubts about psychotherapy in connection with it. So . . . I guess you've got the burden
of proof.

I told you this was a different case.

But *how* different, doctor? *Why* different?

Tweedy feels a moment of anger and grasps the arms of his chair
to let it diffuse. It is not the first time he has had a controversy with
one of the health insurance plans, and he knows deep down that he
is really powerless . . . *tell me,* doctor . . . *prove it,* doctor . . . *show
me,* doctor . . . *they* hold the money, *they* decide . . . He tries to
keep his voice reasonable. . . . As I noted there on the claim form,
the patient has what I call *acute stress reaction of adult life* . . . in
other words he is having one hell of a time adjusting to the fact that
he wants to be a transsexual. . . .

It began in the late 1930s, the idea that doctors could be guaranteed payment for their services, that patients could be guaranteed

payment for their medical bills. It meant protection . . . and it meant the stirrings of a potentially huge new industry. *The health care insurance business.*

First out of the gate were the Blue Cross–Blue Shield Plans, the original "doctor's" plans. Somehow, "policies," "insurance policies," seemed a bit tacky for health care matters, reminders of hard-faced men squeezing quarters and dollars for weekly life insurance premiums from frightened, money-starved citizens during the Depression. Blue Cross was to guarantee hospital bills, Blue Shield was to guarantee doctors' bills.

So the Plans were adopted state by state, devised and supported by the medical establishment. There were limited psychiatric benefits too, though in the beginning no one really could imagine the explosion in psychotherapy that's around today. But if you were admitted to a state hospital or to a medically approved private hospital, medical insurance would cover most of what it cost. The doctors who attended you? Their fees would be covered, as well. And as for treatment, well, remember, this was in the flowering of ECT . . . so you could have fleeting reassurances that even though your body was about to be punished with volts and volts of electricity, *you* didn't have to pay for it. At least.

The Blue Cross–Blue Shield Plans operated as nonprofit corporations and followed the laws of the states where they operated. Rarely did an individual Plan cross state lines, and each operated independently of the others, though the Plans did have a loose sort of federation with an umbrella organization. They grew steadily, both in size and complexity, until now there are more than seventy Plans across the country. Each one provides for psychiatric benefits in one way or another, depending on what state law allows. You don't have to be committable any longer; there are "intermediate" grades of mental disorders that allow you to live at home and go about your business. Treatment for these intermediate-to-mild problems is also paid for.

Following close on the heels of the Blue Cross–Blue Shield Plans were the profit-oriented insurance companies. Let's *sell* health insurance and make some money at it . . . but they knew the tedious task of trying to market a new product on a person-by-person basis. It would take years before there would be any real black ink on the bottom line if they tried to sell consumers individually. But what if . . . they put together a *group* plan and sold it to . . . corporations. With one sale they could sign up thousands of people, reap millions of dollars in premiums, and compete with Blue Cross–Blue Shield.

It worked. And, of course, Blue Cross–Blue Shield saw the opportunities and moved too. Group health insurance spread from business to business, and psychiatric benefits tagged along. . . .

- *Care in outpatient psychiatric facility and services of a psychiatrist: First 5 visits . . .*
- *Care in approved outpatient psychiatric facility and for services of psychiatrist $1,000 per year . . .*
- *Maximum benefit . . . $30,000 during lifetime; exception in-hospital psychiatric care . . .*

Every major company or union has a program, millions of workers are covered. In 1968, for example, the United Auto Workers offered a prepaid mental health benefits program to its members, a program prepared with the advice and assistance of American psychiatry.

But the giant step was really taken in 1965: Medicare. Suddenly millions of people became eligible for government-supported health insurance, people who would not have qualified under any other health insurance plan. The elderly mostly, and the disabled.

And psychiatry was right there, looking to be covered along with surgery, internal medicine, radiology, urology. . . . The Medicare Plan would follow the older Blue Cross–Blue Shield Plans; if you had to be put in a state hospital or needed special care and treatment, your psychiatric needs would probably be covered. But long-term psychotherapy . . . ? A sticky item. Is it provable? Is it *medical?*

Medicare started as a three-and-a-half-billion-dollar plan, but things have changed. It's over forty billion dollars now and still growing. Psychiatric benefits, like most other medical benefits, have expanded. Inpatient psychotherapy is now part of the action as long as it is "efficacious to a person's treatment."

There are limits, however. Medicare will pay only $250 per year for outpatient psychiatric care—short-term psychotherapy. That's a minimal number of sessions.

Still, with the various insurance plans, psychiatry has things pretty much its own way when mind-game problems develop. The medical model pervades . . . sickness, healing, illness, therapy by a *doctor*.

—There must be *physician* description and there must be *physician* review, and then the *physician* must determine that the individual rendering the service is competent to render that service, says a state mental health commissioner when testifying before his state legislature. —In other words, you have to have a *physician* that reviews the treatment plan, says that it is appropriate for the particular needs of the individual, then he would periodically review that to determine whether or not the treatment is provided in accordance with his recommendations . . . [author's italics].

The medical model. In many states psychologists and social workers and any other nonmedical therapist can't qualify. Medicare agrees. Psychiatrists do the billing, they get the checks, they parcel out the proceeds. Except in one instance: psychologists who run diagnostic tests can send their bills directly to Medicare. No psychiatrist has to run interference. Otherwise, psychiatrists do the proposing and the disposing.

Often it's run a bit like a consumer sales office. The boss gets an override, a percentage, on the sales of his employees. The boss doesn't do any real selling, but because he is the boss, he's entitled. The boss in this case is the psychiatrist, and even though a psychologist or social worker might do most, or even all, of the treatment, the bills go out in the psychiatrist's name, signifying he has "guided" or otherwise overseen the treatment. The bills are in *psychiatric* hours and amounts, there is no mention of psychologists or social workers.

It frequently goes like this . . .

if the psychiatrist's usual and customary fee is $50 per hour . . .
if the psychologist's usual and customary fee is $40 per
hour . . .
if the social worker's usual and customary fee is $35 per
hour . . .

All hours are billed at $50 per hour, and when the check comes
in, the psychiatrist pays off the psychologist at $40 per hour and
the social worker at $35 per hour. He can put the balance in his
pocket.

—When a claim comes in over the signature of a psychiatrist,
we have no way of knowing if he has farmed out the work to
others, says an executive of a large, profit-oriented insurance car-
rier. —And we don't bother to check!

—We only pay to *psychiatrists* under Medicare, says the Social
Security Administration.

—I recall a bill from a psychiatrist who tried to bill *honestly*,
says a Blue Cross–Blue Shield executive, —and he broke it down
for psychologists and social workers. "What are you doing, doctor?" we asked. "These are people who work for me," he said.
"You can't *do* that. You've got to charge the same for them as for
yourself," we said. "Then if you want to make an adjustment to
your patients by whatever dollar amount, you can do that inter-
nally." It fouls up our statistical data, you see.

Then he gets an override? He can keep the excess?

—If he chooses to do so, that's not our problem.

The Mother Lode.

It is springtime in Washington, and the second session of the
Ninety-fifth Congress is well into its legislative calendar. In a hear
ing room on the House side, the Subcommittee on Oversight and
Investigations of the Interstate and Foreign Commerce Committee
is taking testimony. Seated facing the committee members at a
table is Katherine C. Meyers, the committee's special assistant. She
is testifying about the Blue Shield Plan for the District of Columbia. . . .

Congressman Albert Gore, Jr., of Tennessee holds up an object for the witness to see. —Will a Blue Shield card like this one entitle somebody who pays into Blue Shield each month an opportunity to have a voice in the policies of Blue Shield in the District of Columbia?

—No, she says, —it will not. The only people who have a vote at meetings are the participating physicians.

—So the physicians totally control the policy?

—Yes.

—Let me get this straight. The people who pay into Blue Shield each month and who are paying for the service have no voice. If the management determines that they are paying too much for a particular medical procedure and recommends that Blue Shield, on their behalf, pay a lower amount, then all the participating doctors are notified of this "heresy." A majority of the participating doctors have to vote to permit Blue Shield to reimburse at a lower level. Is that correct?

—That is correct.

Now have we ever heard of physicians *lowering* their fees? Have we ever heard of physicians who tried to keep their fees within the amounts paid by the insurance carriers? Are physicians likely to vote against their own vested financial interest?

At latest count there are more than thirty psychiatrists per one hundred thousand population in the District of Columbia. There are fewer than ten psychiatrists per one hundred thousand in the rest of the country.

Select the best interpretation:

   (a) There are more mental disorders in Washington
   (b) Psychiatrists like to stick together
   (c) Psychiatrists prefer hot, humid summers
   (d) Anything west of the Potomac is not Vienna
   (e) Medical reimbursement plans are better in Washington

Doctor, it bothers me that medical people seem to control the policies of Blue Shield. Is that fair to those who pay the premiums? Doctors started Blue Shield. It is the doctors' plan.

Yet subscribers *pay* for it.

We recognize that. Each Blue Shield board of directors has seats for public members, for people who represent nonmedical interests.

Doctor, how many of those boards of directors have a *majority* of seats for public members?

(shrugs)

Let me tell *you*, Doctor . . . less than one in three Blue Shield Plans across the country has a majority of public members on their boards. Between forty and fifty Blue Shield Plans, with tens of millions of subscribers, have medical people in the majority on the board.

Is that a real problem?

To some people. There are those who believe that any doctor who sits on a Blue Shield board has an inherent conflict of interest.

Ridiculous.

If your medical practice relies on fee reimbursement from Blue Shield, and you also sit on the Blue Shield board, don't you have pretty good protection? You aren't going to hurt your own interest in any way, are you?

No one thinks of our own situation when we sit on the board.

Can you really be sure of that?

(no response)

The congressional subcommittee found it was not uncommon for some doctors to receive hundreds of thousands of dollars *each year* from Blue Shield, while these same doctors sat on Blue Shield boards of directors.

There are lots of other people on these boards besides doctors, you know.

Sure, but there is doctor domination. Or doctor and hospital representative domination.

You make it sound like a conspiracy.

Try the phrase *conflict of interest.* And this is not to say that you would do anything deliberately wrong. But power is a tricky ingredient.

You suggest our control be eliminated?

That would seem fair.

(no response)

*   *   *

Dr. Harry Tweedy pushes himself away from his desk and stands, sneaking a glance at his Patek Philippe. Damn. If they didn't finish in the next ten minutes he'd have trouble making that party.

Across from him Alex McKay is busy reading what looks like a letter. Tweedy realizes it is one he has written.

Acute stress reaction . . . yes, you mention that, McKay says, looking up. I'm afraid I'm going to have to ask you for some additional information. Let me begin again. We have your diagnosis of Mr. Hershorn, and we need more information. He is seeking transsexual surgery, is he not?

Yes, of course.

Then we have a problem with this claim.

Tweedy points to the letter. The man suffers from acute stress reaction of adult life, just as I wrote it, he says. He's an excellent candidate for surgery and he knows it. But he's having trouble adjusting, is nervous as hell, jittery. The prospect of getting cut and sewn, losing parts of his body even though he claims he wants to, is traumatic.

He doesn't sound like someone I'd recommend for transsexual surgery.

I think he is. But he needs help. We're just going to have to wait and see.

McKay consults the file. I note you saw him four times a week for a little while, then three times a week. Isn't that a bit often for what you're trying to do?

Tweedy realizes suddenly that he is not going to make the party. This bureaucratic idiot is just going to drag everything out. He slams his palms on the desk. Look, how do *you* know what this man needs? Who the hell are you to question me?

McKay's eyes grow sharp for an instant, but he says nothing, letting his fingers play with the corners of the papers.

You're no psychiatrist, that's for sure, Tweedy continues. You'd know what I'm doing is right if you were a psychiatrist.

I'm an internist. But I've talked over this matter with our peer review committee. They are psychiatrists and thought I should come and talk with you. And I've checked through the records.

This isn't the first time your work has been subjected to peer review, is it?

Tweedy shakes his head. Getting angry was stupid.

I want information, that's all, McKay says in a measured voice. Acute stress reaction to adult life should be resolvable inside three months. How long have you been seeing Mr. Hershorn?

Whatever it says in the file.

McKay pushes it toward him. Read it.

Tweedy looks up. He knows the answer. Six months.

And acute stress reaction doesn't require therapy four times a week, three times a week for months and months. McKay's eyes are piercing now.

There didn't seem to be anything else in the diagnostic manual to cover it. I mean DSM III.

And we don't pay unless you find a diagnosis in DSM III, right?

Their eyes lock.

Look, you haven't talked to my patient, Tweedy says. You really don't have the slightest idea of what is going on except what I've written. I also must protect him. Do you think you have the knowledge to second-guess me?

All of us are subject to peer review, McKay says. Perhaps if you could give us more information. If you could let me have the rest of the file.

Tweedy lays his hand on the folder. You know I can't do that.

McKay shrugs. Then we can't really know if you're seeing him as often as you say, or for how long. It will be hard to justify reimbursement.

It is my word and my professional judgment, says Tweedy.

It's *our* money, McKay reminds him softly. On the basis of this, I'm afraid . . . he shrugs. You know how it is.

Psychotherapy and peer review. They are becoming tied to one another as medical insurance coverage broadens. All the medical insurance plans have some provision for peer review, a system where diagnosis and treatment are *reviewed* periodically by medical experts in the same field as the physician looking for insurance reimbursement.

But reviewing psychotherapy just isn't as simple as reviewing an appendectomy. There aren't that many ways to carve out an appendix, the procedures are generally straightforward, and the physician knows what he is looking for. It's three-dimensional medicine.

Not so with mental disorders. Who can tell the color of a depression? How do you operate on an anxiety? Can your fingers touch paranoia? The usual physical dimensions just don't apply. Nor do they apply to psychotherapy, the well-followed mode of treatment. The surgeon will use a scalpel, the psychiatrist . . . ? If analysis and suggestion are the psychiatrists' scalpel, they lack the exactness, the finality of cold, hard steel. In fact, whatever the surgeon's implements, the psychiatrist falls back on medication and analysis . . . intellectualism. *They* are his tools.

In 1979, however, Blue Shield of California decided to set up standards for psychotherapy, the first state to do this. The key phrase was "medically necessary," the treatment had to be *medically necessary*. This, of course, tightened things up a bit, since it was the medical model they were embracing, and some of the behavior-oriented therapies were thus excluded.

They also decided that all cases of psychoanalysis had to have peer review. The need for psychoanalysis and its results can be evaluated, they said; there were, and are, criteria.

Too bad they didn't have these criteria for psychoanalysis a few years earlier. It might have saved the subscribers and the taxpayers hundreds of thousands of dollars. . . .

It was the habit of some psychiatrists who wanted to become psychoanalysts to attach themselves to the staff of a Veterans Administration hospital and become federal employees.

Then they would appear for psychoanalysis . . . knowing that they had to have this exposure if they wanted to become psychoanalysts. Four to five times a week for several years, thousands and thousands of dollars paid out, all the time as federal employees, the bills going to federal Blue Shield . . . their personal analysis at government expense, their training under their own special benefit program.

The bills would come in, and no one caught it . . . this wasn't because the VA psychiatrists had deep problems and *needed* psychoanalysis to function . . . this was to get training so they could become psychoanalysts.

And other people paid the bill.

—You can assume, says a Blue Shield executive, —that many psychoanalysts practicing today who have been attached to Veterans Administration hospitals have probably had their psychoanalysis training paid this way.

Mother Lodes.

Q.— What's the standard limit for outpatient psychotherapy under most private medical insurance policies?

A.— Five hundred dollars.

Q.— Will that cover most problems?

A.— No one really knows.

Q.— Who decides the limit, then?

A.— The company votes in what the insurance cost will bear. The main lobbyists for increasing are the APA and the National Association for Mental Health.

Q.— The limit is not scientifically based?

A.— What a question!

Alex McKay is not really surprised at Tweedy's answer. He has found a pattern in some of these cases . . . the more difficult the doctor is about accepting peer review, the more recalcitrant he is about divulging any file information so a competent review can proceed.

McKay holds up a letter. Here's the first response we got from you. He reads. . . . I code all my patients, and enclose the patient's number. I have been treating him for stress reaction of adult life, and under DSM III he is eligible under your program. This claim should be paid.

Tweedy shrugs. That's my standard response.

You provide us with no diagnosis, no symptomatology, no treatment program. We can't continue payments indefinitely on a claim like that.

Tweedy draws the folder closer. I have given you more information. More than enough, really.

You have now provided us with the patient's name and that he is being treated for stress relating to transsexual surgery.

Dr. McKay, Tweedy says, annoyed now, I have a responsibility to my patients. I cannot broadcast information about them to anyone.

McKay looks at him for a long moment. In the first place we are not just "anyone," he says. We know what it's like to protect a patient's privacy. We on the peer review committee took the same oath as you, we're all doctors. You aren't going to claim some extra consideration just because you happen to deal in psychiatry. That's been tried before.

Tweedy pushes himself to his feet, and turns away to hide his fury. For an instant he is on the verge of ordering McKay from his office. But bucks rest on the amicable outcome of this session.

McKay's face has returned to its lumpy repose. Tweedy's reaction is not untypical for a psychiatrist. McKay knows from experience that when he asks for accountability, psychiatrists will fuss because they aren't used to doing it.

I don't want my patient to suffer, Tweedy says.

McKay says, He won't.

Tweedy looks at McKay. What do you want to know?

Original diagnosis, proposed treatment, duration of treatment . . .

I can't let you have the file, but perhaps I can give you symptomatology, history, how I have been treating him for stress connected with changing his sex.

McKay smiles. Proof is all he's looking for.

Tweedy knows that whatever McKay decides, his medical insurance reimbursement will probably continue.

A psychiatrist in testimony on behalf of the American Psychiatric Association before the House Ways and Means Committee said, a few years back, —Successful psychotherapy requires the absolute guarantee of patient/therapist communications. Confidentiality is a sacred fiduciary relationship and it must be protected. Anything that interferes with the confidentiality of communications adversely affects the ability to treat a patient.

"Absolute" . . . "sacred" . . . words that don't leave much room for compromise. But what if medical reimbursement were on the line? The squeeze is on and these doctors don't like being questioned. Third-party payments are good, but accountability is a bother.

About Insurance Reimbursement

Even by conservative estimates more than 30 million Americans need treatment for mental illness each year, and there are in excess of 180 million Americans covered by some form of health insurance. Many insurance plans have mental health benefits too, and the result is that hundreds of millions of dollars per year are paid out to psychiatrists and other mental health professionals. Psychiatrists have a huge stake in the way the various insurance plans are administered, and each time their share of the mental health insurance pie is thinned, they stand to lose millions.

So they can't be expected to endure such losses like stoics. Most recently the federal Blue Cross–Blue Shield Plans in Washington, D.C., decided to up the copayment share for outpatient mental health benefits by 50 percent, meaning that the patient will have to pay 50 percent more of the psychiatrist's bill. It also means the psychiatrist can't rely on the insurance plans for as much reimbursement and must look to the patient for a greater amount of the fee. The Washington Psychiatric Society called the change . . . *ominous . . . totally unacceptable . . . prejudicial* . . . especially since mental health was the only area singled out for a change in the copayment provision. Other medical specialties weren't affected and continue to operate on the old copayment schedule. But the psychiatrists see this latest change in copayment as a trend and are so disturbed that they have organized an ad hoc committee to examine the changes and are planning a public relations campaign to emphasize why there should be full psychiatric coverage.

A major vexing problem with the Blue Shield Plans remains the fact of doctor control, and this is bound to change, though psychiatrists should not bear an undue amount of the blame. They are, after all, only one among many medical specialties who might sit on the board. However, the Federal Trade Commission will not sit idly by and let those who benefit most from the Plans also control how they are administered. In fact, the Commission has just concluded that in those geographic areas where doctors control the Blue Shield Plans, doctors' fees are *substantially* higher. Changes are coming.

Long-range sights continue to be focused on national health insurance, though prospects for its passage in the near future appear slim. But preparations continue to be made. One of the most controversial aspects is deciding which mental health professionals and which psychotherapies will receive insurance reimbursement. The key word has come to be *efficacy*, which means, in order to be reimbursed the therapies have to be efficacious, to be helpful. Congress is currently wrestling with how one measures the helpfulness of particular therapies, and psychiatrists are urging that scientific research principles be used. Psychologists, however, are claiming that this is an application of the medical model and take issue with this approach. At present a commission composed of psychiatrists, psychologists, social workers, and psychiatric nurses has been established by Congress to evaluate the therapies, using the most acceptable clinical and scientific information available.

In geographic terms the nearest national health insurance program to the United States is in the province of Quebec, Canada. The program has been in existence for about ten years. At a recent APA symposium, the Quebec experience showed that every psychiatrist could expect a full practice, even turning away dozens of patients each week. The individual fees would be lower, but more people would be reached, and the volume of the practice would more than offset the lower fees. Most Quebec psychiatrists seemed pleased with national health insurance, and the message they delivered to their American counterparts was simply this . . . it works!

Fourteen

JOKERS AND WILD CARDS

You know things are going to be a bit tight when you try to walk through the doors of the San Francisco Civic Center without a lapel badge and a security guard blocks your way.

—Sorry, he says, meaning, *watch it!*

—I'm supposed to get my press badge in the press room, you say and wave credentials.

He shakes his head. Immovable, watchful. Other guards stand as a phalanx across the inside front of the huge building, small walkie-talkies in their hands, obviously in contact with unseen reinforcements. It is a disconcerting greeting to the 133rd Annual Meeting of the American Psychiatric Association. Behind the security guards you see a large lobby area speckled with message tables, message boards, and announcements. Some early arrivals are strolling about, reading the paraphernalia that is designed to make their week in San Francisco memorable.

You put the question to the security guard. —Just how *am I* to get to the press room, then?

His distant eyes seem to swallow you up. He points across the street. —Why don't you try the registration office over there, in Brooks Hall?

You look, but all you see is polished mall walkways, benches, flower beds. Brooks Hall? The security guard smiles briefly and nods toward a metal railing that looks like a subway entrance. —There, he says, —that's the way to Brooks Hall.

As you walk underground you can't help but think this is a strange way to enter a convention.

A nonprofessional-looking crowd gathers in front of the Civic Center later that first Monday morning. They are loud, they are feisty, and they have a message.

Most are under forty years of age, the men shaggy-haired, bearded, the women in jeans or long, full skirts and peasant blouses or tee shirts. They are picketing on the sidewalk in a slow oval, waving balloons that urge . . . *Smash the Therapeutic State!* . . . and on their shirts, stenciled boldly . . . *Psychiatry Kills!*

The charter buses from the San Francisco hotels begin arriving at 8:00 A.M., depositing their cargo of visiting psychiatrists. No one has warned the psychiatrists that they will have a reception committee, and when they emerge into the sunlight, many of them raise eyebrows at the commotion. Then, peering straight ahead, they aim for the civic center doors. San Francisco police have the pickets under scrutiny, and the psychiatrists walk by unmolested. The security guards are quick to open the doors, giving a fast eye to the plastic-encased lapel badges.

The pickets claim to be former mental patients, and the harder you study them, the more you realize . . . *they look just like anyone else*! Their tongues aren't wagging idiotically, they don't have bizarre facial tics or wild eyes, they don't laugh uncontrollably or shout hysterically. They are acting peaceably . . . in control! Their signs read . . . *Stop Cruelty to Seniors in Nursing Homes . . . Tranquillity Is Hard to Swallow . . . Stop Forced Overdrugging in Nursing Homes . . . Stop the Torture of Children . . .*

Someone brings a bullhorn, and suddenly you're aware the press is covering this—and so is radio—and television crews have picked up footage for the evening news. The psychiatrists are still arriving on their buses, but their spouses, who accompany them, show more curiosity about what is going on outside the civic center than inside. The audience looks a bit self-conscious to be standing *there*, on the sidewalk, ogling people who, after all, claim to have been *hospitalized* mental patients.

By now the bullhorn is blaring with indictments, personal horror stories of psychiatric mistreatment, real experiences described by the people who have lived through them. The words, when they reach the third floor, are muffled, but the tone is clear. It's outrage and humiliation! . . . *One, two, three, four . . . we won't take your drugs no more . . . Smash the therapeutic state!* . . .

On the third floor of the civic center, in the press room, a public relations man confers with Shervert Frazier, M.D., Director of the American Psychiatric Association Joint Committee on Public Affairs.

Sherve Frazier looks worried. The people outside are not saying nice things about American psychiatry. The APA is going to have to do something. This disruption can't be ignored much longer.

—Talk to them, the public relations man advises.

—But what will we tell them? Sherve asks.

The public relations man shows his irritation at the commotion outside. —They're a bunch of lunatics, you know. They hardly represent the bulk of former mental patients.

Sherve has been through this kind of thing before, and he knows the danger of letting emotions run. —We have to handle this smoothly, he says. The last thing the psychiatrists want is a messy confrontation.

The public relations man stares away for a moment. —Let's tell them that if there is anyone in the convention they want to see, to let us know, and we'll try to arrange it.

—That sounds good, says Sherve, nodding.

That should defuse the little problem. But it doesn't.

Two days later there is a highly anticipated symposium, "Psychiatrists' Values and Their Effects on Psychotherapy," and the panelists include a former president of the American Psychiatric Association and a former president of the American Academy of

Psychoanalysis. The hall is crowded, and the atmosphere is one of good fellowship. For twenty minutes there are pithy comments about the way psychiatrists inject their own personality and values into psychotherapeutic relationships, when . . .

A loud whistle shatters the calm. Five demonstrators, three men and two women, run into the hall from a rear door shouting . . . *Psychiatry Kills* . . . *ECT Kills* . . . They are young, casually dressed, undoubtedly part of the now disbanded picket line of former mental patients, or at least in sympathy with the picketers.

—Get Out! shout the psychiatrists. What the *hell* is this!

Psychiatry Kills . . . they run down to the front, along the side of the dais, blowing whistles . . .

—Get Out! Some psychiatrists are standing, pointing, but none leave their seats.

The demonstrators reach a fire door behind the dais. . . . *We'll be back*, they shout . . . *there are more of us . . . more of us . . .*

They push the fire door open, and they are gone.

Less than thirty seconds have elapsed.

There is an undercurrent of muttering throughout the hall. Who do they think they are? . . . where did they come from? . . . why didn't someone stop them? . . . Ridiculous!

The speaker, another well-known psychiatrist, has not left the lectern during the demonstration. He now clears his throat, pauses while the muttering dies away, and picks up where he was interrupted. *We live by the mortal dominion of chance . . .*

He is met by loud clapping and cheering, as if this is the answer to the demonstrators.

But no sooner does the clapping die away when sirens pick up where the cheers left off. Sirens, engines, noise, here at the hall. Then through the rear door where the demonstrators had burst through moments before are suited-up firemen, escorted by police.

Everyone looks equally confused. An alarm was pulled? A false alarm? What else. The demonstrators, that's who. Disruption. Nonsense. But angering, nevertheless. No respect. How can one continue a reasonable lecture in this kind of atmosphere?

* * *

The psychiatrists have a strong line of defense in San Francisco. After all, they are doctors, men and women of the medical model. In the past decade there have been scientific and medical breakthroughs. Every month brings some evidence of a physiological base for almost every mental problem.

And holding court with the psychiatrists as they retrench into medicine are longtime friends, the drug companies. Pills, prescriptions, psychiatrists. A formidable combination.

Just one look, that's all it takes, to digest the whole bill of goods going down at the convention. In the lobby rotunda are commanding signs announcing special lectures. These lectures, usually named for an honored personality in the trade, are the gems of the convention. There's the Benjamin Rush Lecture, the William C. Menninger Memorial Lecture, the Adolf Meyer Lecture. And on these impressive posters are drug companies' logos. Lederle Laboratories sponsors the Founders Award Lecture . . . Roche Laboratories sponsors the Benjamin Rush Lecture, SmithKlein sponsors the Adolf Meyer Lecture. Symbiosis, interdependency, mutual nurturing . . . all the psychological terms you can think of meaning close, very close togetherness, spring to mind. So does another phrase. *You scratch my back, I'll scratch yours.*

And in the official program of the convention, under bold type that reads Special Acknowledgments: *The American Psychiatric Association expresses its deep appreciation for the support of the following:* . . .

What follows is a list of the special lectures, then other little services offered from the drug boys, such as photographic coverage by Geigy Pharmaceuticals . . . coffee served in the exhibition hospitality lounge by McNeil Laboratories. *The little perks that don't go unnoted.*

Drug promotion often masquerades as education, and the special lectures are only the tip of the iceberg. Symposia for the psychiatrists, six in all and, according to the posters, something *you won't want to miss,* are sponsored by the drug boys. *And there are no other symposia offered.*

Drug company advertising also manages to provide the lifeblood

for numerous magazines. In a recent survey twenty-five out of
twenty-eight medical magazines containing "articles of interest"
were sent free to doctors. Seventy thousand doctors and more had
these dropped into their mailboxes. Without drug money they
would not be published. Without drug ads the publishers would
have no interest in mailing them out.

Psychiatric News, the biweekly newspaper for psychiatrists, published by the American Psychiatric Association, is no slouch when
it comes to sewing up drug ads either. At about $1,200 an ad it
means nice change in the Association's cash register. And the ads
are as Madison Avenue as anything you'll see on TV. Color.
Drama. Eye-catching. Persuasive. Snappy. And yet the same drugs,
month after month after month. The drug names will roll off the
psychiatrist's tongue in the same way *sugar pops* rolls out of the
mouth of a TV-watching preschooler.

And cornering the psychiatric market is no more penny ante
than the cereal vendors cornering the tiny tots' market. Not penny
ante. Chemin de fer.

Recently the detail men of a major drug company got a new
selling tool for the company's antidepressant product. A videotape
symposium on depression, running about ten minutes, was sponsored by the American Psychiatric Association and paid for *by the
drug company*.

The detail men were instructed to play it for the medical people.
Let them see and hear what other doctors think of our product.

*Four to eight million people in the United States are afflicted
with depression* . . . the tape begins . . . *this message is sponsored by
the American Psychiatric Association and financed by* . . .

Several speakers offer their views on how widespread depression
may be, and on the fact that it is probably underdiagnosed. What's
the best way to treat it? Tricyclic antidepressants have been used
more and more in recent years, and the results have been quite
good. Then the final speaker with the *real* message . . . yes, tricyclicates are especially good drugs, and we'd like to recommend one in
particular . . .

It's no surprise that the recommended product is made and sold by the drug company that has financed the videotape.

What is a surprise is that the American Psychiatric Association would lend its name and apparently sees no conflict of interest. The information, they would point out, is distributed, after all, in the name of education.

Some time during the first day of the convention you notice people wearing little round stickers on their badges . . . *ERA Yes!* Someone has been handing them out, and you know that another confrontation is building. The psychiatric media over the past two years has been reporting the on-again, off-again, on-again decision to hold the following year's convention in New Orleans, in a non-ERA-ratified state. It looks as if the last, final stand will be made here, in San Francisco.

No sooner do the former mental patients disband their picketing than a new group of demonstrators, the ERA supporters, take over. But these even include psychiatrists . . . liberationists and psychiatrists against psychiatrists! A picket line is quickly formed, and the buses from the San Francisco hotels that continue to arrive throughout the day to deposit and retrieve visiting psychiatrists find it difficult to locate a clear area.

There is an audience, of course, but somehow the disdain with which the spectators watched the former mental patients is gone. These are *our* people, some of the watching psychiatrists seem to be thinking, *we* can understand. . . .

Still, the spectators don't linger very long. The pickets are now moving in a slow circle, hoisting their signs . . . *APA Is Sexist . . . APA Is Schizoid About ERA . . . APA Has Had a Mental Breakdown . . . APA's Stance on ERA Is Depressing . . .*

There is no banter with the pickets and little overt support. After a few moments of baleful watching, the spectators turn away, and you just can't tell whether any impression has been made.

But inside the civic center the talk flows about ERA and what must be done. There is a special APA board meeting to discuss the next step, and when ERA proponents prevail, there is wild cheering and joy. . . . They will boycott the next convention, if it's held in nonratifying Louisiana.

But somehow the support seems a bit soft. The young resident sporting an ERA sticker has just read his first paper to an American Psychiatric Association convention.

—Are you really going to stay firm and boycott?

A little sheepishly, —No, I'll probably go. I'm on the program committee, so I guess I'll have to be there.

—You could resign.

—I wouldn't do that. He looks a bit startled. —No, I'll be going.

—What about your wife?

—She's a city planner, makes more than I do.

—Would she hold your going to New Orleans against you?

Laughs. —She'd probably go with me. But neither of us is against ERA, not at all . . .

Here and there among the pickets during the week, you notice two women with clipboards standing quietly and occasionally walking up and conversing with spectators. The women are nicely dressed, middle-aged, and pleasant-faced; they seem out of place, somehow, in the activist melee that goes on day after day in front of the Civic Center.

They don't seem a part of *any* demonstration, but each day they are there, and each day they talk to people and get them to read and sign their clipboards.

—What have you got there?

The woman smiles and glances at her companion. —These are petitions, she says, —would you like to sign?

There is a sheet attached to the clipboard, and it protests the use of Soviet psychiatric hospitals as prisons for dissidents and urges that psychiatrists stop being used for the political ends of the state. It protests the jailing of psychiatrists who have dared to rebuke the system.

—Where will you send these?

—To Washington, where they'll be presented to the Soviet embassy and to our government.

How could anyone be against this? There's that vivid precedent of doctors collaborating under Nazism, the subversion of humanitarian ends for political gain. Because of the awful consequences of misuse of psychiatric technique, psychiatrists should want to be the first to complain about what is happening in Soviet Russia . . .

There are only a few names on her petition. —How has support here been for this petition?

She looks uncomfortable. —Not many of the psychiatrists want to sign.

—But there are thousands of them here.

—They're polite about it, but most won't sign.

—Why, then?

It isn't because they don't believe the petition. They *know* what's going on, they aren't blind about their own profession.

She sighs. —Some of them actually look frightened when they tell me they don't want to sign. Others just say they never sign *anything* . . . even something like this. It's too bad, really.

Continuing medical education is offered at every medical convention. To the psychiatrists it means they must obtain a certain number of credit hours of learning *each year* or face the possibility of losing their board certification and professional credentials. They must *keep up*, they must be on top of the latest events in their profession. Opportunities exist all through the year to gain these credits, but it is especially convenient at the APA convention. Hundreds of courses are provided throughout the week, and there is an extremely wide variety of topics. The psychiatrists are urged to take the courses as needed.

But continuing medical education also has meaning for the drug companies. It presents them with a special opportunity at various medical conventions to sell their products, using the technique of drug promotion masquerading as education. If they can put together a program *and* get accreditation *and* expose the doctors to their products . . .

Their chances come when they are allowed to set up exhibits. The APA is happy to set aside some floor area in the exhibition hall . . . for a price. The drug companies pay a fee for the space they use. There will be two kinds of exhibits allowed . . . *scientific* exhibits, which are supposed to have no commercial sponsorship at all, not one word of drug company identification . . . and *technical* exhibits, which are supposed to have an educational character and *to emphasize products, services or instruments.* . . .

As you descend the stairs into subterranean Brooks Hall, you hear the bleeps and ticks and subdued rumble from the exhibition area, and you know it will be jammed. Psychiatrists are like the rest of us when it comes to spectacles. Enough of sitting in converted ballrooms and party rooms, listening to panelists who have little to add to what has gone on before. The exhibits can be fun! Like going to the planetarium or a science museum . . . there are working parts, things *move*, buttons to push, slide demonstrations, things to learn.

The major drug companies are represented in their "technical" exhibits, more than twenty of them "of interest" to psychiatrists. It is important for these companies to be here, and they're willing to pay the price it takes. To put up one of these exhibits, what with design costs, construction costs, shipping and setup, preparation of promotional material, expenses and fee, the cost runs anywhere from $5,000 to $40,000. When the cost of collecting and preparing new data as part of the exhibit is added to that, the cost can go well over $100,000. Such exhibits handsomely support a big chunk of any medical convention. Yet, with only twenty-plus companies setting up exhibits, why does it appear that these booths go on endlessly? Simple. Drug companies have multiple spaces! One has four, another eight, and one . . . twenty-six!

An exhibit in the middle of the hall hits your eye because it looks incongruous in the scientific milieu. It's, well, sort of a Mediterranean garden with trellises and something that looks like a *pond.* Nice boxes of roses and rhododendron and dwarf orange trees edge the retreat. You could get rid of depression in a glade like this. Even if the big tree there in the center is plastic and the trellis is plastic and the pond is something eerie that *shimmers.* And guess what, the *drug* being pushed *is* an antidepressant. Something to take at night. Probably laced with a sleep-inducer. New on the market. Made by Geigy. Well, you can bet the buttons on your blouse that a new drug like this with that sales hooker, P.M., added to it, is going to get big play in the months and maybe years ahead in psychopharm ads.

The psychiatrists knew the name of the old, unimproved drug Geigy was peddling . . . Tofranil, a fast-acting, "effective" antidepressant; but now, *now* with P.M. added to it there is a new dimension. A prescription for day. A prescription for night. Two where there was one.

You must leave the cheerful oasis. Something outsize has caught the eye. An exhibit touting itself as a "unique" experience has professional actors appearing six times a day simulating emotionally disturbed patients and the ways they might respond to different types of therapy. Step right up, folks. Try your skill. The audience is invited to join in this theater of the absurd. Check your diagnostic skills. Check your management expertise. How would you diagnose this woman? What would you prescribe for this man? One wonders if Equity is involved in any of this.

A modular unit, sort of like a minitheater in a shopping mall, intrigues you. Inside it feels like a warm tent on a sunny day. Enclosed. Confidential. A place to rest, be entertained or instructed. There are a couple dozen armchairs, a slide screen, and the ever-present pointer. Lecture-hall paraphernalia.

A pleasant, fiftyish, solid-looking man picks up the pointer. He must go through this demonstration many times a day, but he remains enthusiastic, earnest. He is in the employ of the drug company that set up this warm, cozy modular womb. In one way or another tied to them. Perhaps only for the purposes of this convention, perhaps for other events or for research projects. Whatever, he believes in this drug amitriptyline, a tricyclic antidepressant. His drug company manufactures it *under their own trade name*, which he does not use.

The questions and responses are technical . . . —What cardiovascular complications can there be from tricyclics?

—Tricyclics slow conduction . . .

—And that means . . . ?

—A patient with conduction disease is at greater risk. The important thing is to watch for heart disease.

There is a certain edginess in the audience about the use of tricyclics. Someone mentions the possibility of arrhythmia.

The lecturer's voice drops. He says that if this weren't a drug company exhibit he could talk much more freely. And he talks about the PDR, the *Physicians' Desk Reference*, which is compiled from drug company information supplied on each of the drugs. It lists side effects as well as possible complications . . . a compendium of information so extensive as to release *any* drug company from just about *any* liability.

Now, the lecturer doesn't want to discount PDR, but he wants to make it plain that maybe it's a bit *too cautious*. To emphasize he says that he believes PDR is often written from data taken in the emergency room, where you're liable to face *overdosage*. Then of course you should note that amitriptyline might be contraindicated for many things, and you should follow PDR. But in everyday practice you don't have to be *that* cautious.

The battle between the drug companies to produce that extra something that'll sell more, to put down another drug in place of one's own, the battle goes on, obfuscating and deluding. It is almost like the battle for whiter, brighter teeth on the toothpaste aisle at the supermarket. And it might be a Madison Avenue joke if life, death, and mental health weren't involved.

But you've had enough of the drug companies and the sturdy, well-suited gentlemen who huckster with soft voices and polished pointers. On the other side of the exhibition hall are the scientific exhibits. Could these be as bad? There must be something purer here.

They are less elaborate, and you have hope that something scientific will fall out of them. Papers and news releases have been scattered around, playing up new discoveries and special interests of these people.

At one exhibit a young man, a researcher at a psychiatric institute in the Southwest, is sitting at a table with neat piles of literature. Blown-up photos behind him show a man and woman in the throes of . . . anguish . . . despair. The caption reads, *The problems of depression in office practice.* Depression? In office practice? What can this mean! What panacea is there for this dreadful possibility, whatever it is?

—Your institute did this study? You pick up one of the pamphlets.

—Yes, indeed.

On the back page of the brochure you see a course of action prescribed. . . . begin treatment with an antidepressant, e.g. trimipramine. And there's an asterisk after trimipramine. On the bottom of the page, sure enough, reference is to Surmontil. No drug company listed, but you know the company. This is one of many exhibits. *Scientific, indeed.*

It's almost anticlimactic to ask the studious young man who brought him here, who paid his way, who funded the exhibit, who rented the space, who paid for the study. He is simply trying to do his job, hustle a few brochures about the great benefits of this nice generic drug called trimipramine but sold by this drug company under the name of Surmontil.

Then this really isn't about psychiatrists getting depressed in their offices for whatever reason, it's about *patients.* But a jazzy heading of a "study" has given this drug a nice sales push.

In a few days he'll say good-bye to the Golden Gate and the plastic trellis and plastic trees and the convention shuttle buses and go back to his research base where God knows what new project might be in the offing to be funded by some drug superbucks. What's the harm.

If you can stand it, there are other scientific exhibits in the same vein. These are presented in the name of education. Studies are performed by nonprofit institutions, and this gives credibility to the drug company who has paid for the project. This "scientific" stuff meets criteria set by the American Psychiatric Association so it can be presented in the name of "education."

And it surely is . . . an education.

Congratulations! . . . reads the letter from a San Francisco city official after the psychiatrists have finished their last cups of coffee, have packed it in at their 133rd annual meeting. . . . congratulations to the American Psychiatric Association, to the San Francisco city police, and to the many psychiatrists who showed patience and restraint in the face of demonstrations outside the Civic Center during the convention. If force had been used, there's no telling how many injuries there could have been. . . .

And the doctors present didn't have to treat a single demonstrator.

There was nothing left but to heal themselves.

Fifteen

THE CRUELEST GAME OF ALL

The site is Boston, and the case on the docket is simply . . . *Okin v. Rogers*. The case has to do with human rights, civil rights, the powerful versus the powerless. It has to do with the authority of a state over an individual. It has to do with abrogation of right over one's own person, the right to be viewed as a human worthy of respect. It has to do with psychiatrists and those whom psychiatrists "treat." It has to do with the least of us, and therefore, in the long run, it has to do with all of us.

The case is important. Not because of Okin, who is Robert Okin, Commissioner of the Massachusetts Department of Mental Health, and not because of Rogers, who is Rubie Rogers, an inmate in 1975 of what was then called Boston State Hospital. These are two people who probably in their wildest daydreams would not have imagined that they would one day be pitted against each other. Here they are, part of a drama that is important because it concerns whether psychiatrists should and must have respect for their patients' wishes and whether tyranny sincerely practiced for the "good" of the patient may, in fact, be the most oppressive sort of tyranny there is.

In 1977 Rubie Rogers and Others petitioned the U.S. Federal District Court to restrain Boston State Hospital from forcing medication and seclusion on them and on other patients *except in emergency situations.* The court, in response, issued a temporary restraining order, which Boston State Hospital appealed. By December of that year the First Circuit Court of Appeals upheld the order and the case immediately went to trial. The adversaries were clearly predictable. Joining Okin as defendants were two psychiatrists from the former May and Austin units at Boston State Hospital where Rogers and Others had been incarcerated. The State of Massachusetts itself had a big stake in the matter, since it ran the hospital. It lent its support to the defendants.

On October 29, 1979, the district court issued an order and judgment prohibiting psychiatrists and staff of Boston State Hospital from medicating inpatients of the hospital without their consent or the consent of a guardian *"except where there is a substantial likelihood, or as a result of, extreme violence, personal injury or attempted suicide."* Rogers and Others got what they wanted.

The court based its ruling on a finding of a right to refuse medication inherent in constitutional guarantees of privacy and freedom of speech. Overriding such a right required utmost caution.

Now, it would seem that such a judgment might be considered fair. After all, psychiatrists at the hospital or the staff could *still* restrain or medicate if conditions allowed. But these strictures were not taken with good grace by those in charge. Little by little their *authority* had been eroded over the years. No longer could they lobotomize at will or perform other psychosurgery or give electroshock without having to go through complicated justification. Now come restraints on the use of antipsychotic drugs! And if a patient flatly rejects the shot or the pills, well, there you are. Do these patients really know what's good for them? After all, haven't they waived certain citizen's rights the moment they put foot in the door of a mental institution? When they signed the usual release and contract at the time they entered the building, didn't they give up the right to object to forced medication? And if the psychiatrists are denied the ability to treat these patients the way *they* want to, then why are we calling these places hospitals? Better the state should call them hotels with the rent paid by the Commonwealth at the will of the patient.

It was inevitable that the decision to free the patients from coercion in the name of healing would be appealed. And so it was.

On the sidelines were the American Psychiatric Association and the Massachusetts Hospital Association ready to enter the case as "friends of the court" on behalf of the psychiatrists.

But Rubie Rogers and Others were not alone either. The New York Civil Liberties Union and the Mental Health Law Project also submitted amicus curiae briefs in their support, as did the American Orthopsychiatric Association, The Mental Health Association and the Massachusetts Mental Patients Liberation Front.

For decades, in fact for hundreds of years, patients or victims (depending on the circumstances and the institutions) have pled for surcease of autocratic cruelties. But the current psychiatric inmate's liberation movement did not become organized as such until 1970 with the formation of the Insane Liberation Front in Portland, Oregon. The following year groups were started in New York, Boston, and Vancouver, British Columbia, while at the same time patients' unions were forming in England. Detroit, in 1973, was the site of the first conference on human rights and psychiatric oppression.

The liberation groups are not choosy about the verbiage they use against psychiatrists. They accuse psychiatry of bondage, killing, torture, and coercion. Their stridency is looked at as "inappropriate behavior" by most psychiatrists, and their rage is regarded as evidence that they are nothing more than a bunch of nuts.

Look at them, the shrinks say as the ex-inmates distribute amateurish mimeographed lists of alleged abuses. . . . Look at those dregs who want to take their angers out on us! Who in his right mind would want to get into a dialogue with them!

And you can feel a tingle in the air as the shrinks are buoyed by this criticism. It was bad enough having Ken Kesey out there writing that fanciful book about Randall McMurphy, the "patient" who wouldn't knuckle under to the apparently irrational shrinks who let equally irrational and sadistic staff people harass and mutilate him. And it was bad enough when you had somebody doing a documentary about the way the criminally insane are treated at Bridgewater State Hospital and calling it *Titicut Follies*! . . . Now you've got the lawyers joining hands with the inmates to make it even tougher. The whole system's liable to fall apart. At this rate, what red-blooded medical student would want to go into psychiatry or work with the institutions? Challenging *us*? Do they *know* what can happen?

The first major erosion of psychiatrists' authority to prescribe treatment occurred in the area of psychosurgery. The most infamous psychosurgery technique is the prefrontal lobotomy. This is a true *medical model* tool. That is, its practitioners firmly believed that physical (or physiological) causes rather than psychological causes were at the root of many mental problems. If you had a mental disorder, you were *sick*, and only a doctor could really understand . . . and would be able to operate by cutting into the skull and blotting off a bit of the brain, the so-called diseased part. Direct invasion of the skull had its beginnings in antiquity, going back to the time when primitive man bored holes to allow "ventilation" . . . let the fresh air in and let the evil air out!

We can thank Portugal for producing a stalwart son by the name of Egas Moniz who happened to be a doctor and who experimented with something resembling a dull knife with which he cut patients' prefrontal nerves. He described his new procedure in 1936, and there were some psychiatrists who took great interest in this technique of drilling the skull and sawing slowly back and forth to sever those nerves. Moniz thought it might be good for schizophrenia. Sever connections to those within-the-head screams and hallucination. Give the person a little peace and quiet. His technique of achieving psychic relief was so well received in fact that it won him the Nobel prize.

"Vegetate," not hallucinate, could have been the chant. Moniz was a neurologist and surgeon. But soon this type of psychosurgery was refined so that it wasn't necessary to be a surgeon to perform it. An icepick-like instrument, called a leucotome, soon followed, so anyone, even a psychiatrist, could shove it into the brain at the corner of the patient's eye and jiggle it back and forth. The procedure was not refined, as no one had any real idea of how much fiber to cut, but this was no deterrent. And an added blessing to the psychiatrist was that he could do this job without even an anesthesiologist, if he wished. Electroshock could put the patient under, and the patient not only didn't *feel* the pick but wouldn't remember what happened afterward. Electroconfusion supplied perfect postoperative amnesia.

Within ten years lobotomy psychosurgery was in the big time! While the technique was used in Europe it was embraced with fervor by some in America. The foremost of these was Walter Freeman, M.D., who once estimated that 50,000 prefrontal slicings were done in those years. By some accounts Freeman himself performed more than 4,000.

The intention was to make patients less violent and to clear up their hallucinations. But the results were less than satisfactory and often quite horrible. There was gross impaired intellectual functioning, and while some lobotomized people could perform simple tasks, others could do nothing. And there were instances where this technique to reduce violence had just the opposite effect.

It became apparent that some precautions had to be taken. It goes without saying that the most powerless or potentially dangerous or psychically damaged patients were the prime candidates for such "therapy"; they were the ones without a power base. So it is no surprise that legislation or standards to establish criteria for this therapy were slow in coming.

But there are now some safeguards in many states, thanks to the continued pressure over the decades from relatives or victims and from those within and without the medical profession who see lobotomies as the cruelest form of psychic control.

It is never used in some psychiatric hospitals and rarely used in others. Safeguards in states such as Massachusetts and California now require the opinion of more than one psychiatrist before the operation can be performed. Patient or guardian consent is also solicited. In some areas of the country these would seem meager safeguards, since patient consent is suspect and guardian consent can be issued coercively. But at the least it removes total authority from the psychiatrist.

Even though psychosurgery may be one of the most intrusive procedures to be visited upon a mentally disturbed person, there were psychiatrists who shrieked about *any* challenge to their ultimate authority. *They* would decide who would get a lobotomy . . . when and why. Some psychiatrists even suggested they be made "guardians" of their patients.

Robert Cole, Chief Counsel for Rubie Rogers and Others, argues that physicians themselves cannot and should not be acceptable guardians for patients because of competing interests. There is a built-in conflict of interest.

Competing interests? Isn't the physician on the side of the patient always? Psychiatrists have a stake in protecting other patients and keeping order and stability in the wards. They also may be predisposed to certain modes, if not only *one* mode, of treatment, while a guardian *outside the profession* might look for other alternatives. Or, in basic terms, what's in the best interests of the patient and what's in the best interests of the psychiatrist may not be the same. *Competing* interests.

The second modern assault on the patient's brain *in the guise of helping him* came with injections of a drug called Metrazol. The effect was a grand mal seizure, a major epileptic episode, but it quieted him down afterward . . . it sure did! The hallucinations or the depression was washed away, but you might have to deal with a fractured leg or a broken arm. . . . But his brain wasn't so tortured afterward! Later, Metrazol therapy was replaced with electroshock, but in both cases the brain was bombarded in an effort to cause a strong convulsion.

Patient consent? Ridiculous. After all, the authoritarians knew what was best. What did a patient know? They were to do as they were told, and for a couple of decades well-meaning and not-so-well-meaning psychiatrists literally shocked the hell out of thousands.

But in the past decade small groups of former mental patients and their supporters have banded together to curb the authority of those who would attack their minds, the clinical psychiatrists and the lawmakers who listened to them. And some headway has been made. Since the former patients are no longer locked up, they are able to petition legislators, print handouts, document witnessed abuses. They have become the advocates for one of the most silent and constitutionally deprived groups of people in the land, those with affective disorders requiring psychotropic drugs or threatened by psychosurgery and electroshock.

The Alliance for the Liberation of Mental Patients, a Philadelphia-based group, was one of those that traveled to Berkeley, California, to attend the Eighth Annual Conference on Human Rights and Psychiatric Oppression. The targets of their rage are diffuse. Psychiatrists who practice psychosurgery and electroshock without patient consent are on the list, but the Alliance finds it impossible to limit their disgust here. They find they must indict all psychiatry because the profession under the umbrella of the conservative and politically active American Psychiatric Association chooses to go along with those who ignore the right of patient consent. But the Alliance cannot stop even here. Since major psychotropic drugs with some pretty severe side effects are administered either unwittingly or coercively to thousands of patients, the Alliance has singled out the one drug company that makes the most widely used and most potent of these drugs . . . SmithKlein (formerly Smith, Kline and French). They are the developers and manufacturers of Thorazine. The Alliance claims that SmithKlein in 1978 sold over $60 million worth of psychiatric drugs. And it is not enough to single out Thorazine with its often gruesome side effects of involuntary grimacing, tongue lapping, erratic gait, and excessive dry mouth, they must also indict SmithKlein for its laboratories in Third World countries, and what they refer to as economic exploitation of foreign peoples.

One might be tempted to dismiss the Alliance for the Liberation of Mental Patients as just another wild-eyed bunch of crazies hacking away at the establishment, yet they have managed to get the endorsement of half a hundred or more respectable human rights–oriented organizations. And they are the leaders of a boycott against SmithKlein products including Sea & Ski, Sine-Off, and Love cosmetics. Their cry . . . *"Don't* give your cold to Contac!"

On May 4, 1980, representatives of this group, together with other ex-patients from across the country, met in the San Francisco office of the Bay Area Committee for Alternatives to Psychiatry and discussed safeguards that must be guaranteed to protect mental patients from the autocratic rule of psychiatric doctors.

Their frustration is summed up in a flat statement by Judi Chamberlin, who is affiliated with the Mental Patients Liberation Front in Massachusetts and who was a member of the President's Commission on Mental Health . . . —Everything you do is considered to be a symptom of your illness. If you are angry about being there [in an institution], *that* is not looked on as legitimate. Normal rights, like making a phone call or going outside, are regarded as privileges. Psychiatrists are the culprits of authoritarian rule over mental patients, she says; there *must* be more patient control.

With the Boston State case as an example of how fiercely organized psychiatry will fight to keep calling the shots, one must wonder what there is in the psyche of the physician that makes him *require* this power. Reasoning that mental patients aren't competent to make judgments flies in the face of their legal rights to sign contracts, to vote, to say yea or nay to psychosurgery. The American Psychiatric Association, in its brief, maintains that it's "obviously preferable" that psychiatric treatment be voluntary. —Ultimately, however, they say,—effective clinical care demands that the physician be allowed to *override the committed patient's objection in certain circumstances.* At times, for example, the patient's verbal objection will be patently senseless or will be accompanied by behavior demonstrating ambivalence about the treatment and the loss of the psychotic illness. *Failure to impose treatment in such circumstances is irresponsible* [author's italics]. And furthermore, they argue that if the state isn't *allowed* to force medication, then the patients entitled to it should be released. . . . But to go where? To be jailed or to hit the streets? These are cruel and unreasonable alternatives, ignoring the inherent humanity in every mental patient.

While Judi Chamberlin meets in San Francisco to talk about alternatives to coercive therapy, whether it be lobotomy, electroshock, or major antipsychotic drugs, the attorneys for the American Psychiatric Association, Joel Klein and Ellen Silberman, also argue that the Massachusetts court "simply was mistaken" in assuming that there were alternative methods of treating mental patients, and that . . . —for those patients so seriously ill as to require commitment, medication is invariably an indispensable treatment.

But there is this nagging thought . . . chemically induced convulsions were once considered an *indispensable* treatment . . . and so was electroshock . . . and so were lobotomies. There are too many drastic indispensable treatments to recount, but there was the fire-hose routine, there were wet sheets, there was the straitjacket. For the nonconfessors there was the rack; there was the stake for witches. Tyranny sincerely exercised for the good of the victim.

We can live with the ruling that says we may not force medication on a patient who objects, say the residents at Boston State Hospital. *We can live with it.* And it is the residents who have patient involvement, not senior psychiatrists who have flipped over the challenge to their absolute authority. *We can live with it.* Is there something blowing in the wind?

Coercion and authoritarian management of those with affective disorders, as mental illness is now called, can be more subtle than what we have seen in the institutional setting. It goes on in psychiatric offices and at the community mental health level. Drugging is still the big item, and likely to get even more play in the 1980s. Monitoring who takes what and how much has now been reduced to a science.

There's a little kit offered by drug companies now that will allow the psychiatrist to take a blood sample and find out if the client has been cheating and not taking the medication. Maybe he has been flushing the stuff down the toilet, maybe he's sick and tired of the dry mouth and itchy-skin side effects and wants to take less. No way he can get away with it. He comes to the office as required and he gets stuck for a blood test. As simply as taking a blood-sugar analysis, the psychiatrist can find out in a hurry if this client is doing as he was told. No? Taking too little in the doctor's opinion? Well, no more of this pill at breakfast, that pill at dinner. Won't even bother with time-release submarines that will ensure he gets what he's supposed to. We'll go the injection route. Long-lasting injection. Thought that sucker would fool his doctor, did he? No way. The doctor is certain he knows best.

And at the community mental health centers the bag ladies and young men who now inhabit roach-city hotel rooms wander in for their required checkups. Miss a checkup and it could mean into the slammer or back to the wards. At least that's the threat and not many want to challenge to find out. A lot of clients say, I don't want these shots . . . would like to take a lesser dose . . . maybe the pills instead. Well, who's crazy now? Do these freaks for one minute think they can be in charge of their own destinies *in that manner?*

There is a good check on the blood readings, and the staff makes sure they give their long-lasting antipsychotic injections. Roll them in, check them out. There is *absolute control* with long-lasting injections. Doctor knows what the client ought to get, no questions asked, and he gets it. In and out. If you detect a cattle-car mentality, a scientific approach to the *mental problem*, a mathematical determination for the *final solution* of dealing with those who have affective disorders, you may be on the right track.

In a world where the lesser of us have had to struggle every inch of the way to gain or preserve free choice, where masterminds linking themselves with the moneyed and powerful establishment clutch every wisp of control available, the fine line between respectful treatment and insolent assault is often wobbly. In the name of benevolent authority the lesser of us have suffered irremedial damage.

Women, whose rights have yet to be granted, would do well to question the authority of much psychiatric dictum. Should male chauvinist views be perpetuated in therapy? Should electroshock, which is offered or thrust upon over 100,000 *reported* clients a year, mostly women, be freely tolerated? Is there any real justification for it except where the most immediate threat of self-destruction exists and when no other less assaultive treatment works? There are many psychiatrists who have used it and now find it nothing less than criminal and barbarous.

Should lobotomies be continued except with the most selected discrimination? Should high levels of antipsychotic drugs be administered *with or without consent* without the most conscientious attempt to consult the client or guardian about the side effects? Should the aging be carelessly classified as suffering from lesser or greater forms of senility without the most careful psychological and physical work-up?

Psychiatry is moving more and more into biological and neurological territory. Psychopharmacology is an exploding industry. At a time when government committees are demanding "efficacy" determinations for psychotherapy (that is, therapy through analysis and discussion), in order to set medical payment for treatment more and more psychiatrists will throw up their hands and offer specific medically oriented treatments.

Biologics in the field of psychiatry are an important element in turning the art into "efficacious therapy." For example, enzymes that are normally found in the stomach and intestines have also been discovered in the brain. The brain, then, becomes a hugely complex endocrine organ, a pharmaceutical manufacturing organ making hundreds of psychoactive compounds.

Feeling states such as hopelessness, depression, optimism, can then, some psychiatrists insist, be related to biological events. Through *laboratory tests* likened to those used for other physical work-ups, one might be able to tell what kind of depression this is, what particular drug might be useful. It sounds simple. It sounds scientific. It sounds "'efficacious." It could be quantitatively measured. Congressional committees approving budgets would be satisfied. Governmental departments allocating funds for mental health reimbursement would be satisfied. Insurance carriers would be satisfied.

The simple is always so tempting. Especially when mental health funding comes under close and cynical scrutiny. For what else are we really talking about except funding? Money. How to treat the average Joe and Jane as cheaply and as quickly as possible. How to cut budgets.

Conservatives, be they pressure groups, bureaucrats, or government leaders, have a hard time accepting the abstractions of psychotherapy. Most consider it hogwash and look for the frontier method of dealing with somatic disorders. Drug-em-up, cut-em-up, lock-em-up. How can an intellectually based art like psychotherapy find financial support in a back-to-the-basics decade?

There is a clear signal emanating from the autocracy of the early 1980s that will predict certain things.

Sympathy toward mental illness will wane. Community mental health centers will offer fewer amenities as mayors and governors grab federal bloc grants for less benign purposes.

Jails will increasingly become way stations for the mentally disturbed young, the poor, and the elderly.

The Alcohol, Drug Abuse and Mental Health Administration will find itself with less funding for research and for assisting mental health centers. Centers will increasingly be converted to police stations or mini city halls.

Autocratic rule by psychiatrists in city-run mental hospitals or psychiatric wards will continue, especially away from urban centers. The more *certain* psychiatrists become concerning the efficacy of psychopharmacology as a mode of treatment . . . that drugging really works . . . the more they will insist on the unbridled right to administer.

At the same time patients' rights groups will not only proliferate, they will also join forces with other groups that speak for human rights . . . the American Civil Liberties Union, women's rights groups, homosexual rights groups. The rights wave of the 1980s will adopt the techniques of the 1960s, when organized petitioning began to have effect on doctrinaire opinions. Patients' rights groups, through demonstrations, political education, professional dialogue, and the use of the courts, will continue the argument that the fundamental issue at stake is to foster an honest alliance between therapist and client, one that allows patients the opportunity to participate and consent to treatment in an informed manner. These groups will also demand a workable monitoring system to ensure that paper rights will be translated into effective action and that patients are truly protected by law.

Autocratic psychiatry is approaching the high-water mark. There is a silent minority whose numbers reach into the millions. It is they who will change the face of psychiatry. And it is high time.

SOURCES

Chapter 1—BABEL

AMERICAN PSYCHIATRIC ASSOCIATION. *Diagnostic and Statistical Manual of Mental Disorders.* 3rd. ed. 1980.

DRUMMOND, HUGH. "Dr. D. Is Mad as Hell." *Mother Jones* (December 1979).

"DSM-III Seen as Problem for Analyst." *Psychiatric News* (November 7, 1980).

McDONALD, MARGARET C. "Tourette Syndrome—Neurological?" *Psychiatric News* (April 4, 1980).

NATIONAL INSTITUTE OF MENTAL HEALTH. *Research Grants Sourcebook 1978.* U.S. Department of Health, Education and Welfare, Public Health Service, Alcohol, Drug Abuse and Mental Health Administration.

SOBEL, DAVA. "New Psychiatric Definitions Expected to Affect Therapy." *The New York Times* (December 11, 1979).

Chapter 2—PLAYERS

BIEGEL, ALLAN. "Psychiatric Education at the Crossroads: Issues and Further Directions." *American Journal of Psychiatry*, 136:12 (December 1979).

BURSTEN, BEN. "Psychiatry and the Rhetoric of Models." *American Journal of Psychiatry*, 136:5 (May 1979).

CALLEN, KENNETH E., and DAVIS, DAVID. "What Medical Students Should Know About Psychiatry: The Results of a Survey of Rural Practitioners." *American Journal of Psychiatry*, 135:2 (February 1978).

CAMPBELL, ROBERT J. "Candidates' Statements." *Psychiatric News* (January 18, 1980).

GREENBLATT, M., CAREW, J., and PIERCE, C. M. "Success Rates in Psychiatry and Neurology Certification Examinations." *American Journal of Psychiatry*, 134:11 (November 1977).

HALES, DIANNE. "Recruiting Psychiatrists Seen as Vital Issue." *Psychiatric News* (April 4, 1980).

JANUS, SAMUEL S., ADLER, DAVID W., KOFFLER, JEFFREY M., and SCHWARTZ, ROSS J. "Life Profile of Psychiatric and Other Residents." Paper read at 133rd Annual Meeting of the American Psychiatric Association, San Francisco, California, May 8, 1980.

The Johns Hopkins University Circular, 1979–1980. Johns Hopkins University, School of Medicine, Baltimore, Maryland (November 1979).

KIESLER, C. A. "The Training of Psychiatrists and Psychologists." *American Psychologist*, Vol. 32 (February 1977) 107–8.

LANGSLEY, DONALD G. "Response of the President-elect." 133rd Annual Meeting of the American Psychiatric Association, San Francisco, California, May 5, 1980.

LOONEY, JOHN G., HARDING, RICHARD K., BLOTCKY, MARK J., and BARNHART, F. DAVID. "Psychiatrists' Transition from Training to Career: Stress and Mastery." Paper read at 132nd Annual Meeting of the American Psychiatric Association, Chicago, Illinois, May 1979.

MELCHIODE, GERALD A. "Psychoanalytic Teaching in Medical Education." *American Journal of Psychiatry*, 13:8 (August 1979).

1979–1980 Bulletin. University of Southern California School of Medicine. Los Angeles.

Psychiatry Residency Training Program. 1980, University of Texas Medical Branch, Galveston.

Psychiatric Residency Training Program. 1980, University of Vermont, Burlington.

Stanford University Bulletin, Palo Alto, California: Stanford Medical School (1979–80).

TAYLOR, R. L., and TORREY, F. F. "The Pseudo-Regulation of American Psychiatry." *American Journal of Psychiatry,* 129:6 (December 1972).

"What Is a Psychiatrist?" Washington, D.C.: American Psychiatric Association (1977).

Chapter 3—THE GENDER MENDERS

BELL, A. P., and WEINBERG, M. S. *Homosexualities: A Study of Diversity Among Men and Women.* New York: Simon & Schuster, 1978.

BIEBER, I. *Homosexuality: A Psychoanalytic Study of Male Homosexuals.* New York: Basic Books, 1962.

BRODY, JANE. "Benefits of Transsexual Surgery Disputed as Leading Hospital Halts the Procedures." *The New York Times* (October 2, 1979).

FREUD, SIGMUND. "Letter to an American Mother." *American Journal of Psychiatry,* 107 (1951), 786.

———. "Three Essays of Sexuality." Standard Edition, Vol. 7. London: Hogarth Press, 1953.

HATTERER, L. J. *Changing Homosexuality in the Male.* New York: McGraw-Hill, 1970.

HOOKER, EVELYN. "Homosexuality." *Final Report and Background Papers, National Institute of Mental Health Task Force on Homosexuality.* DHEW Pub. No. (ADM), 76–357 (1972; reprinted 1976).

KATZ, JONATHAN. *Gay American History.* New York: T. Y. Crowell, 1976.

MARMOR, JUDD. "Notes on Some Psychodynamic Aspects of Homosexuality." *Final Report and Background Papers, National Institute of Mental Health Task Force on Homosexuality.* DHEW Pub. No. (ADM), 76–357 (1972; reprinted 1976).

MASTERS, WILLIAM H., and JOHNSON, VIRGINIA E. *Homosexuality in Perspective.* Boston: Little, Brown, 1979.

MASTERS, WILLIAM H., JOHNSON, VIRGINIA E., and KOLODNY, ROBERT C. *Ethical Issues in Sex Therapy.* Boston: Little, Brown, 1977.

Morris, P. A., "Doctors' Attitudes to Homosexuality." *British Journal of Psychiatry*, Vol. 122 (1975), 435–36.

Pear, Robert. "Ban is Affirmed on Homosexuals Entering Nation." *The New York Times* (December 27, 1979).

Pomeroy, W. B. "The Diagnosis and Treatment of Transvestites and Transsexuals." *Journal of Sex and Marital Therapy*, Vol. 3 (Spring, 1975).

Robitscher, Jonas. *The Powers of Psychiatry*. Boston: Houghton Mifflin, 1980.

Rouslin, S. "A Psychoanalytic View of Homosexuality: An interview with Joseph J. Geller, M.D." *Perspective on Psychiatric Care*, 16:2 (1978), 76–79.

Sulloway, Frank. *Freud, Biologist of the Mind*. New York: Basic Books, 1979.

"Summary of Preliminary Findings of Follow Up on 22 Transsexual Patients from the University of Minnesota." Presented at 133rd Annual Meeting of the American Psychiatric Association, San Francisco, California, May 3–9, 1980.

Tripp, C. A. *The Homosexual Matrix*. New York: Signet, 1975.

West, D. J. *Homosexuality Re-examined*. London: Gerald Duckworth & Co., 1977.

Williams, A. H. "Problems of Homosexuality." *British Medical Journal* 3 (August 16, 1975), 426–28.

Chapter 4—COMING THROUGH THE RYE

Douglas, Donald B. "Who Is a Real Alcoholic?" *New York State Journal of Medicine* (April 1976).

Elithorn, A., Wells, F. O., and Galloway, David. "Are Our Barbiturates Really Necessary?" *British Medical Journal* 3 (August 2, 1975), 285.

Gitlow, Stanley E. "A Pharmacological Approach to Alcoholism." *AA Grapevine* (October 1968).

Glaser, Frederick. "Dealing with the Unknown: A Commentary on Three Papers Concerning Alcohol Related Problems." Paper read at 133rd Annual Meeting of the American Psychiatric Association, San Francisco, California, May 6, 1980.

Gottlieb, Richard, Noppi, Theodore, and Strain, James J. "The

Physician's Knowledge of Psychotropic Drugs: Preliminary Results." *American Journal of Psychiatry,* 135:1 (January 1978).

"Interview with Ari Kiev." *Behavioral Medicine* (February 1980).

McDONALD, MARGARET C. "Rand Rethinks Alcoholism Treatment." *Psychiatric News* (April 18, 1980).

"NIAAA Lab Develops New Test for Alcoholism." *Alcohol, Drug Abuse and Mental Health Administration News,* U.S. Department of Health, Education and Welfare, 6:5 (March 7, 1980).

PARRY, HUGH J., CISIN, IRA H., BALTER, MITCHELL B., MELLINGER, GLEN D., and MANHEIMER, DEAN L. "Increasing Alcohol Intake as a Coping Mechanism for Psychic Distress." National Institute of Mental Health paper, Washington, D.C. (*c.* 1974).

RYBACK, RALPH. "Psychological Aspects of Alcohol and Alcoholism." Paper read at Massachusetts Medical Society Course on Alcoholism and Drug Addiction, Sherman Auditorium, Boston University, March 6, 1974.

SCHUCKET, MARC A. "Geriatric Alcoholism and Drug Abuse." *The Gerontologist,* 17:2 (1977).

TRAINOR, DOROTHY. "Search Elusive for 'Alcoholic Personality.'" *Psychiatric News* (October 17, 1980).

"Treating Alcoholism: The Illness, The Symptoms, The Treatment." DHEW Pub. No. (ADM), 77–128 (1974; reprinted 1977).

"You've Been Lied to, Doctor . . ." Advertisement in *Psychiatric News* (July 4, 1980), 10–11.

Chapter 5—VIENNA WALTZ

American Psychiatric Association. *Health Insurance and Psychiatric Care.* Baltimore: Garamond/Pridemark Press, 1972.

BERGMAN, ROBERT L. "A School for Medicine Men." *American Journal of Psychiatry,* Vol. 130 (1973), 663–66.

BOYER, L. BRYCE. "Folk Psychiatry of the Apache," in *Magic, Faith and Healing,* ed. Ari Kiev. Glencoe, Illinois: Free Press, 1964.

BREUER, JOSEF, and FREUD, SIGMUND, in collaboration with Anna Freud. *Studies on Hysteria.* New York: Basic Books, 1957.

COOPER, B., and BROWN, A. C. "Psychiatric Practice in Great Britain and America—A Comparative Study." *British Journal of Psychiatry,* Vol. 113 (1967), 625–36.

DARNTON, NINA, and CORBETT, MARCIA. "The Magic Force of Witch Doctors." *The New York Times* Magazine (October 19, 1980).

FINE, REUBEN. *A History of Psychoanalysis.* New York: Columbia University Press, 1979.

FRANK, JEROME D. *Persuasion and Healing—A Comparative Study of Psychotherapy.* Baltimore: Johns Hopkins University Press, 1961, 1973.

FREEMAN, LUCY. "Immortal Anna O. From Freud to Feminism." *The New York Times* Magazine (November 11, 1979).

FREUD, SIGMUND. "Further Recommendations in the Technique of Psychoanalysis." *Zeitschrift,* Bil.1 (1913).

GELFAND, MICHAEL. "Psychiatric Disorders as Recognized by The Shona," in *Magic, Faith and Healing,* ed. Ari Kiev. Glencoe, Illinois: Free Press, 1964.

HALE, NATHAN G., JR. *Freud and the Americans.* New York: Oxford University Press, 1971.

HAMBURG, DAVID, et al. "Report of Ad Hoc Committee on Central Fact Gathering Data of the American Psychoanalytic Association." *Journal of the American Psychoanalytic Association,* Vol. 15 (1967).

JONES, ERNEST. *The Life and Work of Sigmund Freud.* New York: Basic Books, 1961.

KAPLAN, BERT, and JOHNSON, DALE. "The Social Meaning of Navaho Psychopathology and Psychotherapy," in *Magic, Faith and Healing,* ed. Ari Kiev. Glencoe, Illinois: Free Press, 1964.

KIEV, ARI, ed. *Magic, Faith and Healing.* Glencoe, Illinois: Free Press, 1964.

MACKLIN, R. "The Medical Model in Psychoanalysis and Psychotherapy." *Comprehensive Psychiatry,* Vol. 14 (1973).

MENNINGER, WILLIAM C. *Psychiatry in a Troubled World.* New York: Macmillan, 1948.

MOORE, ROBERT A. "Ethics in the Practice of Psychiatry: Origins, Functions, Models and Enforcement." *American Journal of Psychiatry,* 135:2 (February 1978).

MURPHY, JANE M. "Psychotherapeutic Aspects of Shamanism," in *Magic, Faith and Healing,* ed. Ari Kiev. Glencoe, Illinois: Free Press, 1964.

NELSON, SCOTT H., and TORREY, E. FULLER. "The Religious Functions of Psychiatry." *American Journal of Ortho-psychiatry,* 43:3 (1973).

OPLER, M. K. "Dream Analysis in Ute Indian Therapy," in *Culture and Mental Health,* ed. M. K. Opler. New York: Macmillan, 1959.

————. "Some Points of Comparison Between the Treatment of Functional Disorders by Apache Shamans and Modern Psychiatric Practice." *American Journal of Psychiatry*, 92:1371 (1936).

POSINSKY, S. H. "Yoruk Shamanism." *Psychiatric Quarterly*, Vol. 39 (1965).

PRINCE, RAYMOND. "Indigenous Yoruba Psychiatry," in *Magic, Faith and Healing*, ed. Ari Kiev. Glencoe, Illinois: Free Press, 1964.

QUINN, SUSAN. "Oedipus vs. Narcissus." *The New York Times* Magazine (November 16, 1980).

SHEELEY, W. F. "A Brief History of the Psychiatric Education for the Nonpsychiatrist; II: The Age of Reason—and Beyond." *Psychosomatics*, Vol. 3 (September–October 1962).

————. "A Brief History of Psychiatry for the Doctor; III: The Circle Is Closed." *Psychosomatics*, Vol. 4 (January–February 1963).

SOBEL, DAVA. "Freud's Fragmented Legacy." *The New York Times* Magazine (October 26, 1980).

TORREY, E. FULLER. *The Mind Game: Witchdoctors and Psychiatrists.* New York: Emerson Hall, 1972.

"Training Program in Psychoanalysis." The San Francisco Psychoanalytic Institute Catalogue of Courses, 1979–1980.

WYKERT, JOHN. "Anna O—A Re-evaluation." *Psychiatric News* (May 2, 1980).

Chapter 6—NUTS AND BOLTS

CAMPBELL, ROBERT JEAN, NARDINI, JOHN E., and ADEN, GARY C. "The International Psychiatric Association for the Advancement of Electrotherapy—A Brief History." Handout presented at 133rd Annual Meeting of the American Psychiatric Association, San Francisco, California, May 3–9, 1980.

CULVER, CHARLES M., FERRELL, RICHARD B., and GREEN, RONALD M. "ECT and Special Problems of Informed Consent." *American Journal of Psychiatry* 137:5 (May 1980).

"ECT Study Challenges Common Myths." *Psychiatric News* (July 4, 1980).

HAPGOOD, FRED. "The Unkindest Therapy of All." *Atlantic Monthly* (January 1980).

"Myths About Electro-convulsive Therapy." News release of the 133rd Annual Meeting of the American Psychiatric Association, San Francisco, California, May 8, 1980.

ROBITSCHER, JONAS. *The Powers of Psychiatry.* Boston: Houghton Mifflin, 1980.

TEMKIN, TANYA. "Doctors Sue for Right to Shock." *Madness Network News* (Spring 1978).

WEINER, RICHARD D. "The Psychiatric Use of Electrically Induced Seizures." *American Journal of Psychiatry*, 136:12 (December 1979).

Chapter 7—TURF

ALSOFROM, JUDY. "Psychiatry Faces Survival Battle." *American Medical News* (May 26, 1978).

"APA's Building Plans." *Psychiatric News* (April 18, 1980).

"APA Reaffirms MD Primacy in Treatment." *Psychiatric News* (July 16, 1976).

BOURNE, PETER G. "The Psychiatrist's Responsibility and Public Trust." *American Journal of Psychiatry*, 135:2 (February 1978).

Brief of the American Psychiatric Association as Amicus Curiae, in the United States Court of Appeals for the Fourth Circuit, *Virginia Academy of Clinical Psychologists et al.* v. *Blue Shield of Virginia et al.*, August 27, 1979.

Brief of the American Psychological Association as Amicus Curiae, in the United States Court of Appeals for the Fourth Circuit, *Virginia Academy of Clinical Psychologists et al.* v. *Blue Shield of Virginia et al.*, July 24, 1979.

Complaint filed December 14, 1979, in the District Court of the United States for the Southern District of Ohio, Eastern Division, *State of Ohio ex rel. William J. Brown, Attorney General* v. *Joint Commission on Accreditation of Hospitals.* Draft of remarks by Dr. Herbert Dörken on behalf of Association for the Advancement of Psychology in hearings on Medicare reform before Ways and Means Committee, U.S. House of Representatives, Ninety-sixth Congress, 1st Session, June 18, 27, 1979.

ENGLISH, JOSEPH T. Testimony on behalf of American Psychological Association before the Subcommittee on Health, Committee on Ways and Means, U.S. House of Representatives, Ninety-sixth Congress, 2nd Session, February 12, 1980.

"FTC Staff Recommends Termination of Physician Control over Blue Shield." *Behavior Today*, 10:20 (May 28, 1979).

GARDNER, JANET. "Psychologists vs. Psychiatrists." *The Plain Dealer* (Cleveland) (February 3, 1980).

Hearings on mentally disabled persons Before Senate Judiciary Committee of the Vermont State Senate, Montpelier, Vermont, March 28, 1979.

Hearings Before Subcommittee on Health and the Environment of the Committee on Interstate and Foreign Commerce, U.S. House of Representatives, Ninety-fourth Congress, 2nd Session, August 17, 1976.

Hearings Before Subcommittee on Health and Scientific Research of the Committee on Human Resources, U.S. Senate, Ninety-fifth Congress, 2nd Session, October 9, 10, 13, 1978.

JOHNSON, JAMES H., and WILLIAMS, THOMAS A. "The Psychologist in the Department of Psychiatry." *Professional Psychiatry* (June 1979).

LANGSLEY, DONALD G. "Viewpoint." *Psychiatric News* (September 19, 1980).

LEVIN, HILLEL. "War Between the Shrinks." *New York* Magazine (May 21, 1979).

McDONALD, MARGARET C. "Appeals Court OKs Psychologists' Billing," *Psychiatric News* (July 18, 1980).

―――. "JCAH Agrees to New Wording in Standards." *Psychiatric News* (September 19, 1980).

"Medical Participation in Control of Blue Shield and Certain Other Open-Panel Medical Prepayment Plans." *Staff Report to the Federal Trade Commission and Proposed Trade Regulation Rule*, April 1979.

"Memorandum Supporting Investigation of the Joint Commission on Accreditation of Hospitals and the American Medical Association." Filed by Association for the Advancement of Psychology with Federal Trade Commission, July 1976.

"No Peace In Our Time (iv)." *Advance*, 3:2 (February 1976).

O'KEEFE, ANNE MARIE. News release on appellate argument in *Virginia Academy of Clinical Psychologists et al.* v. *Blue Shield of Virginia et al.* Association for the Advancement of Psychology (February 7, 1980).

O'KEEFE, ANNE MARIE, and McCULLOUGH, STEPHEN J. "Physician Domination in the Health Care Industry: The Pursuit of Antitrust Redress." *Professional Psychology* (August 1979).

"Psychiatry Image Said to Impair Patient Access." *Psychiatric News* (July 21, 1978).

"Psychologists and Psychiatrists Battle over Blue Shield Coverage in Virginia." *Mental Disability Law Reporter* (November–December 1979).

RUSHING, WILLIAM. *The Psychiatric Professions.* Chapel Hill: University of North Carolina Press, 1964.

SOBEL, DAVA. "Psychologists Speak of Rivals and of Pavlov." *The New York Times* (September 7, 1980).

"Tension Rising Between Psychology, Psychiatry." *Clinical Psychiatry News*, 5:11 (November 1977).

TRAINOR, DOROTHY. "Psychiatry Said in Serious Danger of Elimination." *Psychiatric News* (September 1, 1978).

WALSH, JOHN. "Professional Psychologists Seek to Change Roles and Rules in the Field." *Science*, Vol. 203 (January 26, 1979).

Chapter 8—SEDUCTION AND SUPERBUCKS

Hearings Before Subcommittee on Monopoly of the Select Committee on Small Business, United States Senate, Ninety-fourth Congress, 2nd Session, April 28, May 10, 24, 1976.

JELLINEK, MICHAEL, and LAZARE, AARON. "Relations Between Academic Departments of Psychiatry and Pharmaceutical Companies." *American Journal of Psychiatry* 136:6 (June 1979).

MELLINGER, GLEN D., BALTER, MITCHELL B., MANHEIMER, DEAN I., CISIN, IRA H., and PARRY, HUGH J. "Psychic Distress, Life Crisis, and Use of Psychotherapeutic Medications." *Archives of Psychiatry*, Vol. 35 (September 1978).

MINTZ, MORTON. *The Therapeutic Nightmare.* Boston: Houghton Mifflin, 1965.

National Institute of Mental Health. *Research Grants Sourcebook, 1978.* U.S. Department of Health, Education and Welfare, Public Health Service, Alcohol, Drug Abuse and Mental Health Administration.

Principles and Guidelines of Advertising Acceptance, American Psychiatric Association, Revised (January 1978).

Rates and Data, *Psychiatric News* (July 1979–80).

Chapter 9—AT THE PLEASURE OF THE KING

"Another Day of Death," 112:24, *Time* (December 11, 1978), 23–26.

FORT, JOEL. "Doubts About Courtroom Experts." *Human Behavior Magazine* (December 1978).

———. "The Use and Abuse of Expert Testimony." Syllabus prepared for the University of California, Hastings School of Law College of Advocacy, 1976.

LOCKE, ROBERT. "Judge Warns Psychiatrists Against 'Benign Perjury.'" *Burlington Free Press* (February 10, 1980).

"Psychiatry and the Law—End of an Affair?" *Psychiatric News* (June 6, 1980).

ROBITSCHER, JONAS. *The Powers of Psychiatry.* Boston: Houghton Mifflin, 1980.

STERN, SUSAN. "Twinkies Surface in Arkansas Court." *Synapse* (University of San Francisco Medical School newspaper) (May 22, 1980).

SZASZ, THOMAS. "The Political Use of Psychiatry in the United States: The Case of Dan White." Paper read at 133rd Annual Meeting of the American Psychiatric Association, San Francisco, California, May 7, 1980.

"When Psychiatric Witnesses Square Off in the Courtroom." *U.S. News & World Report,* 86:42 (May 7, 1979).

Chapter 10—THE PENILE SYSTEM

"APA to Meet in New Orleans in 1981; Board Rescinds Earlier Boycott Vote." *Psychiatric News* (July 4, 1980).

BENEDEK, ELISSA P., BARTON, GAIL, and BIENICK, CHRISTINE. "Problems for Women in Psychiatric Residency." *American Journal of Psychiatry* 134:11 (November 1977).

BENEDEK, ELISSA P., and POZNANSKI, ELVA. "Career Choices for the Woman Psychiatric Resident." *American Journal of Psychiatry* 137:3 (March 1979).

"ERA Supporters Threaten Walkout After APA Vote." *Psychiatric News* (April 18, 1980).

HAMILTON, MILDRED. "The Psychiatrists Yield to the Feminists over the ERA." *The Tribune* (Oakland) (May 8, 1980).

HATFIELD, LARRY D. "APA Spins Its Official Wheels on ERA." *San Francisco Examiner* (May 6, 1980).

"Historian Says Psychiatry Trails Women's Aspirations." *Psychiatric News* (October 17, 1980).

LANGSLEY, DONALD G. "Viewpoint." *Psychiatric News* (July 18, 1980).

LEWIS, RAY. "Observations on Era." *Psychiatric News* (July 18, 1980).

MENNINGER, WILLIAM C. *Psychiatry in a Troubled World.* New York: Macmillan, 1948.

NAKAO, ANNIE. "Grad Charges Med School with Racial Prejudice." *San Francisco Sunday Examiner & Chronicle* (June 1, 1980).

"No ERA, no APA for Louisiana in 1981." *San Francisco Chronicle* (May 9, 1980).

"Psychiatrists for ERA," Vol. 1, No. 1 (handout of the 133rd Annual Meeting of the American Psychiatric Association, May 3–9, 1980).

SCHIEFELBEIN, SUSAN. "The Female Patient: Heeded? Hustled? Healed?" *Saturday Review*, 7:7 (March 29, 1980).

"Trustees Move 1981 Meeting from Louisiana in ERA Boycott Vote." *Psychiatric News* (June 6, 1980).

"What Is a Psychiatrist?" American Psychiatric Association, Washington, D.C., 1977.

Chapter 11—GOOD-BYE, PEPSI GENERATION

BESDINE, RICHARD W. "Observations on Geriatric Medicine." U.S. Department of Health, Education and Welfare, Public Health Service, National Institutes of Health, DHEW Pub. No. (NIH), 79–162 (1979).

BIRENBAUM, ARNOLD, ARONSON, MIRIAM, and SEIFFER, SAMUEL. "Training Medical Students to Appreciate the Special Problems of the Elderly." *The Gerontologist*, 19:6 (1979).

BLUMENTHON, M. D., DAVIE, JAMES W., and MORYEZ, RICHARD K. "Developing a Curriculum in Psychogeriatrics." *American Journal of Psychiatry* 136:9 (September 1979).

BUTLER, ROBERT N. "Aging: Research Leads and Needs." *Forum on Medicine* (November 1979).

———. "The Alliance of Advocacy with Science." Donald P. Kent Lecture, 1979.

———. "Mission of the National Institute on Aging," *Journal of the American Geriatrics Society*, 25:3 (March 1977).

———. "Thoughts on Geriatric Medicine." National Institute on Aging, Science Writer Seminar Series, DHEW Pub. No. (NIH), 78–1406 (1978).

———. *Why Survive? Being Old in America.* New York: Harper & Row, 1975.

FORD, CHARLES V., and SBORDONE, ROBERT J. "Attitudes of Psychiatrists Towards Elderly Patients." *American Journal of Psychiatry*, 137:5 (May 1980).

FRANKEL, SANFORD I. "Geriatric Psychiatry Training for the General Psychiatric Resident." *American Journal of Psychiatry*, 135:1 (January 1978).

GARETZ, F. K. "Common Psychiatric Syndromes of the Aged." *Minnesota Medicine*, Vol. 57 (1974).

GEIGER, DEBORAH. "How Future Professionals View the Elderly: A Comparative Analysis of the Social Work, Law and Medical Student's Perception." *The Gerontologist*, 18:6 (1978).

HAVRON, DEAN. "Psychiatrist Finds Polypharmacy Problem in a Major Hospital, But Won't Generalize." *Medical Tribune* (October 10, 1979).

Hearings Before Subcommittee on Health and Long-Term Care of the Select Committee on Aging, U.S. House of Representatives, Ninety-fourth Congress, 2nd Session, Bangor, Maine, March 26, 1976.

Hearings Before Subcommittee on Human Services of the Select Committee on Aging, U.S. House of Representatives, Ninety-fifth Congress, 2nd Session, Elmira, New York, December 8, 1978.

HELLENBRANDT, FRANCES A. "The Senile in Our Midst: A Look at the Other Side of the Coin." *The Gerontologist*, 18:1 (1978).

"How to Have a Longer Life and Enjoy It More." Interview with Dr. Robert Butler. *U.S. News & World Report* (July 12, 1976).

Joint Hearing Before Subcommittee on Health and Long-Term Care and the Subcommittee on Aging, U.S. House of Representatives, Ninety-fifth Congress, 2nd Session, Washington, D.C., May 17, 1978.

KRUPKA, LAWRENCE R., and VENER, ARTHUR M. "Hazards of Drug Use Among the Elderly." *The Gerontologist*, 19:1 (1979).

LEWIS, M., and BUTLER, R. *Aging and Mental Health: Positive Psychosocial Approaches*. St. Louis: Mosby, 1973.

LOWENTHAL, M. F., BERKMAN, P. L., BRISSETTE, G. G., BUEHLER, J. A., PIERCE, R. C., ROBINSON, B. C., and TRIER, M. L. *Aging and Mental Disorder in San Francisco*. San Francisco: Jossey-Bass, 1967.

"Mental Health Care and the Elderly: Shortcomings in Public Policy." Report by the Special Committee on Aging, U.S. Senate, November 8, 1971.

MORRANT, J. C. "Medicines and Mental Illness in Old Age." *Journal of the Canadian Psychiatric Association*, 20:309–12 (1975).

"Overdiagnosis of OBS Seen as Tendency." *Psychiatric News* (July 4, 1980).

PRIEN, ROBERT F., BALTER, MITCHELL B., and COFFEY, EUGENE M., JR. "Hospital Surveys of Prescribing Practices with Psychotherapeutic

Drugs." *Archives of General Psychiatry*, Vol. 15 (October, 1978).

Roose, Steven P., Bone, Stanley, Haidorfer, Catherine, Dunner, David L., and Fieve, Ronald R. "Lithium Treatment in Older Patients." *American Journal of Psychiatry*, 136:6 (June 1979).

Rossman, Isadore. "Why We Shy Away from Geriatrics." *Geriatrics* (July 1976).

Seffin, Joan M. "Comment: Some Thoughts About Diseases Presenting as Senility." *The Gerontologist*, 18:1 (1978).

"Senility Reconsidered." Task Force Sponsored by the National Institute on Aging. *Journal of the American Medical Association*, Vol. 244 (July 18, 1980).

Steury, Steven, and Blank, Marie L., eds. *Readings in Psychotherapy with Older People*. DHEW Pub. No. (ADM), 77–409 (1977).

Vestal, Robert E. "Drugs and the Elderly." National Institute on Aging, Science Writer Seminar Series. DHEW Pub. No. (NIH), 78–1449 (1978).

"Weinberg Deplores Paucity of Geriatric Teaching For MDs." *Psychiatric News* (August 15, 1980).

Wershaw, Harold J. "Reality Orientation For Gerontologists: Some Thoughts About Senility." *The Gerontologist*, 17:4 (1977).

Williams, Kenneth H., and Goldstein, Gerald. "Cognitive and Affective Responses to Lithium in Patients With Organic Brain Syndrome." *American Journal of Psychiatry*, 136:6 (June 1979).

Yesavage, Jerome. "Memory, Lost and Found." *The Stanford Magazine*, 8:1 (Spring/Summer, 1980).

Chapter 12—LOONY BINS AND CITY STREETS

American Psychiatric Association. *Health Insurance and Psychiatric Care*. Baltimore: Garamond/Pridemark Press, 1972.

"Are Jails the New Back Wards?" News release at 133rd Annual Meeting of the American Psychiatric Association, San Francisco, California, May 7, 1980.

Berger, Phillip A. "Medical Treatment of Mental Illness." *Science*, Vol. 200 (May 26, 1978).

Bernstein, Stephen B., and MacLennan, Beryee W. "Community Psychiatry with the Communications Media." *American Journal of Psychiatry*, Vol. 128 (1971).

"Call for Action Made for Chronic Patient Problem." *Psychiatric News* (April 4, 1980).

DIETZ, JEAN. "Danger Seen for Future of CMHC Movement." *Psychiatric News* (May 16, 1980).

"Drugs and Psychiatry: A New Era." *Newsweek* (November 12, 1979).

FINK, PAUL J., and WEINSTEIN, P. "Whatever Happened to Psychiatry? The Deprofessionalism of Community Mental Health Centers." *American Journal of Psychiatry*, 136:4A (April 1979).

HABERMAN, CLYDE. "Mental Patients 'Dumped,' Koch Says." *The New York Times* (July 29, 1980).

HANLEY, ROBERT. "Health Officer in Jersey Condemns State Policy on Ex-Mental Patients." *The New York Times* (July 29, 1980).

HARRIS, MICHAEL. "The Mentally Sick Jammed Into Jail." *San Francisco Chronicle* (April 15, 1980).

HERRINGTON, B. S. "Chronic Patients Said 'Transinstitutionalized.'" *Psychiatric News* (October 17, 1980).

HOLLINGSHEAD, AUGUST B., and REDLICH, FREDERICK C. *Social Class and Mental Illness.* New York: John Wiley & Sons, 1958.

KIHSS, PETER. "Influx of Former Mental Patients Burdening City, Albany Is Told." *The New York Times* (November 23, 1980).

LEHRMAN, NATHANIEL S. "Political Pork Barreling: A Danger to Psychiatry's Sickest Patients." News release presented at 133rd Annual Meeting of the American Psychiatric Association, San Francisco, California, May 8, 1980.

"Mental Health Center Services." Guide to services at Community Hospital of the Monterey Peninsula, California, 1980.

WINSLOW, WALTER W. "The Changing Role of Psychiatrists in Community Mental Health Centers." *American Journal of Psychiatry*, 136:1 (January 1979).

Chapter 13—THE MOTHER LODE

American Psychiatric Association. *Health Insurance and Psychiatric Care.* Baltimore: Garamond/Pridemark Press, 1972.

BRODSKY, C. M. "The Systemic Incompatibility of Medical Practice and Psychotherapy." *Diseases of the Nervous System*, Vol. 31 (September 1970).

CHODOFF, PAUL. "Psychiatry and the Fiscal Third Party." *American Journal of Psychiatry*, 135:10 (October 1978).

"Conflicts of Interest on Blue Shield Boards of Directors." Report Together with Separate and Additional Views, Subcommittee on Oversight and Investigations of the Committee on Interstate and Foreign
Commerce, U.S. House of Representatives, Ninety-fifth Congress,
2nd Session, December 1978.

"Digest of Selected Health and Insurance Plans 1977–1979." U.S.
Department of Labor, Bureau of Labor Statistics, Volume I, Health
Benefits, including Supplement No. 1, January 1979.

HALES, DIANNE. "Blue Cross, Blue Shield Tighten Psychiatric Coverages
in East, West." *Psychiatric News* (September 7, 1979).

Hearings on Mental Health Insurance Before Committee on General
and Military Affairs, Vermont State Senate, Montpelier, Vermont,
November 4, 19, 1975, January 4, 1976.

Hearings Before Subcommittee on Interstate and Foreign Commerce,
U.S. House of Representatives, Ninety-fifth Congress, 2nd Session,
April 5, 1978.

HERRINGTON, B. S. "Congress Asks: Does Therapy Work?" *Psychiatric
News* (March 21, 1980).

————. "Klerman Weighs Role in Therapy Efficacy Study." *Psychiatric News* (May 2, 1980).

LUBORSKY, LESTER, SINGER, BARTON, and LUBORSKY, LISE. "Comparative Studies of Psychotherapies." *Archives of General Psychiatry*,
Vol. 32 (August 1975).

MARMOR, JUDD. "Short Term Dynamic Psycho Therapy." *American
Journal of Psychiatry*, 136:2 (February 1979).

MARSHALL, ELIOT. "Psychotherapy Faces Test of Worth." *Science*,
Vol. 207 January 4, 1980).

————. "Psychotherapy Works, But for Whom?" *Science*, Vol. 207
(February 1, 1980).

MATSUNAGA, THE HONORABLE SPARK. "A Perspective on Mental Health
Care for the 1980s." Address at 133rd Annual Meeting of the American Psychiatric Association, San Francisco, California, May 8, 1980.

McDONALD, MARGARET C. " 'Blues' Cut Federal Employees' Benefits."
Psychiatric News (November 7, 1980).

————. "Ohio Sues JCAH in Anti Trust Action." *Psychiatric News*
(March 21, 1980).

"Obstacles in the Pathways to Prepaid Mental Health Care." National
Institute of Mental Health, DHEW Pub. No. (ADM), 76–383
(1977).

PINNEY, E. L., Jr., WELLS, STEPHAN H., and FISHER, BERNARD. "Group

Therapy Training in Psychiatric Residency Programs." *American Journal of Psychiatry*, 135:12 (December 1978).

"Report of the Ad Hoc Committee on Psychotherapy." Herbert A. Holden, M.D., Chairman, Blue Shield of California, 1979. (Adopted by the Blue Shield of California Medical Policy Committee, June 20, 1979.)

SHARFSTEIN, STEPHAN S. "Third-Party Payers: To Be or Not To Be." *Journal of Psychiatry* 135:10 (October 1978).

SHARFSTEIN, STEPHAN S., TOWREY, O. B., and MILOWE, IRWIN D. "Accuracy of Diagnostic Information Submitted to an Insurance Company." *American Journal of Psychiatry* 137:1 (January 1980).

"Study Links Higher Fees to Doctor-Insurer Ties." *The New York Times* (November 24, 1979).

Testimony of Marcia Kraft Goin on behalf of the American Psychiatric Association, American Psychological Association, National Association of Private Psychiatric Hospitals, Before Ways and Means Subcommittee of the Committee on Health, U.S. House of Representatives, Ninety-sixth Congress, 2nd Session, April 17, 1980.

TOWREY, O. B., and SHARFSTEIN, STEPHAN. "Fraud and Abuse in Psychiatric Practice." *American Journal of Psychiatry*, 135:1 (January 1978).

Chapter 14—JOKERS AND WILD CARDS

COX, FRANK. Letter to the editor, *San Francisco Examiner* (May 13, 1980).

FELDMAN, HAROLD S. "Treatment of Acutely Disturbed Schizophrenic Criminal Offenders." Pamphlet from Scientific Exhibit at 133rd Annual Meeting of American Psychiatric Association, San Francisco, California, May 3–9, 1980.

GERSHON, SAMUEL. "Depression: An Ancient and Ubiquitous Disease." Pamphlet from Scientific Exhibit at 133rd Annual Meeting of American Psychiatric Association, San Francisco, California, May 3–9, 1980.

Hearings Before Subcommittee on Monopoly of the Select Committee on Small Business. U.S. Senate, Ninety-fourth Congress, 2nd Session, April 28, May 10, 24, 1976.

Hearings Before Subcommittee on Monopoly of the Select Committee on Small Business, U.S. Senate, Ninety-fourth Congress, 2nd Session, May 26, 27, 1976.

McLaughlin, Blaine E. "The Problems of Depression In Office Practice." Pamphlet from Scientific Exhibit at 133rd Annual Meeting of the American Psychiatric Association, San Francisco, California, May 3–9, 1980.

"Study Finds Newer Drug Therapy Aids Aggressive, Schizophrenic Criminals." News release from Lederle Laboratories at 133rd Annual Meeting of the American Psychiatric Association, San Francisco, California, May 4, 1980.

"You Are Invited . . ." Handout from The Roche Interactive Learning Center at 133rd Annual Meeting, American Psychiatric Association, San Francisco, California, May 3–9, 1980.

Chapter 15—THE CRUELEST GAME OF ALL

Herrington, B. S. "APA Joins Drug Refusal Case Appeal," *Psychiatric News* (April 18, 1980).

Mares, Bill. "Medicine, Psychiatry Reunited." *Burlington Free Press* (December 10, 1979).

McKinney, Joan. "Ex-Patients Take On Psychiatric System," *The Tribune* (Oakland) (May 4, 1980).

Robitscher, Jonas, *The Powers of Psychiatry*. Boston: Houghton Mifflin, 1980.

"Survivors of Psychiatric Assault Accuse APA of Crimes Against Humanity." News release from International Conference on Human Rights and Psychiatric Oppression at 133rd Annual Meeting of American Psychiatric Association, San Francisco, California, May 3–9, 1980.

"The New York Times National Economic Survey." *The New York Times* (January 6, 1980).

"Thorazine Treatment or Torture?" News release from Alliance For the Liberation of Mental Patients at 133rd Annual Meeting of the American Psychiatric Association, San Francisco, California, May 3–9, 1980.

INDEX